Curriculum Units

1 **How Many of Each?**
Addition, Subtraction, and the Number System 1

2 **Making Shapes and Designing Quilts**
2-D Geometry

3 **Solving Story Problems**
Addition, Subtraction, and the Number System 2

4 **What Would You Rather Be?**
Data Analysis

5 **Fish Lengths and Animal Jumps**
Measurement

6 **Number Games and Crayon Puzzles**
Addition, Subtraction, and the Number System 3

7 **Color, Shape, and Number Patterns**
Patterns and Functions

8 **Twos, Fives, and Tens**
Addition, Subtraction, and the Number System 4

9 **Blocks and Boxes**
3-D Geometry

How Many of Each?
Addition, Subtraction, and the Number System 1 **UNIT 1**

Spiral to Infinity Steve Allen

"Fractal images are often made up of small images-within-images, constantly repeating and going smaller and smaller."– Steve Allen

Investigations

IN NUMBER, DATA, AND SPACE®

GRADE

1

How Many of Each?

Addition, Subtraction, and the Number System 1

UNIT 1

scottforesman.com

Editorial offices: Glenview, Illinois • Parsippany, New Jersey • New York, New York
Sales offices: Boston, Massachusetts • Duluth, Georgia
Glenview, Illinois • Coppell, Texas • Sacramento, California • Mesa, Arizona

TERC

The Investigations curriculum was developed by TERC, Cambridge, MA.

This material is based on work supported by the National Science Foundation ("NSF") under Grant No. ESI-0095450. Any opinions, findings, and conclusions or recommendations expressed in this material are those of the author(s) and do not necessarily reflect the views of the National Science Foundation.

ISBN: 0-328-23726-4

ISBN: 978-0-328-23726-5

8 9 10-V003-15 14 13 12 11 10 09 08

CC:N2

TERC

Co-Principal Investigators

Susan Jo Russell

Karen Economopoulos

Authors

Lucy Wittenberg
Director Grades 3–5

Karen Economopoulos
Director Grades K–2

Virginia Bastable
(SummerMath for Teachers, Mt. Holyoke College)

Katie Hickey Bloomfield

Keith Cochran

Darrell Earnest

Arusha Hollister

Nancy Horowitz

Erin Leidl

Megan Murray

Young Oh

Beth W. Perry

Susan Jo Russell

Deborah Schifter
(Education Development Center)

Kathy Sillman

Administrative Staff

Amy Taber
Project Manager

Beth Bergeron

Lorraine Brooks

Emi Fujiwara

Contributing Authors

Denise Baumann

Jennifer DiBrienza

Hollee Freeman

Paula Hooper

Jan Mokros

Stephen Monk
(University of Washington)

Mary Beth O'Connor

Judy Storeygard

Cornelia Tierney

Elizabeth Van Cleef

Carol Wright

Technology

Jim Hammerman

Classroom Field Work

Amy Appell

Rachel E. Davis

Traci Higgins

Julia Thompson

Note: Unless otherwise noted, all contributors listed above were staff of the Education Research Collaborative at TERC during their work on the curriculum. Other affiliations during the time of development are listed.

Collaborating Teachers

This group of dedicated teachers carried out extensive field testing in their classrooms, met regularly to discuss issues of teaching and learning mathematics, provided feedback to staff, welcomed staff into their classrooms to document students' work, and contributed both suggestions and written material that has been incorporated into the curriculum.

Bethany Altchek
Linda Amaral
Kimberly Beauregard
Barbara Bernard
Nancy Buell
Rose Christiansen
Chris Colbath-Hess
Lisette Colon
Kim Cook
Frances Cooper
Kathleen Drew
Rebeka Eston Salemi
Thomas Fisher
Michael Flynn
Holly Ghazey
Susan Gillis
Danielle Harrington
Elaine Herzog
Francine Hiller
Kirsten Lee Howard
Liliana Klass
Leslie Kramer
Melissa Lee Andrichak
Kelley Lee Sadowski
Jennifer Levitan
Mary Lou LoVecchio
Kristen McEnaney
Maura McGrail
Kathe Millett
Florence Molyneaux
Amy Monkiewicz
Elizabeth Monopoli
Carol Murray
Robyn Musser
Christine Norrman
Deborah O'Brien
Timothy O'Connor
Anne Marie O'Reilly
Mark Paige
Margaret Riddle
Karen Schweitzer
Elisabeth Seyferth
Susan Smith
Debra Sorvillo
Shoshanah Starr
Janice Szymaszek
Karen Tobin
JoAnn Trauschke
Ana Vaisenstein
Yvonne Watson
Michelle Woods
Mary Wright

Advisors

Deborah Lowenberg Ball,
University of Michigan

Hyman Bass, Professor of Mathematics and Mathematics Education
University of Michigan

Mary Canner, Principal, Natick Public Schools

Thomas Carpenter, Professor of Curriculum and Instruction,
University of Wisconsin-Madison

Janis Freckmann, Elementary Mathematics Coordinator,
Milwaukee Public Schools

Lynne Godfrey, Mathematics Coach,
Cambridge Public Schools

Ginger Hanlon, Instructional Specialist in Mathematics,
New York City Public Schools

DeAnn Huinker, Director, Center for Mathematics and
Science Education Research, University of Wisconsin-Milwaukee

James Kaput, Professor of Mathematics, University of
Massachusetts-Dartmouth

Kate Kline, Associate Professor, Department of Mathematics
and Statistics, Western Michigan University

Jim Lewis, Professor of Mathematics,
University of Nebraska-Lincoln

William McCallum, Professor of Mathematics,
University of Arizona

Harriet Pollatsek, Professor of Mathematics,
Mount Holyoke College

Debra Shein-Gerson, Elementary Mathematics Specialist,
Weston Public Schools

Gary Shevell, Assistant Principal,
New York City Public Schools

Liz Sweeney, Elementary Math Department,
Boston Public Schools

Lucy West, Consultant, Metamorphosis:
Teaching Learning Communities, Inc.

This revision of the curriculum was built on the work of the many authors who contributed to the first edition (published between 1994 and 1998). We acknowledge the critical contributions of these authors in developing the content and pedagogy of *Investigations*:

Authors

Joan Akers

Michael T. Battista

Douglas H. Clements

Karen Economopoulos

Marlene Kliman

Jan Mokros

Megan Murray

Ricardo Nemirovsky

Andee Rubin

Susan Jo Russell

Cornelia Tierney

Contributing Authors

Mary Berle-Carman

Rebecca B. Corwin

Rebeka Eston

Claryce Evans

Anne Goodrow

Cliff Konold

Chris Mainhart

Sue McMillen

Jerrie Moffet

Tracy Noble

Kim O'Neil

Mark Ogonowski

Julie Sarama

Amy Shulman Weinberg

Margie Singer

Virginia Woolley

Tracey Wright

Contents

UNIT 1

How Many of Each?

Investigations

CURRICULUM

Overview of Program Components

FOR TEACHERS

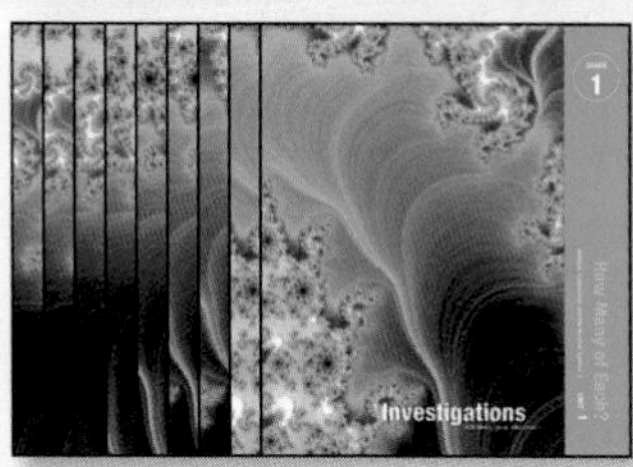

The **Curriculum Units** are the teaching guides. (See far right.)

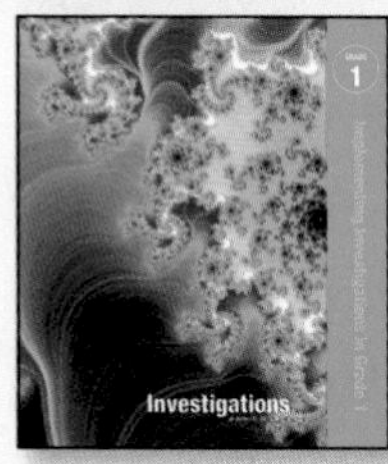

Implementing Investigations in Grade 1 offers suggestions for implementing the curriculum. It also contains a comprehensive index.

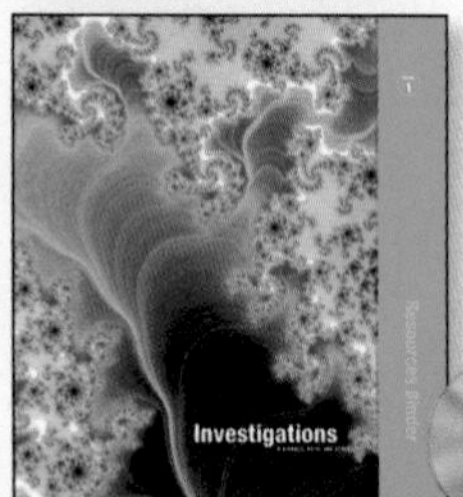

The **Resources Binder** contains all the Resource Masters and Transparencies that support instruction. (Also available on CD.) The binder also includes a student software CD.

FOR STUDENTS

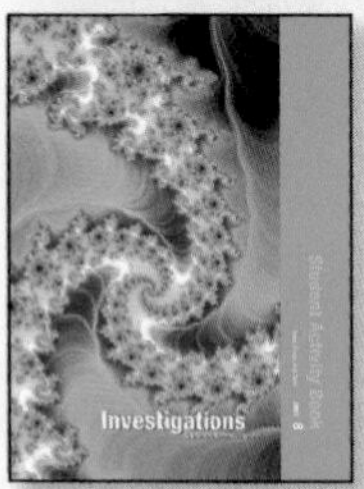

The **Student Activity Book** contains the consumable student pages (Recording Sheets, Homework, Practice, and so on).

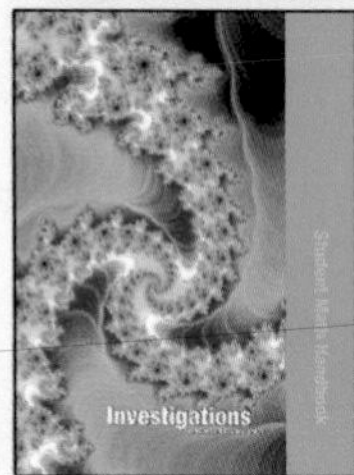

The **Student Math Handbook** contains Math Words and Ideas pages and Games Directions.

The *Investigations* Curriculum

Investigations in Number, Data, and Space® is a K–5 mathematics curriculum designed to engage students in making sense of mathematical ideas. Six major goals guided the development of the *Investigations in Number, Data, and Space®* curriculum. The curriculum is designed to:

- Support students to make sense of mathematics and learn that they can be mathematical thinkers
- Focus on computational fluency with whole numbers as a major goal of the elementary grades
- Provide substantive work in important areas of mathematics—rational numbers, geometry, measurement, data, and early algebra—and connections among them
- Emphasize reasoning about mathematical ideas
- Communicate mathematics content and pedagogy to teachers
- Engage the range of learners in understanding mathematics

Underlying these goals are three guiding principles that are touchstones for the *Investigations* team as we approach both students and teachers as agents of their own learning:

1. *Students have mathematical ideas.* Students come to school with ideas about numbers, shapes, measurements, patterns, and data. If given the opportunity to learn in an environment that stresses making sense of mathematics, students build on the ideas they already have and learn about new mathematics they have never encountered. Students learn that they are capable of having mathematical ideas, applying what they know to new situations, and thinking and reasoning about unfamiliar problems.

2. *Teachers are engaged in ongoing learning* about mathematics content, pedagogy, and student learning. The curriculum provides material for professional development, to be used by teachers individually or in groups, that supports teachers' continued learning as they use the curriculum over several years. The *Investigations* curriculum materials are designed as much to be a dialogue with teachers as to be a core of content for students.

3. *Teachers collaborate with the students and curriculum materials* to create the curriculum as enacted in the classroom. The only way for a good curriculum to be used well is for teachers to be active participants in implementing it. Teachers use the curriculum to maintain a clear, focused, and coherent agenda for mathematics teaching. At the same time, they observe and listen carefully to students, try to understand how they are thinking, and make teaching decisions based on these observations.

Investigations is based on experience from research and practice, including field testing that involved documentation of thousands of hours in classrooms, observations of students, input from teachers, and analysis of student work. As a result, the curriculum addresses the learning needs of real students in a wide range of classrooms and communities. The investigations are carefully designed to invite all students into mathematics—girls and boys; members of diverse cultural, ethnic, and language groups; and students with a wide variety of strengths, needs, and interests.

Based on this extensive classroom testing, the curriculum takes seriously the time students need to develop a strong conceptual foundation and skills based on that foundation. Each curriculum unit focuses on an area of content in depth, providing time for students to develop and practice ideas across a variety of activities and contexts that build on each other. Daily guidelines for time spent on class sessions, Classroom Routines (K–3), and Ten-Minute Math (3–5) reflect the commitment to devoting adequate time to mathematics in each school day.

About This Curriculum Unit

This **Curriculum Unit** is one of nine teaching guides in Grade 1. The first unit in Grade 1 is *How Many of Each?*

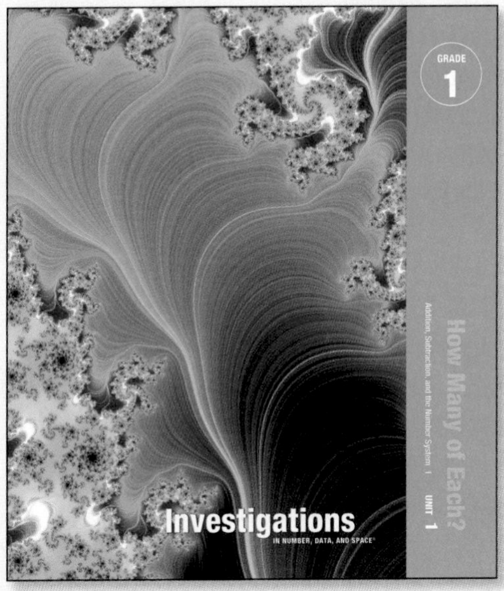

- The **Introduction and Overview** section organizes and presents the instructional materials, provides background information, and highlights important features specific to this unit.
- Each Curriculum Unit contains several **Investigations.** Each Investigation focuses on a set of related mathematical ideas.
- Investigations are divided into one-hour **Sessions,** or lessons.
- Sessions have a combination of these parts: **Activity, Discussion, Math Workshop, Assessment Activity,** and **Session Follow-Up.**
- Each session also has one or more **Classroom Routines** that are done outside of math time.
- At the back of the book is a collection of **Teacher Notes** and **Dialogue Boxes** that provide professional development related to the unit.
- Also included at the back of the book are the **Student Math Handbook** pages for this unit.
- The **Index** provides a way to look up important words or terms.

Overview

OF THIS UNIT

Investigation	Session	Day
INVESTIGATION 1 **Counting and Quantity** Students are introduced to the *Morning Meeting* routine, which continues throughout the year. They also become familiar with many of the math materials they will use throughout the year.	**1.1** Morning Meeting: Daily Schedule	1
	1.2 Morning Meeting: Calendar	2
	1.3 Morning Meeting: Weather	3
	1.4 Collect 20 Together	4
INVESTIGATION 2 **Counting and Comparing** Students engage in several activities that focus on counting, comparing, and ordering quantities. They are also introduced to two more yearlong classroom routines, which focus on counting forward and back and on developing visual images of numbers.	**2.1** Start With/Get To	5
	2.2 Staircases	6
	2.3 Counting What's in a Mystery Box	7
	2.4 Comparing Quantities	8
	2.5 Counting Backward	9
	2.6 Assessment: Count 20 and Quick Images	10
	2.7 Ordering Numbers	11
INVESTIGATION 3 **Combining** Students play several games that involve combining two quantities. They are also introduced to and solve addition story problems.	**3.1** Double Compare and Double Compare Dots	12
	3.2 Five-in-a-Row	13
	3.3 Addition Story Problems	14
	3.4 Roll and Record	15
	3.5 More Addition Story Problems	16
	3.6 Assessment: Double Compare and Combining Games	17
	3.7 How Many in All?	18
INVESTIGATION 4 **Composing Numbers** Students work on finding different 2-addend combinations of the same number. They solve several How Many of Each? problems and complete a unit assessment.	**4.1** Seven Peas and Carrots	19
	4.2 Three Towers	20
	4.3 Heads and Tails	21
	4.4 How Many Am I Hiding?	22
	4.5 Nine Peas and Carrots	23
	4.6 Combinations of Seven	24
	4.7 End-of-Unit Assessment	25

Each *Investigations* session has some combination of these five parts: **Activity, Discussion, Math Workshop, Assessment Activity,** and **Session Follow-Up.** These session parts are indicated in the chart below. Each session also has one or more **Classroom Routines** that are done outside of math time.

Activity	Discussion	Math Workshop	Assessment Activity	Session Follow-Up	Classroom Routines: *Morning Meeting*	Classroom Routines: *Start With/ Get To*	Classroom Routines: *Quick Images*
●●		●		●	●		
●	●	●		●	●		
●	●	●		●	●		
●	●	●		●	●		
●●	●			●	●		
●	●	●		●		●	
●	●	●		●		●	
●	●	●		●		●	
●	●	●		●	●		
●		●	●	●		●	
●●	●			●			●
●●		●		●		●	
●●		●		●			●
●●	●			●		●	
●●		●		●	●		
●	●	●		●			●
	●	●	●	●		●	
●●	●			●			●
●●	●			●	●		
●●	●			●			●
●●		●		●		●	
●●	●			●			●
●●	●			●		●	
	●	●		●			●
			●	●	●		

Mathematics

IN THIS UNIT

How Many of Each? is the first of nine units in the Grade 1 sequence and the first of four units in the Grade 1 number strand. These units develop ideas about counting and quantity, the composition of numbers, and the operations of addition and subtraction. The mathematical focus of this unit is on building number sense through counting and comparing quantities, and through composing and decomposing numbers. Students also work with the operation of addition, developing strategies for combining quantities. As the first unit of the year, this unit also introduces the mathematical tools, processes, and ways of working that will be the foundation of math class this year. As part of this work, students are introduced to several yearlong classroom routines that offer regular practice with counting, developing visual images of quantities, collecting and analyzing data, and working with time and sequence.

This unit builds on all of the work students did in the three kindergarten number units. Much of that work focused on counting. Students learned the number sequence and the connection between numbers in the rote counting sequence and quantities and written numbers. Repeatedly counting sets of objects helped them learn to say one number for each object and develop a system for keeping track of what had been, and what remained to be, counted. Students also encountered addition and subtraction situations as they acted out and solved story problems and as they played games that focused on composing and decomposing numbers.

This unit focuses on 5 Mathematical Emphases:

1 Counting and Quantity **Developing strategies for accurately counting a set of objects by 1s**

Math Focus Points

- Counting a set of up to 20 objects by 1s
- Practicing the rote counting sequence forward and backward, from 1 to 30
- Connecting number names and written numbers to the quantities they represent
- Developing and analyzing visual images for quantities up to 10

Almost all students entering first grade know the oral counting sequence, but they vary tremendously in their ability to accurately count a set of objects and then understanding of the quantities that the counting numbers represent. For instance, they may be able to say the counting sequence up to 20, but given a set of 20 objects, they will miscount them. Activities throughout this unit give students repeated practice with the counting sequence, both forward and backward, and with counting and keeping track of sets of objects. They also help students connect the number names with the written numbers and the quantities that they represent.

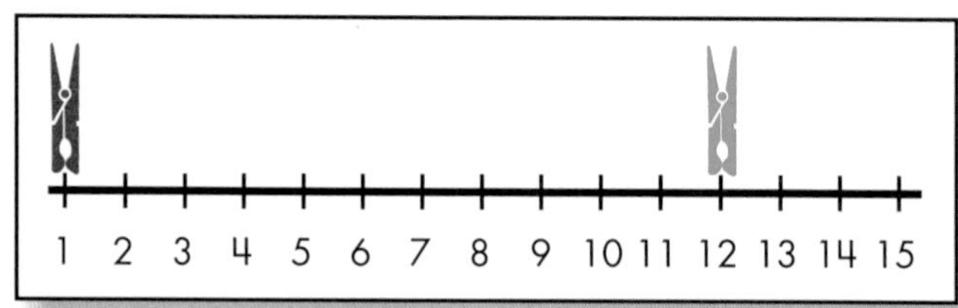

In the Start With/Get To Routine, students practice counting forward and back.

2 Counting and Quantity **Developing an understanding of the magnitude and position of numbers**

Math Focus Points

- Ordering a set of numbers and quantities up to 12
- Comparing two quantities up to 20 to see which is larger
- Developing an understanding of how the quantities in the counting sequence are related: each number is 1 more or 1 less than the number before or after it

Counting and understanding quantities involves understanding the relationships between and among numbers. As students are developing accurate counting strategies, they are also building an understanding of how the numbers in the counting sequence are related—each is 1 more (or 1 less) than the number before (or after) it. As students build this understanding, they are able to order and compare quantities and develop a sense of how big numbers and the quantities they represent are. The work in Grade 1 of understanding "1 more than or 1 less than" expands as students build their understanding of the base 10 number system. In later grades, students begin to think about the relationship among larger numbers as being 10, 100, or 1,000 more than another number.

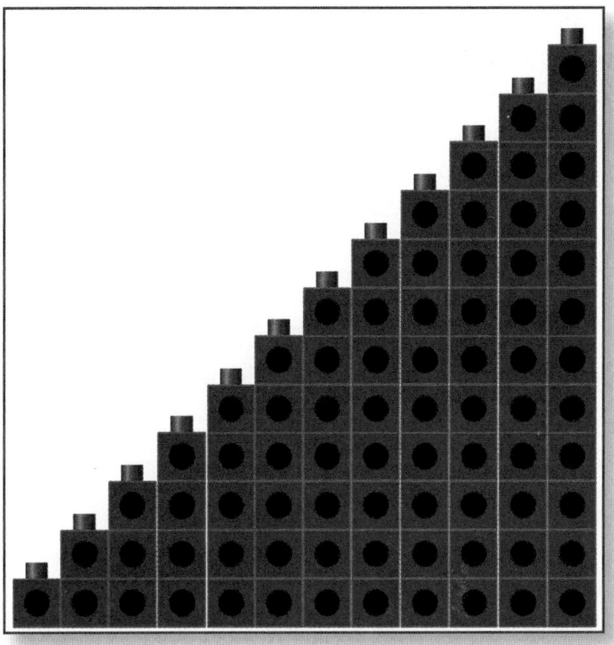

3 Number Composition **Composing numbers up to 10 with 2 addends**

Math Focus Points

- Finding and exploring relationships among combinations of numbers up to 10
- Recording combinations of two numbers that make a certain total
- Solving a problem with multiple solutions
- Solving a problem in which the total and one part are known

Understanding how numbers can be composed and decomposed, and being able to work with numbers in flexible ways lay crucial groundwork for future work in addition and subtraction. In Grade 1, one important idea is that quantities can be composed and decomposed in different ways and yet the quantity remains the same.

Students have repeated experiences breaking one number (a whole) into two parts or combining two parts to form a whole. They begin to consider the relationship between the parts, noticing, for example, that when the whole remains the same, as one part increases the other part decreases. See **Algebra Connections in This Unit,** page 16, for more on this.

4 Whole Number Operations **Making sense of and developing strategies to solve addition problems with small numbers**

Math Focus Points

- Visualizing and retelling the action in an addition situation
- Modeling the action of an addition problem with counters or drawings
- Finding the total of two or more quantities up to a total of 20 by counting all, counting on, or using number combinations
- Seeing that adding the same two numbers (e.g., 4 and 3) results in the same total, regardless of context (e.g., number cubes, cards, objects)

This unit focuses primarily on addition. (Subtraction will be a focus of the second number unit.) Many of the games and activities involve students in comparing and combining two amounts and offer practice with single-digit addition facts. Most first graders *count all* to add two numbers—count out the number in one group, count out the number in the second group, and then count them all from 1. Some students *count on* from one number, and a few may use numerical reasoning, such as *using a known combination* (say 4 + 4) to solve an unknown combination (4 + 5).

At the same time, students are developing strategies for solving story problems. In this first unit, much of this work involves making sense of the action in a story and visualizing the sequence and result of events. Students listen to and retell stories, as well as solve problems that involve combining two or more amounts. Students are also asked to consider related problems (3 crayons + 3 crayons and 3 crayons + 4 crayons, for example) and to think about how they are related and how one problem might help solve another. Although many beginning first graders may not yet see connections between such problems, asking students to look for relationships among problems encourages an important and useful mathematical habit. See **Algebra Connections in This Unit,** page 16, for more on this.

Students solve story problems.

5 Whole Number Operations **Using manipulatives, drawings, tools, and notation to show strategies and solutions**

Math Focus Points

- Using the number line as a tool for counting
- Introducing standard notation for comparing quantities (greater than, less than, and equal to)
- Introducing and using standard notation (+ and =) to represent addition situations
- Recording a solution to a problem
- Representing number combinations with numbers, pictures, and/or words

Throughout this unit and throughout the *Investigations* curriculum, students use mathematical tools and representations to model and solve problems in order to clarify and communicate their thinking. For example, students are introduced to the number line as a tool for counting, and they use cubes to model and solve story problems. Although first graders will vary widely in their ability to represent their mathematical work on paper, they are encouraged to do so in ways that make sense to them. Many use some combination of pictures, words, numbers, and, after they have been introduced to them, mathematical symbols. This early experience with representation continues to develop and mature over the course of Grade 1 and elementary school.

This Unit also focuses on

- Exploring the characteristics of cubes, pattern blocks, Geoblocks, and Power Polygons

Classroom Routines focus on

- Developing strategies for counting accurately
- Using the calendar as a tool for keeping track of time
- Developing vocabulary to talk about time (morning, noon, midday, afternoon, etc.) and sequence (first, next, last, before, after, and so on)
- Collecting and recording data
- Estimating quantities up to about 30
- Adding or subtracting small amounts to/from a familiar number
- Connecting written numbers and number names
- Using the number line as a tool for counting
- Practicing the rote counting sequence forward and backward
- Developing and analyzing visual images for quantities up to 10
- Recreating an arrangement of objects
- Finding the total of two or more single-digit quantities

Students apply their growing knowledge of numbers, quantities, and the operation of addition in all of the units in Grade 1, including geometry and data. In the second number unit *Solving Story Problems,* students count and compare larger quantities. They continue to compose and decompose numbers into several parts, with the added challenge of finding all the possible ways to decompose a number into two parts. Students continue to work on the operation of addition, revisiting familiar activities with variations that encourage students to move from *counting all* to *counting on* if they are ready. In the second number unit *Solving Story Problems,* students are also introduced to the operation of subtraction. As with addition, students' work focuses on developing an understanding of the operation and on strategies for solving subtraction problems.

Assessment

IN THIS UNIT

ONGOING ASSESSMENT: Observing Students at Work

The following sessions provide **Ongoing Assessment: Observing Students at Work** opportunities:

- **Session 1.1, p. 31**
- **Session 1.2, p. 35**
- **Session 1.3, p. 40**
- **Session 1.4, pp. 45 and 46**
- **Session 2.1, pp. 56 and 57**
- **Session 2.2, pp. 62 and 63**
- **Session 2.3, p. 68**
- **Session 2.4, p. 74**
- **Session 2.6, p. 85**
- **Session 2.7, p. 91**
- **Session 3.1, pp. 103 and 104**
- **Session 3.2, p. 109**
- **Session 3.3, p. 114**
- **Session 3.4, p. 122**
- **Session 3.5, p. 127**
- **Session 3.6, p. 132**
- **Session 3.7, p. 140**
- **Session 4.1, p. 151**
- **Session 4.2, p. 157**
- **Session 4.3, pp. 164 and 165**
- **Session 4.4, p. 169**
- **Session 4.5, p. 173**
- **Session 4.7, p. 182**

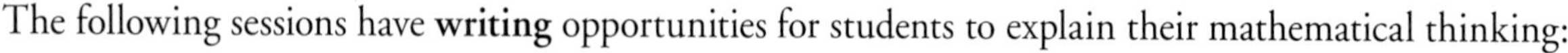

WRITING OPPORTUNITIES

The following sessions have **writing** opportunities for students to explain their mathematical thinking:

- **Session 2.6, p. 85**
  M23, Assessment: Counting 20
- **Session 3.3, p. 113**
  Student Activity Book, p. 21
- **Session 3.3, p. 118**
  Student Activity Book, p. 22
- **Session 3.5, p. 127**
  Student Activity Book, p. 27
- **Session 3.6, p. 132**
  M32, Assessment: *Double Compare*
- **Session 4.1, p. 149**
  Student Activity Book, p. 33
- **Session 4.5, p. 173**
  Student Activity Book, p. 43
- **Session 4.7, pp. 181–182**
  M39–M40, End-of-Unit Assessment

PORTFOLIO OPPORTUNITIES

The following sessions have work appropriate for a **portfolio**:

- **Session 2.6, p. 85**
  M23, Assessment: *Counting 20*
- **Session 3.3, pp. 113 and 118**
  Student Activity Book, pp. 21–22
- **Session 3.6, p. 132**
  M32, Assessment: *Double Compare*
- **Session 4.1, p. 149**
  Student Activity Book, p. 33
- **Session 4.5, p. 173**
  Student Activity Book, p. 43
- **Session 4.7, pp. 181–182**
  M39–M40, End-of-Unit Assessment

Assessing the Benchmarks

Observing students as they engage in conversation about their ideas is a primary means to assess their mathematical understanding. Consider all of your students' work, not just the written assessments. See the chart below for suggestions about key activities to observe.

Benchmarks in This Unit	Key Activities to Observe	Assessment
1. Count a set of up to 20 objects.	**Sessions 1.2–1.4:** Exploring Math Tools ✓ **Session 1.4:** *Collect 20 Together*	**Session 2.6 Assessment Activity:** Counting 20 **Session 3.6 Assessment Activity:** *Double Compare* **Session 4.7 End-of-Unit Assessment:** How Many Cookies?
2. Compare and order quantities to 20.	**Sessions 2.2–2.4, and 2.7:** Staircases and Ordering Numbers	**Session 3.6 Assessment Activity:** Double Compare
3. Combine two small quantities.	**Sessions 3.1–3.7:** Combining Games and Story Problems	**Session 3.6 Assessment Activity:** *Double Compare* **Session 4.7 End-of-Unit Assessment:** How Many Cookies?
4. Interpret (retell the action and sequence) and solve addition story problems.	**Sessions 3.1–3.7:** Combining Games and Story Problems	**Session 4.7 End-of-Unit Assessment:** How Many Cookies?
5. Find more than one combination of two addends for a number up to 10 (e.g., 7 is 4 and 3 and is also 5 and 2).	**Sessions 4.1–4.7:** How Many of Each? Problems	**Session 4.7 End-of-Unit Assessment:** Eight Fruits

Relating the Mathematical Emphases to the Benchmarks

Mathematical Emphases	Benchmarks
Counting and Quantity Developing strategies for accurately counting a set of objects by ones	**1**
Counting and Quantity Developing an understanding of the magnitude and position of numbers	**2**
Whole Number Operations Making sense of and developing strategies to solve addition problems with small numbers	**3 and 4**
Number Composition Composing numbers up to 10 with two addends	**5**
Whole Number Operations Using Manipulatives, drawings, tools, and notation to show strategies and solutions	**1–5**

Algebra Connections

IN THIS UNIT

In this unit, your students will have opportunities to engage with ideas that lay a foundation for algebra. To the surprise of many, 6-year-olds can and do think algebraically. Part of the work of Grade 1 is helping students learn to verbalize those thoughts, both as a way to engage with generalizations about number and operations and as a foundation for meaningful use of algebraic notation in the future. Consider the following vignette:

Ms. Banks' class is playing Double Compare. *Each child lays out two number cards; the child whose combined quantity is larger says "me" and collects the cards. As Ms. Banks walks around the room, she sees that children are playing successfully. For example, when William turns over a 2 and a 6, and Marta turns over a 3 and a 4, they count up the totals; William says "me" and gathers the cards.*

But soon Ms. Banks realizes that there are several pairs of children who are saying "me" or "you" before they could possibly have time to find the sum of their numbers—and they are always right! As she watches, she stops one pair. Paula has just laid out a 2 and a 4, and Allie has just laid out a 3 and a 4.

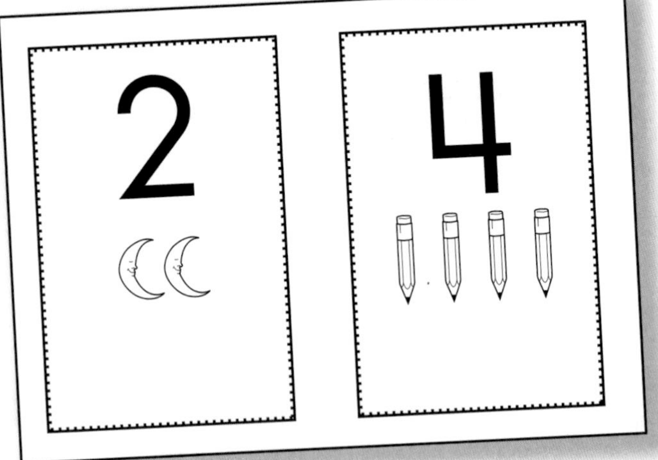

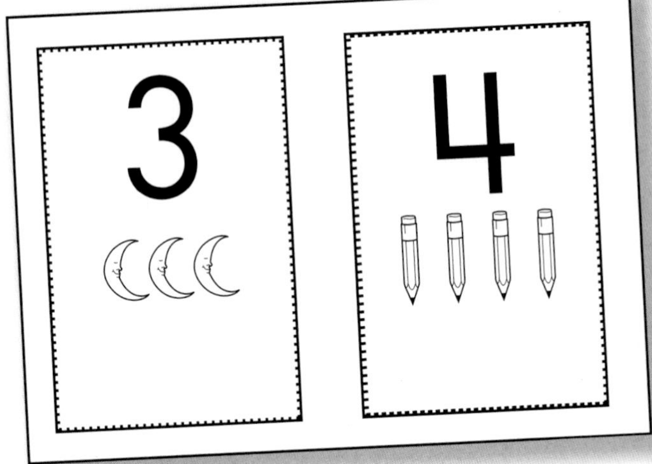

She asks, "Paula, how did you know to say 'you,' and Allie, why did you say 'me' so quickly?" The girls explain that because 3 is larger than 2, 3 and 4 must be larger than 2 and 4. They are sure of that; they don't need to add. As the teacher goes from group to group, she realizes that a few pairs are playing with the same rule in mind: if one number is larger than a second, and the same number is combined with each, then the first combination will be larger than the second.

For more information, see **Teacher Note:** *Double Compare: Strategies for Combining and Comparing,* page 201.

Adding the Same Amount to Different Amounts

As young children begin to learn about numbers and operations, they begin to see regularities in our number system and to think about what stays the same among things that are changing. The regularity, or generalization, described above—if one number is larger than another, and the same number is added to each, the first total will be larger than the second—is one example. Although many first graders are not yet ready to think about generalizations across all numbers, this is true of any three numbers. For example, because $36 < 54$, $36 + 98 < 54 + 98$.

You may find that a few of your students already come from Kindergarten thinking about regularities in the number system such as this one; others may begin to think in these ways during this unit; others still later in the year. Students will have many opportunities to think about and use such ideas throughout the year.

At this age, students should be encouraged to articulate the reasoning behind their quick responses ("How did you know to say 'me' so quickly?"). Although they have in mind a generalization, their explanations are likely to be in terms of specific numbers. "6 and 3 is more than 6 and 1 because 3 is bigger than 1." Or "I had 4 and she had 4, and then I had a higher number." A next step is to ask students to consider whether it works for other numbers ("Does it only work for 6?" Or "Does it only work for 4?"). Some students initially may not be able to respond to such questions. As the year continues, they will become more practiced at explaining their thinking and may eventually be able to articulate this generalization: "If my number is bigger than your number and we both add the same number to our numbers, my total is bigger than yours." Years from now, they will be able to express the idea in algebraic notation: *If* a, b, and c *are numbers and if* $a > b$, *then* $a + c > b + c$.

Some students may use cubes to explain their generalizations.

For most adults, such notation (the use of variables, operations, and equal signs) is the chief identifying feature of algebra. The notation, however, expresses rules about how operations work that students can reason out for themselves. This *reasoning*—about how numbers can be put together and taken apart under different operations—and *not* the notation, is the work of elementary students in algebra. *Investigations* students are encouraged to verbalize the generalizations they see about numbers and operations, and to explain and justify them by using materials and tools, such as cubes.

Adding 1 to an Addend

Consider another algebraic idea that many students discover and explore as they work on the concept of addition. As students begin to learn their addition combinations, there are some that are easier to remember than others. For example, they tend to learn first their doubles (e.g., 3 + 3) and the combinations of 10 (e.g., 2 + 8). Then they use what they know to derive facts they do not remember.

This idea is related to the first about comparing totals. For example, compare 5 + 5 and 5 + 6. Students who have thought about the previous question can say that 5 + 6 is the larger sum, but by how much? Some children will be confident that it is larger by 1. If 5 + 5 = 10, then 5 + 6 must be 10 + 1, which equals 11. The idea behind the example illustrated here is that if 1 is added to one of two addends, the total increases by 1.

In this unit, you will find some students beginning to use this key idea when solving problems with numbers that are close to combinations they know. If they know that 3 + 3 = 6, then they will conclude that 3 + 4 = 7 because 4 is 1 more than 3, and 7 is one more than 6. They may also use the reverse: If 4 + 4 = 8, then 3 + 4 must be 7 because 3 is one less than 4, and 7 is one less than 8. When you notice students using such reasoning, ask them to explain. How do they verbalize the idea? Can they show their reasoning with cubes?

Sample Student Work

When you ask students to explain, it might at first be difficult for them to articulate their thinking. However, by hearing similar kinds of questions repeatedly, some of your students will start to anticipate them and will begin to have ideas to offer. As the year continues, you will find that more students learn to articulate their thinking and, with these ideas in the air, more students will begin to use them. You might hear such language as, "I know that $4 + 4 = 8$. So $5 + 4 = 9$. You're just adding one more and putting it on the 4 so it can turn to a 5. Then the 8 changes to a 9." At a more general level, a student might say, "If you're adding two numbers and add 1 to one number, your answer goes to the next number." Years from now, students will be able to express this idea in algebraic notation: *If* a, b, *and* c *are numbers and if* $a + b = c$, *then* $(a + 1) + b = c + 1$. Or, even more generally: *If* d *is another number and if* $a + b = c$, *then* $(a + d) + b = c + d$.

The examples shown above illustrate the kind of early algebraic reasoning that is fully accessible to elementary-aged students. This early algebra work involves students in reasoning, generalizing, representing, and communicating. It is not so much about finding an answer to a particular problem, but about describing a way to find answers to a *whole class* of problems. For example, the relationship between $4 + 4$ and $5 + 4$ is not only useful for finding the sum of $5 + 4$. This relationship also applies more generally to any problems that add 1 to one of the addends (e.g., $34 + 56 = 90$, so $34 + 57 = 91$).

Note: In the text for the sessions, you will find **Algebra Notes** that identify where these early algebra discussions are likely to arise. Some of the **Teacher Notes** and **Dialogue Boxes** further elaborate the ideas and illustrate students' conversations about them.

Classroom Routines

IN THIS UNIT

Classroom Routines offer practice and review of key concepts for this grade level. These daily activities, to be done in ten minutes outside of math class, occur in a regular rotation every 4–5 days. Specific directions for the day's routine are provided in each session. For the full description and variations of each classroom routine see *Implementing Investigations in Grade 1.*

Morning Meeting

Students count the number of children in the class in more than one way, and at various times. They use the calendar to count days and to keep track of time and events, and the Daily Schedule to think about time and sequence. They collect and analyze data about the weather.

Math Focus Points

- Developing strategies for counting accurately
- Using the calendar as a tool for keeping track of time
- Developing vocabulary to talk about time (morning, noon, midday, afternoon, etc.) and sequence (first, next, last, before, after, and so on)
- Collecting and recording data
- Estimating quantities up to about 30
- Adding or subtracting small amounts to/from a familiar number

Start With/Get To

Students identify a chosen number and find it on the number line. They count from 1 to the chosen number, using the number line to keep track of the count. Later, they count back from the chosen number to 1.

Math Focus Points

- Connecting written numbers and number names
- Using the number line as a tool for counting
- Practicing the rote counting sequence forward and backward

Quick Images

Students see a dot image, or several dot images shown at the same time, and determine the total number of dots. Students explore the idea that the same quantity can be arranged differently, and practice adding single-digit numbers.

Math Focus Points

- Developing and analyzing visual images for quantities up to 10
- Recreating an arrangement of objects
- Finding the total of two or more single-digit quantities

Practice and Review

IN THIS UNIT

Practice and review play a critical role in the *Investigations* program. The following components and features are available to provide regular reinforcement of key mathematical concepts and procedures.

Books	Features	In This Unit . . .
Curriculum Unit	**Classroom Routines** offer practice and review of key concepts for this grade level. These daily activities, to be done in ten minutes outside of math class, occur in a regular rotation every 4–5 days. Specific directions for the day's routine are provided in each session. For the full description and variations of each classroom routine see *Implementing Investigations in Grade 1.*	• **All sessions**
Student Activity Book	**Daily Practice** pages in the *Student Activity Book* provide one of three types of written practice: **reinforcement** of the content of the unit, **ongoing review,** or **enrichment** opportunities. Some Daily Practice pages will also have Ongoing Review items with multiple-choice problems similar to those on standardized tests.	• **All sessions**
	Homework pages in the *Student Activity Book* are an extension of the work done in class. At times they help students prepare for upcoming activities.	• **Session 2.5** • **Session 2.7** • **Session 3.2** • **Session 3.4** • **Session 3.5** • **Session 4.4** • **Session 4.5**
Student Math Handbook	**Math Words and Ideas** in the *Student Math Handbook* are pages that summarize key words and ideas. Most Words and Ideas pages have at least one exercise.	• **Student Math Handbook, pp. 6–8, 17–29, 31–37, 44–49**
	Games pages are found in a section of the *Student Math Handbook.*	• **Student Math Handbook, pp. G1, G2, G3, G6, G7, G9, G13, G14, G19, G25**

Supporting the Range of Learners

Sessions	1.2	1.4	2.1	2.2	2.3	2.4	2.5	2.6	2.7	3.1	3.2	3.3	3.4	3.6	4.1	4.2	4.3	4.4	4.5
Intervention		•		•	•	•		•		•		•	•	•	•	•	•	•	•
Extension			•	•	•		•		•		•	•	•				•	•	•
ELL	•			•		•				•					•				

Intervention

Suggestions are made to support and engage students who are having difficulty with a particular idea, activity, or problem.

Extension

Suggestions are made to support and engage students who finish early or may be ready for additional challenge.

English Language Learners (ELL)

As English Language Learners work through the material of this unit, they must become fluent with the names of numbers and their written representations. They also need to learn and practice the language of addition. English Language Learners must be able to recognize and use addition-related words such as *add, in all, combine, plus,* and *sum.* You can teach some of this vocabulary directly, using demonstrations or native-language translations. You can support your students' vocabulary growth by encouraging them to use new words in context as they engage in the activities.

You can assess students' understanding with simple questions, such as "Paula has 3 cubes and Deshawn has 4. Who has *more,* Paula or Deshawn?" To develop English Language Learners' speaking skills, have them create groups of objects of different sizes and ask one another questions about the groups. Students will solidify their vocabulary through practical application as they participate in classroom activities and discussions.

English Language Learners must also grasp the concept of comparison in order to understand the material in this unit. They must understand and be able to use comparatives and superlatives. (See Session 2.2, page 61.) After English Language Learners have learned the comparative and superlative forms *bigger/biggest* and *smaller/smallest,* they will be able to apply these forms to other words (e.g., *shorter/shortest, taller/tallest*). You can introduce these words on an as-needed basis in the context of various activities.

Working with the Range of Learners: Classroom Cases is a set of episodes written by teachers that focuses on meeting the needs of the range of learners in the classroom. In the first section, *Setting up the Mathematical Community,* teachers write about how they create a supportive and productive learning environment in their classrooms. In the next section, *Accommodations for Learning,* teachers focus on specific modifications they make to meet the needs of some of their learners. In the last section, *Language and Representation,* teachers share how they help students use representations and develop language to investigate and express mathematical ideas. The questions at the end of each case provide a starting point for your own reflection or for discussion with colleagues. See *Implementing Investigations in Grade 1* for this set of episodes.

INVESTIGATION 1

Mathematical Emphasis

Counting and Quantity Developing strategies for accurately counting a set of objects by ones

Math Focus Points

- Counting a set of objects up to 20 by ones

This Investigation also focuses on

- Exploring the characteristics of cubes, pattern blocks, Geoblocks, and Power Polygons
- Developing strategies for counting accurately
- Using the calendar as a tool for keeping track of time
- Developing vocabulary to talk about time (morning, noon, midday, afternoon, etc.) and sequence (first, next, last, before, after, etc.)
- Collecting and recording data
- Estimating quantities up to about 30
- Adding or subtracting small amounts to/from a familiar number
- Connecting written numbers and number names
- Using the number line as a tool for counting
- Practicing the rote counting sequence forward and backward
- Developing and analyzing visual images for quantities up to 10
- Recreating an arrangement of objects
- Finding the total of two or more single-digit quantities

Counting and Quantity

SESSION 1.1 p. 26	Student Activity Book	Student Math Handbook	Professional Development: Read Ahead of Time
Morning Meeting: Daily Schedule Students learn two parts of the *Morning Meeting* routine—the *Daily Schedule* and *Attendance*—that will continue all year. The class establishes routines for using, caring for, and storing math materials. Students spend their first Math Workshop exploring connecting cubes, pattern blocks, Geoblocks, and Power Polygons. The session ends with a short discussion about Math Workshop and the manipulatives.	1		• **Part 2: *Using Investigations*** in *Implementing Investigations in Grade 1:* Components of the Program • **Mathematics in This Unit,** p. 10 • **Part 4: Classroom Routines** in *Implementing Investigations in Grade 1:* Morning Meeting • **Teacher Notes:** Counting Is More Than 1, 2, 3, p. 192; Talking About Shapes, pp. 189–191 • **Dialogue Box:** Mine Is a Sailboat, p. 224
SESSION 1.2 p. 32			
Morning Meeting: Calendar Students are introduced to another part of the *Morning Meeting* routine, the *Calendar.* They continue to explore cubes, pattern blocks, Geoblocks, and Power Polygons during Math Workshop, giving the teacher an opportunity to assess students' counting skills. The session ends with a short discussion about interlocking cubes.	2	17, 18, 19	• **Teacher Note:** Observing Students as They Count, p. 193
SESSION 1.3 p. 38			
Morning Meeting: Weather Students are introduced to the final part of the *Morning Meeting* routine, collecting data about the weather. Math Workshop focuses on counting and exploring materials. The session ends with a discussion about pattern blocks.	3	17, 21–23	
SESSION 1.4 p. 43			
Collect 20 Together Students are introduced to a counting game, *Collect 20 Together.* Math Workshop continues. The session ends with a discussion about Geoblocks.	4	21–23; G1	

Classroom Routines See page 20 for an overview.

Morning Meeting

- Daily Schedule: Prepare a daily class schedule.
- Yearlong calendar: Prepare a yearlong calendar and display it in the classroom.
- Monthly calendar: Prepare the calendar displaying the current month.
- Monthly weather chart: Prepare a monthly weather chart showing typical weather in your area.
- Yearlong weather chart: Prepare a yearlong weather chart showing typical weather in your area.

Materials to Gather	Materials to Prepare
• **Connecting cubes** (class set) • **Pattern blocks** (class set) • **Geoblocks** (class set) • **Power Polygons** (class set)	• **Daily Schedule** Prepare a daily class schedule and post it where all students can see it. See example on page 27. • **M1–M2, Family Letter** Make copies. (1 per student)
• **Crayons or markers** (several per class) • **Connecting cubes** (class set) • **Pattern blocks** (class set) • **Geoblocks** (class set) • **Power Polygons** (class set) • **Chart paper**	• **M3, Assessment Checklist: Counting 20** ☑ Make copies. Write students' names on the recording sheets. (as needed) • **Class yearlong calendar** Prepare and post a yearlong calendar. • **Class pocket monthly calendar** Use the removable numbers to prepare the class pocket calendar displaying the current month.
• **M3, Assessment Checklist: Counting 20** ☑ (from Session 1.2) • **Connecting cubes** (class set) • **Pattern blocks** (class set) • **Geoblocks** (class set) • **Power Polygons** (class set) • **Chart paper**	• **Class monthly weather chart** Prepare a monthly weather chart showing typical weather in your area. • **Class yearlong weather chart** Prepare and post a yearlong weather chart showing typical weather in your area.
• **M3, Assessment Checklist: Counting 20** ☑ (from Session 1.2) • **Dot cubes** (1 per pair) • **Counters** (about 25 per pair) • **Connecting cubes** (class set) • **Pattern blocks** (class set) • **Geoblocks** (class set) • **Power Polygons** (class set) • **Chart paper**	• **M4, *Collect 20 Together*** Make copies. (as needed) • **M5, Twenty-Frame** Make copies. (as needed; optional)

☑ Checklist Available

SESSION 1.1

Morning Meeting: Daily Schedule

Math Focus Points

- Developing vocabulary to talk about time and sequence (*first, next, last, before, after, during,* and so on)
- Counting a set of objects up to 20 by 1s
- Exploring the characteristics of cubes, pattern blocks, Geoblocks, and Power Polygons

Vocabulary

schedule
estimate

Today's Plan			Materials
ACTIVITY 1 Introducing *Morning Meeting:* Daily Schedule and Attendance	20 MIN	CLASS	• Daily Class Schedule
ACTIVITY 2 Introducing Math Tools	10 MIN	CLASS	• Connecting cubes; pattern blocks; Geoblocks; Power Polygons
MATH WORKSHOP 3 Exploring Math Tools 3A Exploring Connecting Cubes 3B Exploring Pattern Blocks 3C Exploring Geoblocks 3D Exploring Power Polygons	30 MIN		3A • Connecting cubes 3B • Pattern blocks (class set) 3C • Geoblocks (class set) 3D • Power Polygons (class set)
SESSION FOLLOW-UP 4 Daily Practice			• *Student Activity Book,* p. 1 • M1–M2, Family Letter*

*See *Materials to Prepare,* p. 25.

Classroom Routines

Morning Meeting This routine, which consists of four activities (*Daily Schedule, Attendance, Calendar,* and *Weather*), will be introduced during the activities in this Investigation. For a complete description of this routine, see Part 4: Classroom Routines in *Implementing Investigations in Grade 1:* Morning Meeting.

ACTIVITY

Introducing *Morning Meeting*: Daily Schedule and Attendance

Classroom routines are an ongoing part of the K–2 *Investigations* curriculum. The *Morning Meeting* routine includes the following activities, which are a regular part of many primary classrooms and are full of mathematical potential:❶

- Daily Schedule
- Attendance
- Calendar
- Collecting Weather Data

Direct students' attention to your posted Daily Schedule.

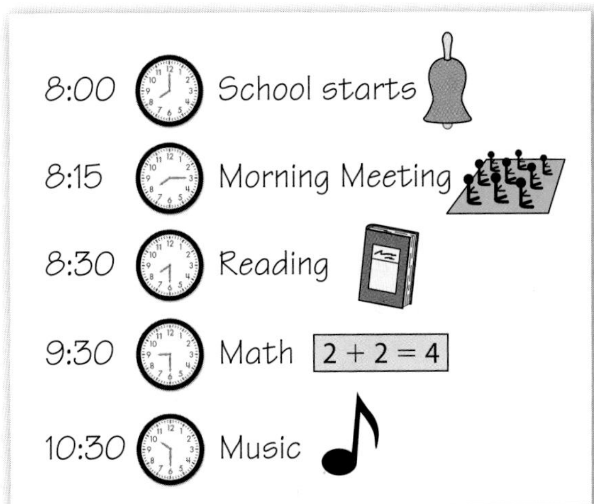

This is our daily schedule. It will tell us what is happening today. The *first* thing we are doing this morning is Morning Meeting. *After* Morning Meeting, who can look and tell us what they think comes *next?*

As they discuss the daily schedule, students are making sense of words such as *first, next, last, before, after, during, early, later,* and *at the beginning* (or *end*) *of.*

In this first session, briefly discuss the schedule for the day, focusing on the sequence of events.

For attendance, decide together whether to count only students or to include adults in your daily count.

Professional Development

❶ **Part 4: Classroom Routines** in ***Implementing Investigations in Grade 1:*** Morning Meeting

Professional Development

❷ **Teacher Note:** Counting Is More Than 1, 2, 3, p. 192

Look around our classroom. About how many children do you think are in our class? That's called making an estimate. When you estimate, you try to figure out *about* how many of something there are.

Take a few estimates. Then explain what attendance is and why it is important.

Who has an idea about how we could figure out *exactly* how many students are here today? It's important that we count carefully so that we're really sure how many children are here and how many are absent.

Ask several students to suggest different ideas for counting the number of students in the class.

Students might say:

"We could each stand up and say a number."

"Everybody could stand up. I'll count them all. They can sit down when I've counted them."

"We can each take a cube and then count the cubes."

Try several of the ways that students suggest to establish and confirm the total number of students in your class. Be sure to count around the class as one strategy.

It is important to establish and double-check the total number of students in your class. This will be an important number in your classroom this year, one that may become a landmark number for many of your students because of the regularity with which they explore it.

[Paula] suggested counting around our circle, and we did that, starting with [Diego] and ending with [Carol]. What do you think would happen if we counted starting with [Carol] and ending with [Diego]?

Some first graders will not know or be sure that if they count the students in a different order, it will result in the same total number. The attendance routine offers many opportunities to pose questions like this that help develop students' understanding of the important ideas that comprise the skill of counting, such as conservation of quantity.❷

ACTIVITY

Introducing Math Tools

10 MIN CLASS

Briefly introduce students to the connecting cubes, pattern blocks, Geoblocks, and Power Polygons.

As we learn about mathematics this year, we will be using many different things to help us solve problems. We will be using tools such as these cubes and blocks as we solve mathematics problems and play math games.

Show students each manipulative, and ask whether they are familiar with any of these materials, how they have used them in the past, and whether they know the names of the materials. As they hear words like *rectangle, hexagon,* or *pyramid* used correctly and in context, students will begin to learn them naturally.③

With the introduction of any new material, it is important to establish clear ground rules. You will want to discuss where the materials are stored and how they will be used and cared for.④

As students explore math tools, they become familiar with some of the important attributes of those tools.

Professional Development

③ **Teacher Note:** Talking About Shapes, p. 189

④ **Part 2: Using *Investigations*** in *Implementing Investigations in Grade 1:* Components of the Program

Professional Development

5 **Part 2: How to Use Investigations** in *Implementing Investigations in Grade 1:* Components of the Program

3 MATH WORKSHOP

Exploring Math Tools

30 MIN

Math Workshop is a format that recurs throughout the *Investigations* curriculum.5 Students will continue with these Math Workshop activities in Sessions 1.2, 1.3, and 1.4.

For the next few days, we'll be having a Math Workshop as a part of every math class. You will be using connecting cubes, pattern blocks, Geoblocks, and Power Polygons. Each of these math tools will be in a different part of the classroom. I'd like everybody to work with each of these—the cubes, the pattern blocks, the Geoblocks, and the Power Polygons—at least once during the next few days.

Explain how many students can be at each "center" at one time. Depending on how you have organized your classroom, you could indicate this by the number of chairs at a certain table or by posting the information on the board. Tell students that they can work with just one other classmate or in small groups. Help them choose which material to use today, monitoring the number of students at each center. Remind students that these materials will be available for a few days.

3A Exploring Connecting Cubes

PAIRS GROUPS

Students become familiar with connecting cubes by exploring them freely.

3B Exploring Pattern Blocks

PAIRS GROUPS

Students become familiar with pattern blocks by exploring them freely.

3C Exploring Geoblocks

PAIRS GROUPS

Students become familiar with Geoblocks by exploring them freely.

3D Exploring Power Polygons

PAIRS GROUPS

Students become familiar with Power Polygons by exploring them freely.

ONGOING ASSESSMENT: Observing Students at Work

This is a time to establish expectations and routines for using math materials and for working productively during Math Workshop.

- **What do students do with the manipulatives?** Do they follow the guidelines for taking them out? Using them? Caring for them? Storing them? Cleaning up?⑥
- **Are students able to follow the Math Workshop format?** Do they understand what activities are available and how many students can be at one center?

About 10 to 15 minutes before the end of class, ask students to clean up their materials, check the floor for stray cubes or blocks, and return all materials to their containers. It is a good idea to give students a warning a few minutes before the end of a work period to alert them that a transition is about to occur.

SESSION FOLLOW-UP

Daily Practice and Homework

Daily Practice: For reinforcement of this unit's content, have students complete *Student Activity Book* page 1.

Family Letter: Send home copies of Family Letter (M1–M2).

Professional Development

⑥ **Dialogue Box:** Mine Is a Sailboat, p. 224

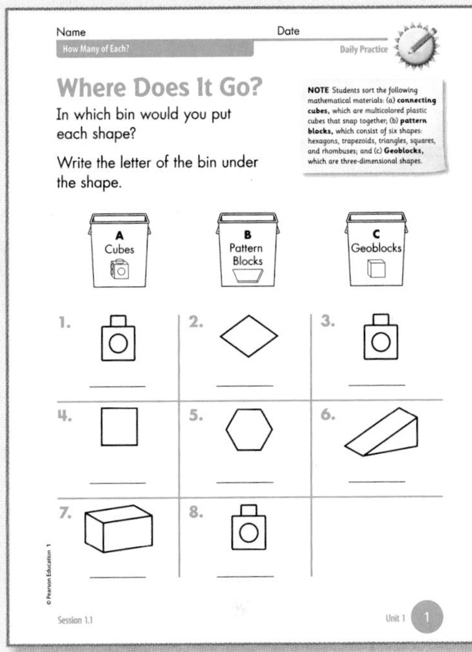

Name Date

How Many of Each? Daily Practice

Where Does It Go?

In which bin would you put each shape?

Write the letter of the bin under the shape.

NOTE Students sort the following mathematical materials: (a) **connecting cubes,** which are multicolored plastic cubes that snap together; (b) **pattern blocks,** which consist of six shapes: hexagons, trapezoids, triangles, squares, and rhombuses; and (c) **Geoblocks,** which are three-dimensional shapes.

A Cubes | B Pattern Blocks | C Geoblocks

1. 2. 3. 4. 5. 6. 7. 8.

© Pearson Education 1

Session 1.1 Unit 1 1

▲ Student Activity Book, p. 1

SESSION 1.2

Morning Meeting: Calendar

Math Focus Points

- Exploring the characteristics of cubes, pattern blocks, Geoblocks, and Power Polygons
- Counting a set of objects up to 20 by 1s

Vocabulary

calendar

Today's Plan			Materials
1 ACTIVITY **Introducing *Morning Meeting:* Calendar**	15 MIN	CLASS	• Class pocket monthly calendar* • Class yearlong calendar*
2 MATH WORKSHOP **Exploring Math Tools** 2A Exploring Connecting Cubes 2B Exploring Pattern Blocks 2C Exploring Geoblocks 2D Exploring Power Polygons	35 MIN		• M3* ✓ 2A • Connecting cubes 2B • Pattern blocks 2C • Geoblocks 2D • Power Polygons
3 DISCUSSION **What Did You Notice?**	10 MIN	CLASS	• Chart paper; connecting cubes (as needed)
4 SESSION FOLLOW-UP **Daily Practice**			• *Student Activity Book,* p. 2 • *Student Math Handbook,* pp. 17, 18, 19

*See *Materials to Prepare,* p. 25.

Classroom Routines

Morning Meeting Continue to follow the *Daily Schedule* and *Attendance* activities introduced in Session 1.1.

ACTIVITY

1 Introducing *Morning Meeting:* Calendar

Introduce another part of the *Morning Meeting* routine, the Calendar, by pointing out the yearlong calendar that you have posted.①

Who knows what this is? It is a calendar. Most times we see only the page for the month that's happening right now. This calendar shows all the *months,* in *order,* in one place. This will be up here all year to help us think about the order of the months, how long they are, and how long a *year* is.

Together as a class, read the names of the months and count how many there are.

Do any of you have calendars at home? What do you or your family use it for?

Using children's ideas, explain that the calendar is a tool and that one of the things that people use a calendar for is to keep track of time and special events.

We're also going to have a calendar for the month that is happening right now. Does anyone know the name of the month that we are in right now? It's [September], the first month of school. Can someone find [September] on our whole-year calendar?

Classroom Routines: Morning Meeting *helps students see and use the calendar as a tool for keeping track of time and events.*

Professional Development

① **Part 4: Classroom Routines** in *Implementing Investigations in Grade 1:* Morning Meeting

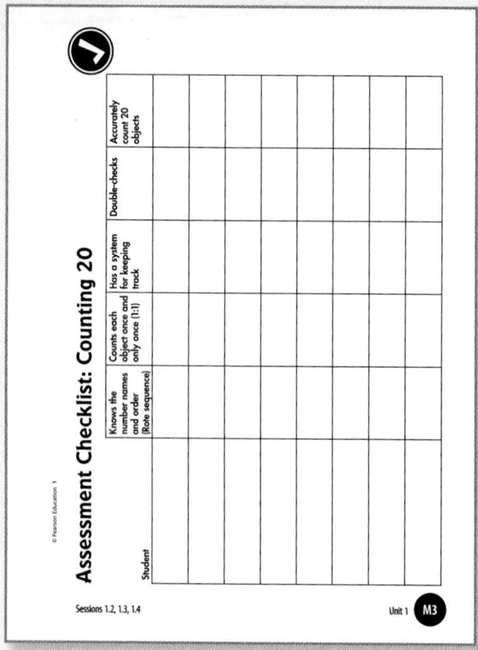
Assessment Checklist: Counting 20

Student	Knows the number names and order (Rote sequence)	Counts each object once and only once (1:1)	Has a system for keeping track	Double-checks	Accurately count 20 objects

Sessions 1.2, 1.3, 1.4 Unit 1 M3

▲ Resource Masters, M3

Direct students' attention to the monthly calendar, and ask what they notice about the calendar for [September]. Some students will focus on the arrangement of the numbers, others on the total number of days, and still others on the special occasions noted on particular days.

Encourage students to figure out which number on the calendar represents today, and ask them how they knew. Model counting to the number that is today's date. Also, ask what day of the week today is and how they could figure that out.

MATH WORKSHOP

2 Exploring Math Tools

35 MIN

Students continue with the activities begun during Math Workshop in Session 1.1.

Remind students of the available activities. Review the rules you established about how materials will be used and cared for, and have a brief conversation about any issues, such as sharing, that came up in Session 1.1. Also explain that today as you circulate, you will be asking some students to count out a set of about 20 cubes, pattern blocks, Geoblocks, or Power Polygons for you.

Some students will need help remembering which activities they have or have not yet done; others will need encouragement to choose a new material to explore.

The activities in this Math Workshop offer an opportunity to informally assess students' counting skills. As you observe students at work with the materials, ask individual students to count out 20 of whatever material they are working with. When partially done, ask how many they have so far. When finished, ask how they know that there are 20. Record your observations on Assessment Checklist: Counting 20 (M3).

2A Exploring Connecting Cubes

PAIRS GROUPS

For complete details about this activity, see Session 1.1, pages 30–31.

2B Exploring Pattern Blocks

PAIRS GROUPS

For complete details about this activity, see Session 1.1, pages 30–31.

2C Exploring Geoblocks

PAIRS GROUPS

For complete details about this activity, see Session 1.1, pages 30–31.

2D Exploring Power Polygons

PAIRS GROUPS

For complete details about this activity, see Session 1.1, pages 30–31.

ONGOING ASSESSMENT: Observing Students at Work

As they explore these materials, students practice counting sets of objects.❸ ❹ Use Assessment Checklist: Counting 20 (M3) to record your observations. See sample on page 36.

- **Are students fluent with the names and sequence of the numbers?**
- **How accurate and confident are students as they count?** Do they say one number word for each object? Do they skip (or double count) any? Can they keep track of which items they have and have not counted?
- **Do students have a way of double-checking their count?**

For information about what to look for as students use the materials, see Session 1.1, page 31.

DIFFERENTIATION: Supporting the Range of Learners

ELL Some English Language Learners may not know how to count in English. Although they will acquire this knowledge through day-to-day exposure, you can provide additional practice during each day's Math Workshop. Work with individual students or with a small group on the number sequences 1–5, 1–10, and then 1–20 until students can count independently in English from 1–20.

Professional Development

❸ **Teacher Note:** Counting Is More Than 1, 2, 3, p. 192

❹ **Teacher Note:** Observing Students as They Count, p. 193

Assessment Checklist: Counting 20

Student	Knows the number names and order (Rote sequence)	Counts each object once and only once (1:1)	Has a system for keeping track	Double-checks	Accurately counts 20 objects

DISCUSSION

3 What Did You Notice?

Math Focus Points for Discussion

- Exploring the characteristics of connecting cubes

Because Math Workshop will be an integral part of math this year, spend a few minutes talking with students about how this session went in terms of management and logistics.

Topics might include:

- Using and sharing materials
- Caring for and storing materials
- Noise level
- Working together
- Working purposefully

Talk with students about how Math Workshop is going and about the mathematics of one of the materials they have been exploring. You might ask questions such as these:

- How can we describe the cubes?
- What can you do with the cubes?
- What can you tell us about the connecting cubes?

Record students' ideas on a sheet of chart paper you can post for their reference.

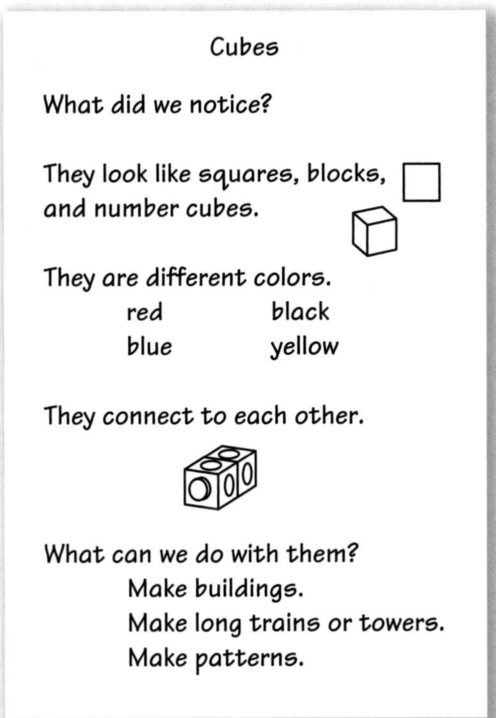

We'll be using cubes often in math this year. We will use them to help us count, to think about patterns, to solve problems and show our thinking, and to build different structures.

SESSION FOLLOW-UP

Daily Practice

Daily Practice: For reinforcement of this unit's content, have students complete *Student Activity Book* page 2.

Student Math Handbook: Students and families may use pages 17, 18, 19 for reference and review. See pages 243–252 in the back of this unit.

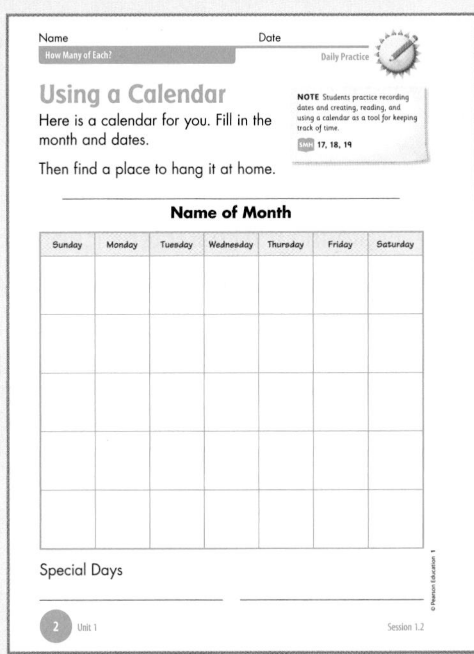

Name Date

How Many of Each? Daily Practice

Using a Calendar

Here is a calendar for you. Fill in the month and dates.

Then find a place to hang it at home.

NOTE Students practice recording dates and creating, reading, and using a calendar as a tool for keeping track of time.

SMH 17, 18, 19

Name of Month

Sunday	Monday	Tuesday	Wednesday	Thursday	Friday	Saturday

Special Days

2 Unit 1 Session 1.2

© Pearson Education 1

▲ Student Activity Book, p. 2

Morning Meeting: Weather

Math Focus Points

- Exploring the characteristics of cubes, pattern blocks, Geoblocks, and Power Polygons
- Counting a set of objects up to 20 by 1s

Vocabulary

data

Today's Plan		Materials
ACTIVITY 1 Introducing *Morning Meeting:* Weather	15 MIN CLASS	• Class yearlong weather chart*; class monthly weather chart*; crayons or markers (several per class)
MATH WORKSHOP 2 Exploring Math Tools 2A Exploring Connecting Cubes 2B Exploring Pattern Blocks 2C Exploring Geoblocks 2D Exploring Power Polygons	35 MIN	• M3 ✓ (from Session 1.2) 2A • Connecting cubes 2B • Pattern blocks 2C • Geoblocks 2D • Power Polygons
DISCUSSION 3 What Did You Notice?	10 MIN CLASS	• Pattern blocks; chart paper
SESSION FOLLOW-UP 4 Daily Practice		• *Student Activity Book*, p. 3 • *Student Math Handbook*, pp. 17, 21–23

*See *Materials to Prepare*, p. 25.

Classroom Routines

Morning Meeting Continue to follow the *Daily Schedule, Attendance,* and *Calendar* activities introduced in Sessions 1.1 and 1.2.

ACTIVITY

Introducing *Morning Meeting*: Weather

Explain to students that the last part of the *Morning Meeting* routine will be to collect and record data about the weather. First, discuss the categories on your posted weather charts (i.e., sunny, cloudy, rainy, snowy, and so on, depending on your climate).➊

On these charts, we'll keep information, or **data**, about the weather all year long. What is the weather today? It's [rainy], so where should we put an X on the chart? [Jacob] says that it's also [windy], so where else should we put an X?

Demonstrate marking an X in the appropriate boxes on the yearlong chart.

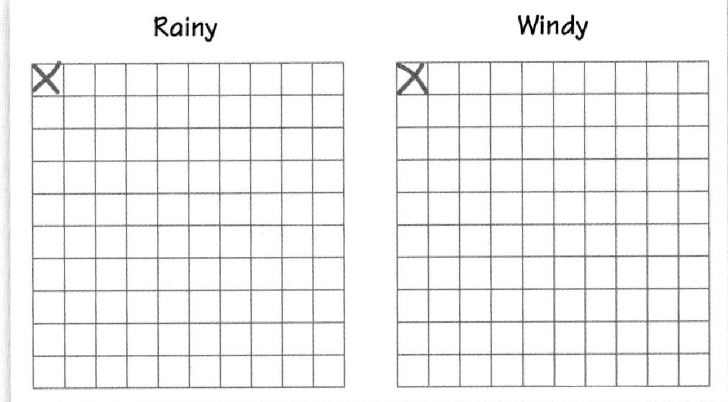

Then explain that you will also keep track of the data for each month because that will give you the chance to look at information in different ways. Ask students to help you record today's data on your [September] weather chart.

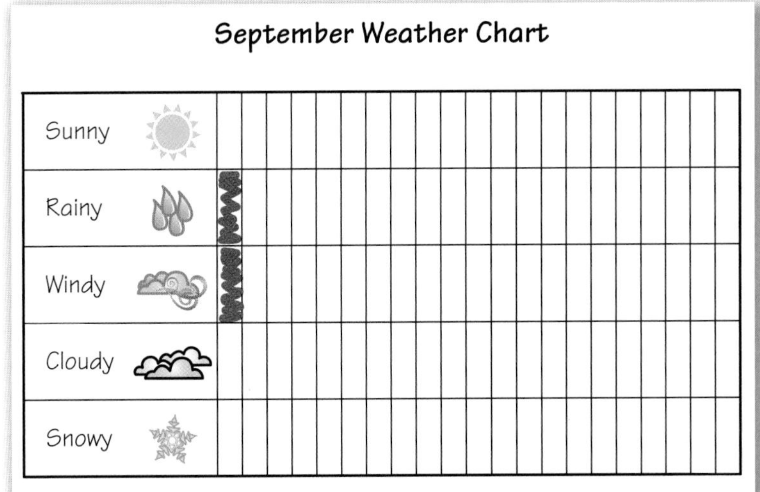

Professional Development

➊ **Part 4: Classroom Routines** in *Implementing Investigations in Grade 1:* Morning Meeting

MATH WORKSHOP

Exploring Math Tools

35 MIN

Students continue with the same Math Workshop activities as in Session 1.2.

Briefly discuss any issues that have been coming up (such as sharing or noise) and review any guidelines as necessary (such as putting materials away when finished with them).

Remind students that they should get to each Math Workshop activity at some point and that you will be asking students to count for you as you walk around the room. Continue to record your observations on Assessment Checklist: Counting 20 (M3).

2A Exploring Connecting Cubes

PAIRS GROUPS

For complete details about this activity, see Session 1.1, pages 30–31.

2B Exploring Pattern Blocks

PAIRS GROUPS

For complete details about this activity, see Session 1.1, pages 30–31.

2C Exploring Geoblocks

PAIRS GROUPS

For complete details about this activity, see Session 1.1, pages 30–31.

2D Exploring Power Polygons

PAIRS GROUPS

For complete details about this activity, see Session 1.1, pages 30–31.

ONGOING ASSESSMENT: Observing Students at Work

For information about what to observe as students use the materials, see Session 1.1, page 31. For information about what to observe as students count, see Session 1.2, page 35.

DISCUSSION

3 What Did You Notice?

Math Focus Points for Discussion

- Exploring the characteristics of pattern blocks

Spend a few minutes talking about how Math Workshop is going and about the mathematics of one of the materials students have been exploring. You might ask questions such as these:

- How can we describe the pattern blocks?
- What can you do with the pattern blocks?
- What did you notice about the pattern blocks?
- How are the pattern blocks the same as or different from the Power Polygons?

Record students' ideas on a sheet of chart paper that you can post for their reference.

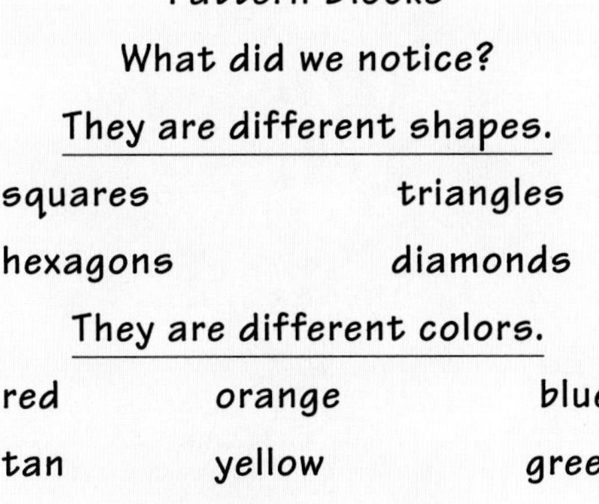

Some fit together.

What can we do with them?

Make designs.

Make pictures.

Make patterns.

Name Date

How Many of Each? Daily Practice

How Many Apples?

There were 7 apples on each tree. Some fell off. Write how many apples are still on the tree and how many fell off.

NOTE Students practice counting and breaking a number into two parts (e.g., 7 = 4 + 3).

SMH 46–47

1. On ____ Off ____
2. On ____ Off ____
3. On ____ Off ____
4. On ____ Off ____
5. On ____ Off ____
6. On ____ Off ____

Session 1.3 Unit 1 3

▲ Student Activity Book, p. 3

End the discussion by sharing with students some of the things they will be doing with pattern blocks over the course of first grade.

We'll be using pattern blocks and Power Polygons during math this year to think about shapes and to build designs. They can also help us count, solve problems, or show our thinking.

4 SESSION FOLLOW-UP
Daily Practice

Daily Practice: For reinforcement of this unit's content, have students complete *Student Activity Book* page 3.

Student Math Handbook: Students and families may use *Student Math Handbook* pages 17, 21–23 for reference and review. See pages 243–252 in the back of this unit.

Collect 20 Together

Math Focus Points

- Counting a set of objects up to 20 by 1s
- Exploring the characteristics of cubes, pattern blocks, Geoblocks, and Power Polygons

Today's Plan		Materials
1 ACTIVITY **Introducing *Collect 20 Together***	10 MIN CLASS	• Dot cubes; counters
2 MATH WORKSHOP **Exploring Math Tools** 2A Exploring Connecting Cubes 2B Exploring Pattern Blocks 2C Exploring Geoblocks 2D Exploring Power Polygons 2E *Collect 20 Together*	40 MIN	• M3 ✓ * (from Session 1.2) 2A • Connecting cubes 2B • Pattern blocks 2C • Geoblocks 2D • Power Polygons (class set) 2E • M4*; M5* • Dot cubes (1 per pair); counters (about 25 per pair)
3 DISCUSSION **What Did You Notice?**	10 MIN CLASS	• Geoblocks (as needed); chart paper
4 SESSION FOLLOW-UP **Daily Practice**		• *Student Activity Book,* p. 4 • *Student Math Handbook,* pp. 21–23; G1

*See *Materials to Prepare,* p. 25.

Classroom Routines

Morning Meeting Follow the *Morning Meeting* routine with students daily, outside of your formal math time: review the day's schedule, take attendance, establish the current day on the calendar and count to that number, and record the day's weather. This routine should quickly become a familiar daily activity that takes only 5 to 10 minutes.

ACTIVITY

Introducing *Collect 20 Together*

10 MIN CLASS

Introduce *Collect 20 Together* to the entire class by playing a demonstration game, perhaps assembling students in a circle on the floor. Enlist two student volunteers to play, or play the game yourself with a student partner. It is important to emphasize that partners will be *working together* to collect 20 counters.

Today you and a partner are going to play a game called *Collect 20 Together*. You will take turns rolling a dot cube and taking that many counters. Keep rolling until you and your partner have collected 20 counters. The two of you win when you can show that you've collected at least 20 counters *together*.

Let's watch a sample game. [Deshawn] rolled 2. How many counters does he take?

What number did [Stacy] roll? [Stacy] rolled 5. How many counters does she add to the group? How many do they have altogether? Is that more or less than 20? How do you know?

Students might say:

"If you count the 2, then the 5, it's 7."

"Deshawn took 2 counters so I counted the new counters: 3, 4, 5, 6, 7. There are 7."

"I just knew that there were 7 counters because 2 and 5 together is 7."

Play for another turn or two, or until you think students understand the game, continuing to ask students how they figured out how many counters in all.

Explain that the game is over as soon as the players have at least 20 counters. Depending on what they roll, they may get 20 exactly or they may end up with a few more than 20.

MATH WORKSHOP

Exploring Math Tools

40 MIN

This is the first time a new activity has been introduced to Math Workshop. Remind students that this new activity is available, and explain that this is the last day to explore cubes, pattern blocks, Geoblocks, and Power Polygons.①

As you circulate, continue to ask individual students to count out 20 objects for you. Record your observations on Assessment Checklist: Counting 20 (M3).

2A Exploring Connecting Cubes

PAIRS GROUPS

For complete details about this activity, see Session 1.1, pages 30–31.

2B Exploring Pattern Blocks

PAIRS GROUPS

For complete details about this activity, see Session 1.1, pages 30–31.

2C Exploring Geoblocks

PAIRS GROUPS

For complete details about this activity, see Session 1.1, pages 30–31.

2D Exploring Power Polygons

PAIRS GROUPS

For complete details about this activity, see Session 1.1, pages 30–31.

ONGOING ASSESSMENT: Observing Students at Work

For information about what to observe as students use the materials, see Session 1.1, page 31. For information about what to observe as students count, see Session 1.2, page 35.

2E *Collect 20 Together*

PAIRS

Partners play a game in which they work together to collect at least 20 counters. Have available copies of *Collect 20 Together* (M4) as needed.

Teaching Note

① **Making Math Materials Available** Reassure students that math manipulatives will continue to be an important part of math class. Consider how to make materials available at other times of the day, such as during indoor recess or free time.

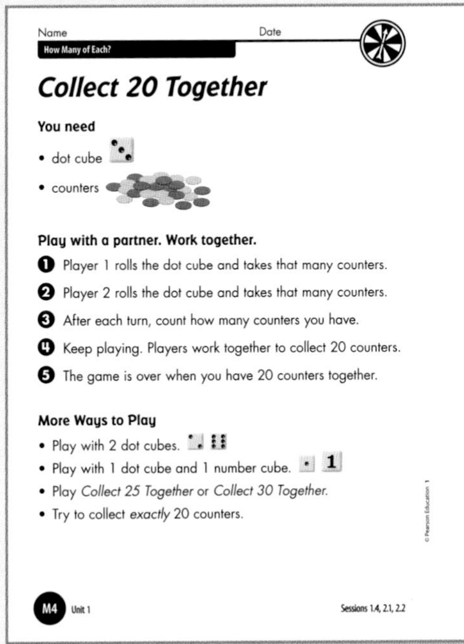

Name Date

How Many of Each?

Collect 20 Together

You need

- dot cube
- counters

Play with a partner. Work together.

1. Player 1 rolls the dot cube and takes that many counters.
2. Player 2 rolls the dot cube and takes that many counters.
3. After each turn, count how many counters you have.
4. Keep playing. Players work together to collect 20 counters.
5. The game is over when you have 20 counters together.

More Ways to Play

- Play with 2 dot cubes.
- Play with 1 dot cube and 1 number cube.
- Play *Collect 25 Together* or *Collect 30 Together*.
- Try to collect *exactly* 20 counters.

M4 Unit 1 Sessions 1.4, 2.1, 2.2

▲ Resource Masters, M4

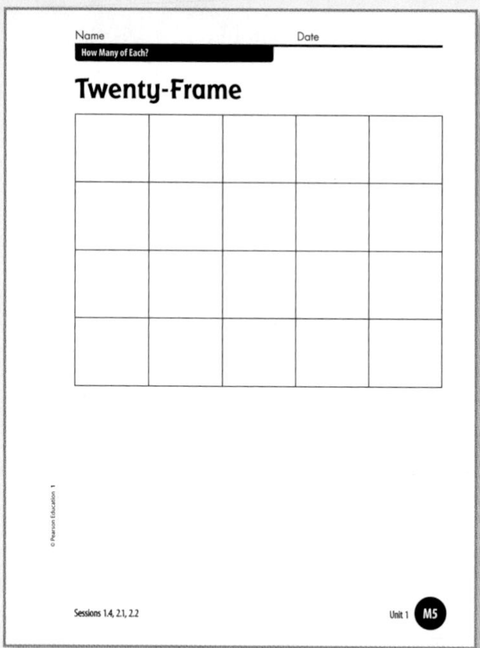
Name Date

How Many of Each?

Twenty-Frame

© Pearson Education 1

Sessions 1.4, 2.1, 2.2 Unit 1 M5

▲ Resource Masters, M5; T1

Collect 20 Together *offers students repeated opportunities to count and recount sets of objects.*

ONGOING ASSESSMENT: Observing Students at Work

Students become familiar with the dot images for 1–6, and practice counting as they collect counters and keep track of the number they have in all. Use this activity to continue to assess students' abilities to count to 20.

- **How do students decide how many counters to take?** Do they recognize the dot patterns, or do they have to count the dots?
- **How do students figure out and keep track of how many counters they have at the end of each turn?** Do they count all? Do they organize or remember, and then count on from the previous total?
- **How fluent and accurate are students in their counting?** What errors do you notice?

DIFFERENTIATION: Supporting the Range of Learners

Intervention Students who are having difficulty counting and keeping track of 20 objects can play to a smaller number, such as 15 or 10. They can use Twenty-Frame (M5) to help them organize and keep track of the counters.

DISCUSSION

3 What Did You Notice?

Math Focus Points for Discussion

- Exploring the characteristics of Geoblocks

Spend a few minutes talking about Math Workshop. Because this is the first time pairs of students have played a game together, you might need to spend some time on management-related topics such as working together, noise level, or being a good partner.

Finally, spend a few more minutes talking about the Geoblocks.

- How can we describe the Geoblocks?
- What can you do with the Geoblocks?
- What did you notice about the Geoblocks?

Record students' ideas on a sheet of chart paper for their reference.

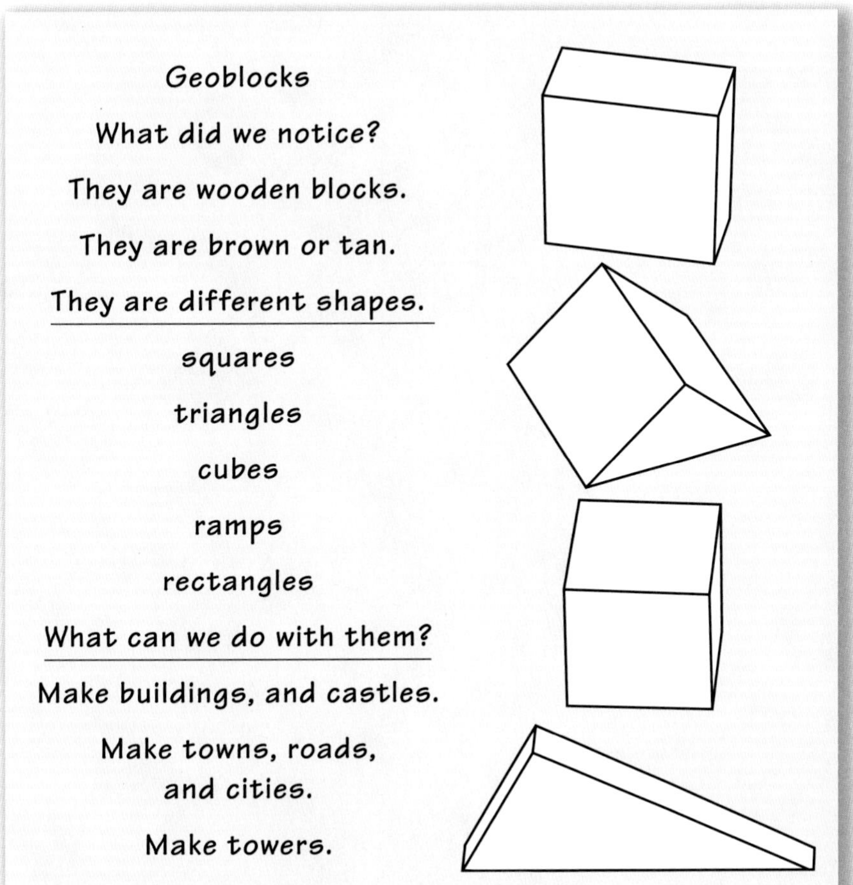

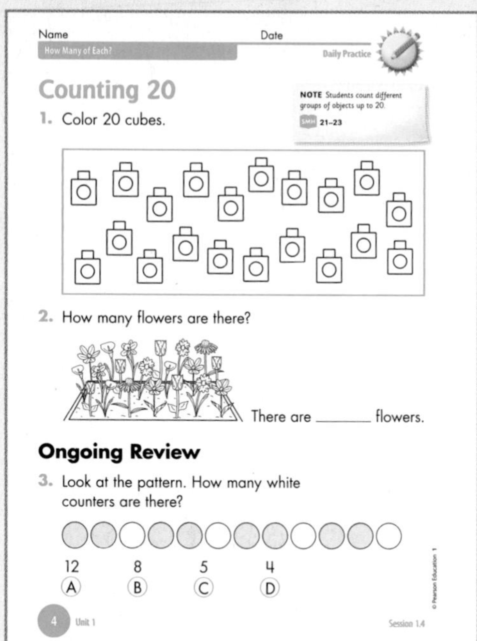
Name Date
How Many of Each? Daily Practice

Counting 20

NOTE Students count different groups of objects up to 20.
SMH 21–23

1. Color 20 cubes.

2. How many flowers are there?

There are ______ flowers.

Ongoing Review

3. Look at the pattern. How many white counters are there?

12 (A) 8 (B) 5 (C) 4 (D)

© Pearson Education 1

4 Unit 1 Session 1.4

▲ Student Activity Book, p. 4

End the discussion by sharing with students some of the things they will be doing with Geoblocks over the course of first grade.

We'll be using Geoblocks during math this year, especially when we are thinking and talking about shapes. We'll also be using them to build things.

4 SESSION FOLLOW-UP

Daily Practice

Daily Practice: For reinforcement of this unit's content, have students complete *Student Activity Book* page 4.

Student Math Handbook: Students and families may use *Student Math Handbook* pages 21–23 and G1 for reference and review. See pages 243–252 in the back of this unit.

INVESTIGATION 2

Mathematical Emphases

Counting and Quantity Developing strategies for accurately counting a set of objects by ones

Math Focus Points

- Counting a set of up to 20 objects by 1s
- Practicing the rote counting sequence forward and backward, from 1 to 30
- Connecting number names and written numbers to the quantities they represent
- Developing and analyzing visual images for quantities up to 10

Counting and Quantity Developing an understanding of the magnitude and position of numbers

Math Focus Points

- Ordering a set of numbers and quantities up to 12
- Comparing two quantities up to 20 to see which is larger
- Developing an understanding of how the quantities in the counting sequence are related: each number is 1 more or 1 less than the number before or after it

Whole Number Operations Using manipulatives, drawings, tools, and notation to show strategies and solutions

Math Focus Points

- Using the number line as a tool for counting
- Introducing standard notation for comparing quantities (greater than, less than, and equal to)
- Recording a solution to a problem

Counting and Comparing

	Student Activity Book	Student Math Handbook	Professional Development: Read Ahead of Time
SESSION 2.1 p. 54			
Start With/Get To Students are introduced to another of the yearlong routines, *Start With/Get To.* In this counting routine, students are given a start number and an end number, and they count from one to the other. In this context, students are introduced to a number line as another mathematical tool. The whole class plays and discusses *Collect 20 Together.*	5	21–23, 26, 31; G1	• **Part 4: Classroom Routines** in *Implementing Investigations in Grade 1:* Start With/Get To • **Part 2: Using Investigations** in *Implementing Investigations in Grade 1:* Components of the Program • **Dialogue Box:** *Start With/Get To,* p. 225
SESSION 2.2 p. 60			
Staircases Students are introduced to Staircases, an activity in which they build and order a set of cube towers from 1 through 12. Math Workshop focuses on counting and ordering quantities, and linking quantities to written and spoken numbers. The session ends with a discussion about using a twenty-frame to play *Collect 20 Together.*	6	21–23; G1	
SESSION 2.3 p. 65			
Counting What's in a Mystery Box Students are introduced to a counting activity in which pairs count and record the number of items in a Mystery Box. Math Workshop continues, and the session ends with a discussion based on cube staircases for which students figure out which step is missing.	7–8	6–8, 21–23	• **Part 1: Collaborating with the Authors** in *Implementing Investigations in Grade 1:* The Teacher-Student-Curriculum Partnership
SESSION 2.4 p. 71			
Comparing Quantities Students are introduced to two new games, *Compare Dots* and *Compare,* in which they figure out which of two cards has more objects. Math Workshop continues, and the session ends with a discussion about cube staircases that introduces the idea of counting backward.	9	21–23; G2, G3	• **Algebra Connections in this Unit,** p. 16 • **Dialogue Box:** Discussing Staircases, pp. 226–227

Classroom Routines See page 20 for an overview.

Start With/Get To

- A basket
- M6–M7, *Start With/Get To* cards, numbers 1–30
- Clothes pins (2)
- Class number line

Quick Images

- T2; T7: Dot Cards, Sets A and B. Cut apart the cards and store them in an envelope or in the plastic sleeve of the Resources Binder.

Materials to Gather	Materials to Prepare
• **Materials for *Collect 20 Together*** See Session 1.4, p. 25. • **T1, Twenty-Frame** (optional) • **Basket** (1 per class); **red clothespin, green clothespin** (1 each per class)	• **M5, Twenty-Frame** If you did not make copies for Session 1.4, make copies for use in this session and in Session 2.2. (as needed) • **M6–M7, *Start With/Get To* Cards, Set A** Make copies on cardstock, if available. You may want to laminate the copies. Cut apart the cards, from 1 through the number of students in the class. Place the cards in a basket. • **M9–M10, Family Letter** Make copies. (1 per student) • **Number line** Display the class number line. Make sure that it shows the numbers from 1 to at least 30.
• **Materials for *Collect 20 Together*** See Session 1.4, p. 25. • **Connecting cubes** (about 100 per pair)	• **M5, Twenty-Frame** Make copies. (1 per pair plus extras) • **Connecting cubes with labels** Label cubes from 1–12 and place them in a resealable plastic bag. (6–8 sets per class; 1 set per pair)
• **Connecting cubes** (about 100 per pair) • **Connecting cubes labeled 1–12** (1 set per pair; from Session 2.2)	• **M8, Mystery Boxes** Make copies. Depending on how quickly students work, some students might work with 3 or 4 boxes. (as needed) • **Mystery Boxes** Prepare 6–8 covered, opaque boxes, each containing a different set of countable objects (buttons, seashells, keys, pennies, plastic spoons, etc.). Label each box with a letter, beginning with A. Prepare boxes containing 10–15 items, 15–20 items, and one with up to 30 items.
• **T2, Dot Cards, Set A** (optional) • **Mystery Boxes** (1 per pair; from Session 2.3) • **Materials for Staircases** See Session 2.2. • **Counters** (10 per pair)	• **M8, Mystery Boxes** Make copies. (1 per student; from Session 2.3) • **M11, Dot Cards, Set A** For each deck, make 4 copies on cardstock, if available. You may also want to laminate the copies. Cut them apart to make one deck. (1 deck per pair) • **M12, *Compare Dots*** Make copies. (as needed) • **M13–M16, Primary Number Cards** Make copies on cardstock, if available. You may also want to laminate the copies. Cut apart to make one deck. (1 deck per pair) • **M17, *Compare*** Make copies. (as needed)

Overhead Transparency

Counting and Comparing, *continued*

Session	Student Activity Book	Student Math Handbook	Professional Development: Read Ahead of Time
SESSION 2.5 p. 77 **Counting Backward** Students learn a new variation of *Start With/Get To* that involves counting backward. Math Workshop continues. The session ends with a discussion of the Mystery Box data.	7, from Session 2.3, 10–12	6–8, 26	• **Dialogue Box:** Counting What's in a Mystery Box, p. 228
SESSION 2.6 p. 82 **Assessment: Counting 20 and Quick Images** Students are introduced to the last of the yearlong routines, *Quick Images,* which focuses on developing visual images of quantities. They complete a counting assessment and end the session with a Math Workshop about comparing numbers.	13	6–8, 21–23, 26, 31; G2, G3	• **Part 4: Classroom Routines** *Implementing Investigations in Grade 1,* Quick Images • **Teacher Note:** Assessment: Counting 20, p. 194; Counting Is More Than 1, 2, 3, p. 192; Observing Students as They Count, p. 193 • **Dialogue Box:** Seeing Dot Images, p. 229
SESSION 2.7 p. 88 **Ordering Numbers** Students learn and do a new activity that involves ordering four numbers or quantities. The session ends with a discussion about comparing numbers and the language and notation mathematicians use to do this.	14–16	43–45	• **Teacher Note:** Introducing Notation, Part 1, p. 198

Materials to Gather	Materials to Prepare
• **Materials for *Start With/Get To*** See Session 2.1. • **Materials for *Compare Dots*** See Session 2.4. • **Materials for Compare** See Session 2.4. • **9″ x 12″ envelope or folder for storing math materials at home** (1 per student; optional)	• **M8, Mystery Boxes** Make copies. (as needed; from Session 2.3) • **M18–20, Dot Cards, Sets B, C, D** For each deck, make 4 copies on cardstock, if available. You may also want to laminate the copies. Cut them apart to make separate decks. (as needed; optional) • **M13–M16, Primary Number Cards** Make a second deck for each student to take home. (1 deck per student) • **M17, *Compare*** Make copies. (1 per student to take home) • **M21–M22, Family Letter** Make copies. (1 per student) • **Chart paper** Title a piece of chart paper "Mystery Data." Prepare a chart listing each mystery box by letter. Record the numbers students counted for each box. See page 80 for an example.
• **Materials for *Compare Dots*** See Session 2.4. • **Materials for Compare** See Session 2.4. • **Dot Cards, Sets B, C, D** (as needed; from Session 2.5; optional) • **Counters** (about 10 per student)	• **M23, Assessment: Counting 20** Make copies. (1 per student) • **T2, Dot Cards, Set A** Cut apart the cards. Store the cards in an envelope or in the plastic sleeve of the Resources Binder. • **Countable materials** Title a piece of chart paper "Mystery Box Data" Place about 30 countable objects in a bin. (as needed; optional)
• **Dot Cards, Set A** (1 deck per class; from Session 2.4; optional) • **Primary Number Cards** (1 deck per pair; from Session 2.4) • **Homework materials: Primary Number Cards** (sent home in Session 2.5) • **Connecting cubes** (about 40 per pair)	

Overhead Transparency

Start With/Get To

Math Focus Points

- Practicing the rote counting sequence forward and backward, from 1 to 30
- Using the number line as a tool for counting
- Counting a set of up to 20 objects by ones

Vocabulary

count
number line

Today's Plan			Materials
1 ACTIVITY **Introducing *Start With/Get To***	15 MIN	CLASS	• M6–M7* • Basket; number line*; red clothespin, green clothespin
2 ACTIVITY ***Collect 20 Together***	30 MIN	PAIRS	• M4 (from Session 1.4); M5* (from Session 1.4; optional)* • Dot cubes; counters
3 DISCUSSION **Strategies for Counting Accurately**	15 MIN	CLASS	• T1 (optional)
4 SESSION FOLLOW-UP **Daily Practice**			• *Student Activity Book,* p. 5 • *Student Math Handbook,* pp. 21–23, 26, 31; G1 • M9*–M10*, Family Letter

*See *Materials to Prepare,* p. 51.

Classroom Routines

Morning Meeting Follow your daily *Morning Meeting* routine as a class. Review the day's schedule, take attendance, establish the current day on the calendar and count to that number, and record the day's weather.

ACTIVITY

1 Introducing *Start With/Get To*

Start With/Get To is another of the ongoing classroom routines in Grade 1.[1]

Before introducing this activity to students, select the highest number you will use—the number of students in your class—and set it aside so that it will be the first number used for this sample activity.

Today we're going to learn another routine that we will do all year. It's called *Start With/Get To.* First, we pick a number to start with; next, we pick a number to get to; and then we count. Today I'd like to start with 1. And we're going to get to, or count to, the number I pull from this basket. [Pull out the number that represents the number of students in your class.] The number is [25]. [Hold up the card.] What number is this? Suppose that we did not know this number. How could we figure out what number this is?

Students might say:

"We could look on the number line."

"We could look at the calendar."

We're going to start with 1 and get to [25]. One place in our classroom that you can look to find the numbers in order is here on this number line. See how it starts at 1 and then goes up 1 by 1, all the way to [the last number]? How could we find [25]?

Have students help you find [25] on the number line. Some might "just know" the number; others might count up to it. After students have found it, mark your starting and ending numbers on the number line, using a green clothespin for the *start with* number and a red clothespin for the *get to* number. Count from 1 together as a class, pointing to each number on the number line as students say it.[2]

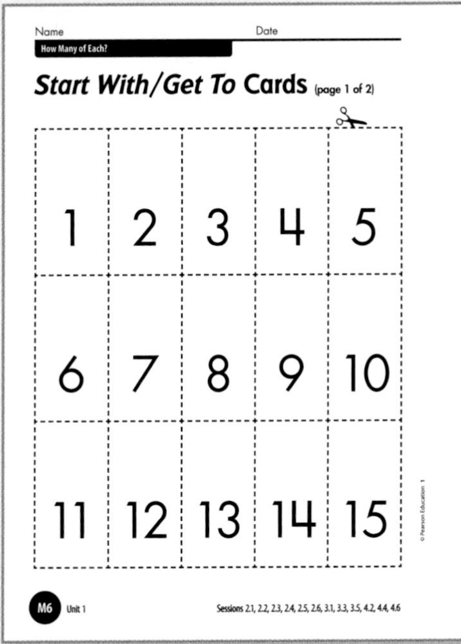

Name Date

How Many of Each?

Start With/Get To Cards (page 1 of 2)

1	2	3	4	5
6	7	8	9	10
11	12	13	14	15

© Pearson Education 1

M6 Unit 1 Sessions 2.1, 2.2, 2.3, 2.4, 2.5, 2.6, 3.1, 3.3, 3.5, 4.2, 4.4, 4.6

▲ Resource Masters, M6

Professional Development

[1] **Part 4: Classroom Routines** in *Implementing Investigations in Grade 1:* Start With/Get To

[2] **Dialogue Box:** *Start With/Get To*, p. 225

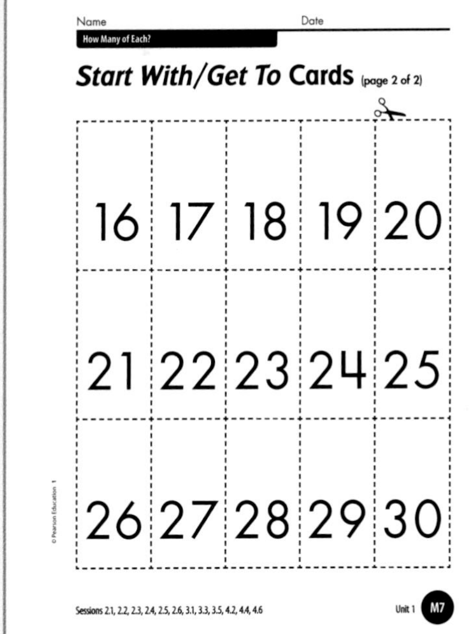

Name Date

How Many of Each?

Start With/Get To Cards (page 2 of 2)

16	17	18	19	20
21	22	23	24	25
26	27	28	29	30

© Pearson Education 1

Sessions 2.1, 2.2, 2.3, 2.4, 2.5, 2.6, 3.1, 3.3, 3.5, 4.2, 4.4, 4.6 Unit 1 M7

▲ Resource Masters, M7

The Start With/Get To *routine helps students practice the rote counting sequence.*

Repeat the activity, asking a different student to pick the *get to* card. Have students count forward together as a class. You can keep the numbers that have been chosen out of the basket until the next variation is introduced, or you can put them back in the basket.

Because every number from 1 to [25] is in the basket, you may have some very short counting sequences. Use those examples to have conversations with students about the distance between those numbers.

[Neil] picked the 3. Will we say a lot of numbers this time? How many numbers will we say if we start at 1 and get to 3? How do you know?

ONGOING ASSESSMENT: Observing Students at Work

As students count, they are connecting the counting numbers to the written numbers on the number line.

- **How comfortable are students with the rote counting sequence?** What errors do you notice?
- **Do students use the number line to figure out what comes next in the counting sequence?** Are they connecting the number names to the numbers on the line?
- **Do any students comment on how far apart the numbers will be on the number line?** About how many (a lot or a few) numbers will be said?

ACTIVITY 2

Collect 20 Together

Explain that today, everyone will play *Collect 20 Together* again.3

Today everybody is going to play *Collect 20 Together.* What do we need to play? How do we play the game?

After reviewing the rules and the materials needed (a dot cube and 25 counters per pair), focus students' attention on the discussion that will happen at the end of class.

After everyone has played a few rounds of *Collect 20 Together,* we are going to have a discussion about how you are counting and keeping track of the counters in your game. So while you are playing, think about *how* you and your partner are playing.

ONGOING ASSESSMENT: Observing Students at Work

Students are becoming familiar with the dot images for 1–6, and practicing counting and keeping track of a set of objects.

- **Do students recognize the 1–6 dot patterns or do they have to count the dots?**
- **How do they figure out and keep track of how many counters they have at the end of each turn?** Do they count all? Organize or remember, and then count on?
- **How fluent and accurate are they in their counting?** What errors do you notice?

Focus your observations of students on counting strategies in preparation for the discussion at the end of this session. For example, note students who have a good system for organizing and/or keeping track of a count, those who "just know" how to add one more, and/or those who do not have to recount the whole set from 1 each time they add more counters.

DIFFERENTIATION: Supporting the Range of Learners

Extension Students who need more challenge can play with the goal of collecting *exactly* 20 counters.

As you observe students playing, you will notice that some pairs play very quickly, turning this into a game of roll and take, roll and take.

Professional Development

3 **Part 2: Using *Investigations*** in *Implementing Investigations in Grade 1:* Components of the Program

To encourage more thoughtful play, periodically ask pairs, or even the whole class, to pause in their game. Then, ask questions such as these:

- Take a moment to figure out how many counters you have right now. If you rolled a 1 next, how many would you have? How do you know?
- Take a moment to figure out how many counters you have right now. How many more do you need to reach 20?

DISCUSSION

Strategies for Counting Accurately

15 MIN CLASS

Math Focus Points for Discussion

- Counting a set of up to 20 objects by ones

As I walked around, I saw many different ways students were playing this game. It was challenging to keep track of so many counters! Let's play a sample game so that people can share their strategies for counting *accurately.*

Play a sample game of *Collect 20 Together* with the class, asking students who are using strategies you wish to highlight to find the total after each turn. The main focus of this discussion should be strategies for counting accurately.

How do you keep track of the counters? Do you need to count all of them when you add more?

Students might say:

"I touch each one as I count."

"I just know how many I have when I add one more. It's the next number."

"I keep the counters in rows of 5, so it's easier to count and recount."

As you demonstrate counting during this discussion, use problematic strategies you have noticed (such as skipping some counters or numbers, or double-counting others). Ask students to watch you carefully and comment on what they see. This can provide a chance to talk about the importance of double-checking.

Finally, share the Twenty-Frame (M5) with students or use the transparency (T1). If you introduced this to any students during Session 1.4, you might ask them to explain it to their classmates.

I have something here called a twenty-frame. Why do you think it's called a twenty-frame? How many squares do you think there are in each *row?*

Establish that there are 4 rows with 5 squares in each row.

The twenty-frame is one way to help us keep track of our counters as we play *Collect 20 Together.* Let's play one more game and see how it works.

Play another game of *Collect 20 Together,* this time placing each counter in its own square on the twenty-frame. After each roll, ask students how many counters there are in all and how they know. Some students will count from 1 every time, but others will use the rows of 5 in some way as they count. The twenty-frame also makes questions such as the following more accessible to first graders:

[Toshi] said that there were 13 altogether. *How many more* counters do we need to get to 15? To 20?

Most students are likely to count the number of empty squares to solve this problem.

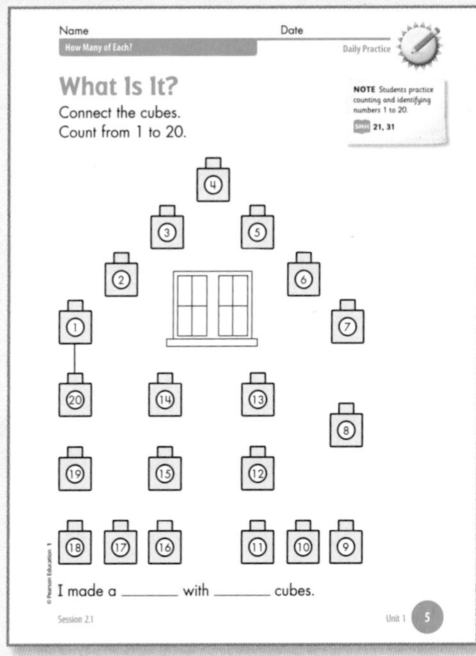
Name Date
How Many of Each?
Daily Practice

What Is It?

Connect the cubes.
Count from 1 to 20.

NOTE Students practice counting and identifying numbers 1 to 20.
SMH 21, 31

I made a ______ with ______ cubes.

© Pearson Education 1

Session 2.1

Unit 1 5

▲ **Student Activity Book, p. 5**

SESSION FOLLOW-UP

Daily Practice

Daily Practice: For reinforcement of this unit's content, have students complete *Student Activity Book* page 5.

Student Math Handbook: Students and families may use *Student Math Handbook* pages 21–23, 26, 31 and G1 for reference and review. See pages 243–252 in the back of this unit.

Family Letter: Send home copies of the Family Letter (M9–M10).

Staircases

Math Focus Points

- Counting a set of up to 20 objects by 1s
- Connecting number names and written numbers to the quantities they represent
- Ordering a set of numbers and quantities up to 12

Vocabulary

smallest
largest
in order

Today's Plan		Materials
1 ACTIVITY **Introducing Staircases**	15 MIN CLASS	• Connecting cubes labeled 1–12*; connecting cubes
2 MATH WORKSHOP **Counting and Ordering Quantities** 2A *Collect 20 Together* 2B Staircases	30 MIN	2A • Materials from Session 1.4 p. 43 2B • Connecting cubes; connecting cubes labeled 1–12*
3 DISCUSSION **Using a Twenty-Frame**	15 MIN CLASS	• M5* • Dot cube; counters
4 SESSION FOLLOW-UP **Daily Practice**		• *Student Activity Book,* p. 6 • *Student Math Handbook,* pp. 21–23; G1

*See *Materials to Prepare,* p. 51.

Classroom Routines

Start With/Get To: Start With 1 As you did in Session 2.1, explain that you will *start with* 1. Ask a volunteer to mark the number 1 on the number line. Choose a card to determine what number you will *get to.* Ask students what number is shown on the card and to help you mark it on the class number line. As a class, count from 1 using the number line to keep track of the count.

1 ACTIVITY
Introducing Staircases

Introduce Staircases by showing students the labeled single cubes facing up and out of order.

What numbers do you see? What's the smallest number? The largest number?

Students should notice that all of the numbers from 1 through 12 are present. When they do, count from 1 to 12 with the class, pointing to each number as you say it. Do not reorder the cubes yet.

We're going to start making a staircase of cubes to match these numbers. We'll start with 1, the first step. The first step should have one cube in it, and it already does. So let's try building another step. Who wants to choose a number so that we could build a step for it? How many cubes should be in that step?

Remind students that there is already one cube in the step and that you want the final step to have the number of cubes in it that is on the label. So to build the step for 5, you will need to add only 4 cubes. Continue with this until you have a few steps built.

After you have built all the steps, you need to put them in order from the smallest step to the largest step.❶

Show students how steps 1 to 5 would look in order.

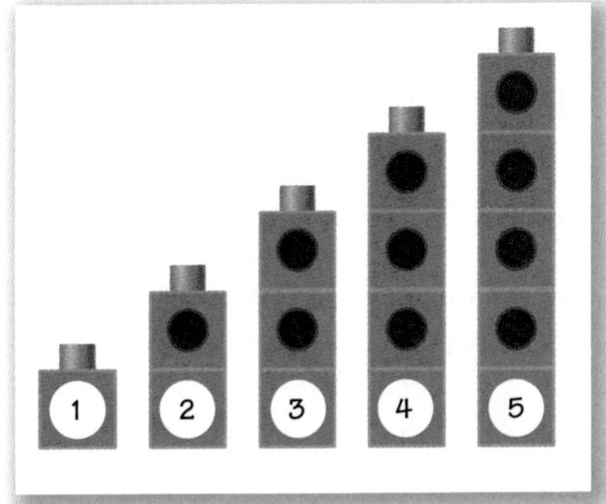

Differentiation

❶ **English Language Learners** Building staircases can help English Language Learners with comparatives and superlatives. Work with a small group of English Language Learners to demonstrate the meanings of the words *small/smaller/smallest* and *big/bigger/biggest*. Build several staircases and ask, Which step is *smaller,* this one or that one? Which step is the *smallest?* Which step is *bigger* than this one? Which step is the *biggest?* Students can practice the vocabulary by making their own staircases and describing them to one another.

MATH WORKSHOP

Counting and Ordering Quantities

30 MIN

Two activities are available for students, *Collect 20 Together* with a twenty-frame and Staircases. Everyone should try *Collect 20 Together* at least once in this Math Workshop because the discussion at the end of this session will be about how the twenty-frame makes the game different. The number of cubes you have will probably determine how many students or pairs can work on Staircases at one time.

2A *Collect 20 Together*

PAIRS

Pairs play *Collect 20 Together,* using Twenty-Frame (M5). Continue observing students' abilities to count and keep track of objects (see Session 1.4, page 46), but pay particular attention to how they use the twenty-frame. Ask students how many they have so far, and how many more they need to get to 20.

ONGOING ASSESSMENT: Observing Students at Work

Using the twenty-frame introduces a system for keeping track of the counters. It can also help students count more accurately, and even count on and/or use groups of 5.

- **Do students use the twenty-frame as part of their strategy?** (e.g., "One row is 5, and 2 more is 6, 7." Or "I just need to count the empty spaces, and that tells me how many more I need to get to 20.")

DIFFERENTIATION: Supporting the Range of Learners

Extension Challenge those students who are ready for it to find a way to record their play. At the end of each turn, they should record both the number rolled and the total number of counters.

2B Staircases

PAIRS

Using a set of cubes labeled 1–12, students work with a partner to build a staircase of connecting cubes.

I'm interested in seeing your staircase when you have finished. After you have shown it to me, you can unsnap your steps and put the number cubes back in the bag for someone else to use.

ONGOING ASSESSMENT: Observing Students at Work 

Students are connecting the written numbers with the quantities they represent and practicing counting, comparing, and ordering numbers.

- **How fluent and accurate are students as they count cubes?** What errors do you notice? Do they count the labeled cube?
- **Do they build steps randomly or in some order?** Do they first build the 1 step, then the 2? Do they count each step from 1 or do they build a matching step and then add 1 more?
- **Can students order the steps accurately?**

DIFFERENTIATION: Supporting the Range of Learners 

Intervention Some students may need to first focus on building a staircase for 1–6, and then add on subsequent steps. Also, if students' steps keep falling over, have them lay their staircases flat rather than standing them up.

Extension Students who quickly and easily complete their steps can continue to build steps for larger numbers. They can also play the following game: one student closes his or her eyes while the other student removes one or more steps. The first student figures out what steps are missing and explains how she or he knows.

Building and ordering staircases helps students see how counting by 1s is a process of adding 1 more.

Name Date

How Many of Each? Daily Practice

Which Number Is Greater?

NOTE Students compare two numbers and identify the greater.

SMH 26, 46–47

Circle the clown in each picture who is balancing more balls.

1. 2. 3. 4. 5. 6.

6 Unit 1 Session 2.2

© Pearson Education 1

▲ Student Activity Book, p. 6

3 DISCUSSION

Using a Twenty-Frame

15 MIN CLASS

Math Focus Points for Discussion

- Counting a set of up to 20 objects

Today you played *Collect 20 Together* with a twenty-frame. How was it different?

Students might say:

"It was easier to keep track of the counters."

"It was easier to see how many more you need."

Play a game as a class, asking students who used the twenty-frame in different ways to share their strategies with the whole group. Choose students who will illustrate the following strategies:

- Counting on from 5, 10, or 15 to figure out how many counters there are;
- Counting the empty squares to figure out how many more are needed to reach 20;
- Using 5 as a landmark; for example, "I know there are 5 in a row, and I have all but one square filled in that row, so it's 4."

4 SESSION FOLLOW-UP

Daily Practice

Daily Practice: For reinforcement of this unit's content, have students complete *Student Activity Book* page 6.

Student Math Handbook: Students and families may use *Student Math Handbook* pages 21–23 and G1 for reference and review. See pages 243–252 in the back of this unit.

Counting What's in a Mystery Box

Math Focus Points

- Connecting number names and written numbers to the quantities they represent
- Ordering a set of numbers and quantities up to 12
- Recording a solution to a problem

Today's Plan		Materials
1 ACTIVITY **Introducing Mystery Boxes**	10 MIN CLASS	• *Student Activity Book,* p. 7 • Mystery Box (1 per class)*
2 MATH WORKSHOP **Counting, Ordering, and Representing** 2A Mystery Boxes 2B Staircases	40 MIN	2A • *Student Activity Book,* p. 7 • M8 (as needed)* • Mystery Boxes (1 per pair)* 2B • Materials from Session 2.2, p. 60
3 DISCUSSION **Which Step Is Missing?**	10 MIN CLASS	• Staircase for numbers 1–12 (1 per class; from Math Workshop)
4 SESSION FOLLOW-UP **Daily Practice**		• *Student Activity Book,* p. 8 • *Student Math Handbook,* pp. 6–8, 21–23

*See *Materials to Prepare,* p. 51.

Classroom Routines

Start With/Get To: Starts With 1 **Choose a *get to* number. Ask students to find and mark the number on the class number line. As a class, count together, from 1 to the *get to* number.**

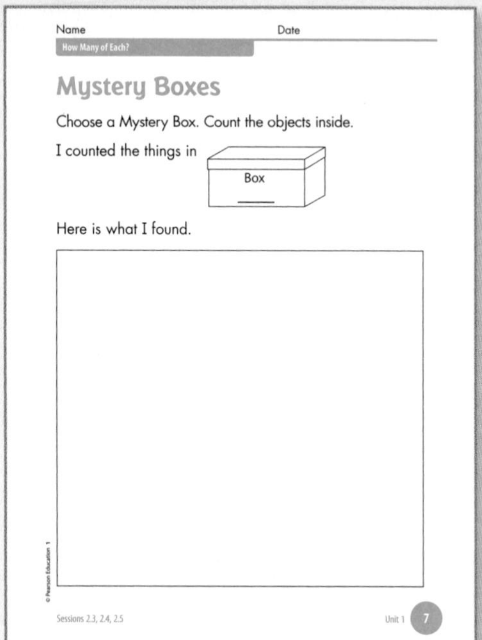
Name Date
How Many of Each?

Mystery Boxes

Choose a Mystery Box. Count the objects inside.

I counted the things in Box ____

Here is what I found.

Sessions 2.3, 2.4, 2.5 Unit 1 7

▲ Student Activity Book, p. 7; Resource Masters, M8

Teaching Note

➊ **Mystery Box Amounts** Some teachers play up the mystery part of this activity and have students work in the hall, or in secret, to build excitement for the "unveiling."

ACTIVITY

Introducing Mystery Boxes

Bring one or all of the Mystery Boxes you have prepared to the meeting area. Explain that inside each Mystery Box is a set of objects. Students will work with a partner to count *together* what is inside and keep it a secret. Each student will make her or his own representation that shows *what* is inside, and *how many* there are inside, on *Student Activity Book* page 7.

Because this is the first time you will ask students to record their work, you might want to take a few minutes to talk about this aspect of the task.

Suppose that I counted the things in Box [A], and I found out that there were 12 cars in the box. I want to write that on my paper. What if I don't know how to write a 12? What are some things I could do to figure out how to write a 12?

Students might say:

"You could ask a friend."

"You could count to 12 on the calendar."

"You could look on the number line."

We've been talking a lot about how to count carefully and accurately. One of the strategies that keeps coming up is *double-checking,* or *counting again.* You should remember to double-check when you count.

Explain where the Mystery Boxes will be located and how pairs should cycle through this choice during Math Workshop. For example, if you have 6 boxes, then 12 students can work on this activity at a time. Some students will want to investigate more than one box.➊

Students should turn in completed papers to you, so that you can prepare the data for the discussion at the end of Session 2.5.

MATH WORKSHOP

40 MIN

Counting, Ordering, and Representing

Many first grade teachers believe that having an activity available for two or three days seems to be the right amount of time, and so *Collect 20 Together* is not included as an activity in this session's Math Workshop. However, your students may benefit from more (or less) time with *Collect 20 Together* (or other future activities). These are choices you, as the person who knows your students best, must make.③

2A Mystery Boxes

PAIRS

Students count the contents of a Mystery Box and make a representation that shows what and how many are in the box. As you circulate, remind students that they are to *work together* to count all the objects in the box, and then *each* complete *Student Activity Book* page 7. Encourage students to use numbers to show how many items are in the box.

Have copies of Mystery Boxes (M8) available for students who might work with more than 1 box.

Sample Student Work

Professional Development

③ **Part 1: Collaborating with the Authors** in *Implementing Investigations in Grade 1:* The Teacher-Student-Curriculum Partnership

Students work together to count the items in a Mystery Box.

ONGOING ASSESSMENT: Observing Students at Work

As students count sets of objects, they are practicing the rote sequence and developing strategies for counting accurately. They are also working to represent their work.

- **How accurate are students in their counting? What errors do you notice?** Do students double-check their work? Compare their counts with those of a partner?
- **How do students record their work?** Do they use numbers? Pictures? Words? Do they show every item? Show one item and the total number?
- **Do students know what numbers to write for a given quantity?** If not, do they have a strategy for figuring it out? What tools do they use?

DIFFERENTIATION: Supporting the Range of Learners

Intervention Students who need practice counting smaller quantities should investigate one of the boxes with 10–15 items. Some students may benefit from seeing how others have recorded their work. You might take dictation for these students, showing them how the words and numbers you have written represent their work.

Extension Those students who are more adept at counting can work with boxes with 20–30 items.

2B Staircases

For complete details about this activity, see Session 2.2, pages 61–63.

Ask one student to save his or her staircases for you to use during the discussion.

DISCUSSION

3 Which Step Is Missing?

Math Focus Points for Discussion

- Ordering a set of numbers and quantities up to 12

Have a brief discussion about the Staircase activity. You will need one complete set of steps for the numbers 1–12, arranged randomly.

Here is one complete set of steps that [Chris] made during Math Workshop today. I'd like you to help me put them in order. Which step should we place *first?*

Ask volunteers to help you order the steps, explaining why they chose the step they did, and how they knew where to place it.

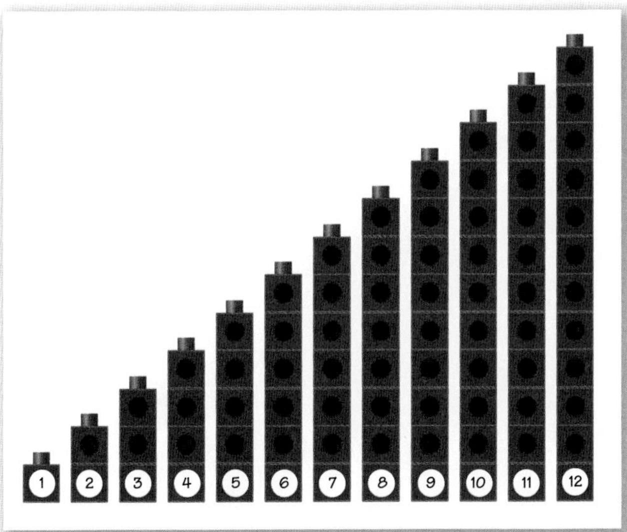

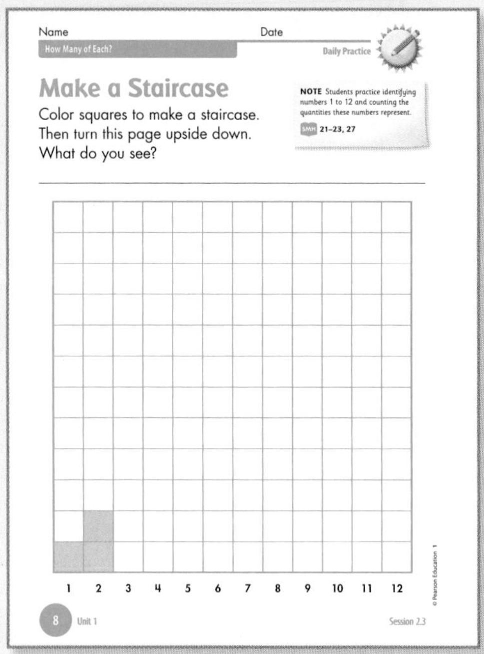

Name Date

How Many of Each? Daily Practice

Make a Staircase

Color squares to make a staircase.
Then turn this page upside down.
What do you see?

NOTE Students practice identifying numbers 1 to 12 and counting the quantities these numbers represent.

SMH 21–23, 27

1 2 3 4 5 6 7 8 9 10 11 12

8 Unit 1 Session 2.3

© Pearson Education 1

▲ Student Activity Book, p. 8

When the steps are in order, play a few rounds of the following game:

OK, everybody close your eyes. I'm going to take a step away. When you open your eyes, think quietly to yourself about which step is missing and how you know. Ready?

Remove one step and arrange the others so that they are all touching. Ask students which number they think is missing and how they figured it out. Some will see the missing number, and others will notice a visual difference in the line of steps and then figure out what number belongs there. To challenge students, remove more than one step or remove two consecutive steps.

4 SESSION FOLLOW-UP

Daily Practice

Daily Practice: For reinforcement of this unit's content, have students complete *Student Activity Book* page 8.

Student Math Handbook: Students and families may use *Student Math Handbook* pages 6–8, 21–23 for reference and review. See pages 243–252 in the back of this unit.

Comparing Quantities

Math Focus Points

- Ordering a set of numbers and quantities up to 12
- Comparing two quantities up to 10 to see which is larger
- Developing an understanding of how the quantities in the counting sequence are related: each number is 1 more or 1 less than the number before or after it

Vocabulary

more
larger
counting back

Today's Plan		Materials
1 ACTIVITY Introducing *Compare Dots* and *Compare*	15 MIN CLASS	• M11; T2 • M13–M16*
2 MATH WORKSHOP Comparing Numbers 2A *Compare Dots* 2B *Compare* 2C Mystery Boxes 2D Staircases	30 MIN	2A • M11*; M12* • Connecting cubes (optional) 2B • M17* • Primary Number Cards; counters; connecting cubes (optional) 2C • M8* • Materials from Session 2.3, p. 65 2D • Materials from Session 2.2, p. 60
3 DISCUSSION Counting Forward and Back	15 MIN CLASS	• Staircases for numbers 1–12 (from Math Workshop)
4 SESSION FOLLOW-UP Daily Practice		• *Student Activity Book,* p. 9 • *Student Math Handbook,* pp. 21–23; G2, G3

*See *Materials to Prepare,* p. 51.

Classroom Routines

Start With/Get To: Start With 1 Choose a *get to* number. Ask students to find and mark the number on the class number line. As a class, count together, from 1 to the *get to* number.

Differentiation

➊ **English Language Learners** Before the full-class demonstration, preview the concept of *more* and the rules of the games with English Language Learners. In this way, English Language Learners will be able to participate more fully in the full-class discussion and will be better prepared to play the games with their native English-speaking peers.

Professional Development

➊ **Algebra Connections in this Unit,** p. 16

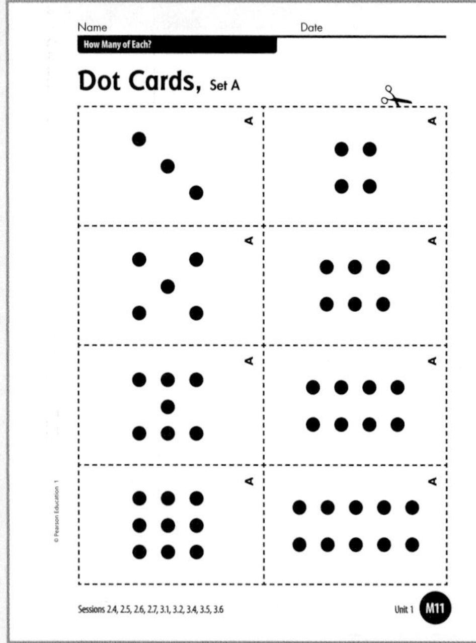
Name Date
How Many of Each?
Dot Cards, Set A
Sessions 2.4, 2.5, 2.6, 2.7, 3.1, 3.2, 3.4, 3.5, 3.6
Unit 1 M11

▲ Resource Masters, M11; T2

ACTIVITY

15 MIN CLASS

Introducing *Compare Dots* and *Compare*

Introduce *Compare Dots* and *Compare* to the entire class by playing a demonstration game of each. Either ask for two volunteers to play the game, or choose one student to play with you. Deal out the deck of cards to each player.➊ Note that transparent Dot Cards are available for the overhead (T2) to assist you in introducing *Compare Dots.*

Today we're going to play two new games. One is called *Compare Dots,* and the other is called *Compare.* They are played the same way, but they use different decks of cards.

First let's learn *Compare Dots.* The goal of this game is to figure out which of two cards has more dots. Both players turn over a card at the same time. The player who has the card with more dots says "Me" and takes those cards.

Hold up the cards that each player turned over.

[Libby] turned over this card [5 dots], and [Danielle] turned over this card [7 dots]. Which card has more dots? How do you know which shows a larger number?

Ask students to explain their strategies.

Students might say:

"I counted the dots. Libby has 5 and Danielle has 7. 7 is more than 5."

"I could just see that Danielle's card has more dots."

Continue with a few more turns until most students understand the game.

Sometimes you both might turn up the same card. When that happens, both of you just turn over the next card. Then the player who has the card with the most dots says "Me" and takes all the cards. The game is over when all of the cards have been turned over.

When students understand *Compare Dots,* it should be easy to quickly introduce *Compare.* The rules are exactly the same as *Compare Dots,* but students use the Primary Number Cards (M13–M16) to play. Note that students can play with or without the Wild Cards. Wild Cards can be any number.

Students learn to compare numbers by playing games such as Compare Dots.

MATH WORKSHOP

Comparing Numbers

30 MIN

Explain to students that at the end of math class today, you will be discussing the Staircases activity. Any students who have yet to visit that choice should do so today.

2A Compare Dots

PAIRS

Pairs play *Compare Dots* as you demonstrated. Have available copies of *Compare Dots* (M12) as needed.

2B Compare

PAIRS

Pairs play *Compare.* Each player turns over a card. The player with the larger number says "Me" and takes the cards. If players turn over the same number, then both players turn over the next card. Play continues until there are no cards left.

Have counters and copies of *Compare* (M17) available for students to use as needed.

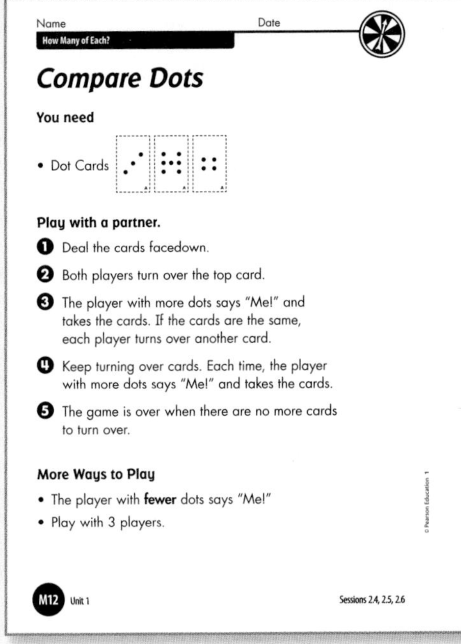

Name Date

How Many of Each?

Compare Dots

You need

- Dot Cards

Play with a partner.

1. Deal the cards facedown.
2. Both players turn over the top card.
3. The player with more dots says "Me!" and takes the cards. If the cards are the same, each player turns over another card.
4. Keep turning over cards. Each time, the player with more dots says "Me!" and takes the cards.
5. The game is over when there are no more cards to turn over.

More Ways to Play

- The player with **fewer** dots says "Me!"
- Play with 3 players.

© Pearson Education 1

M12 Unit 1 Sessions 2.4, 2.5, 2.6

▲ Resource Masters, M12

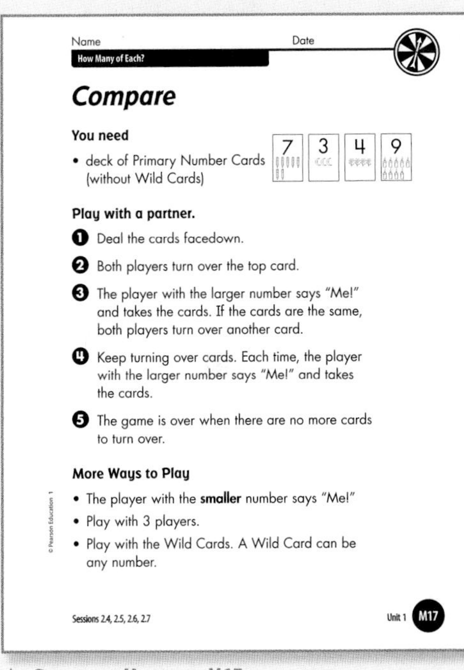

Name Date

How Many of Each?

Compare

You need

- deck of Primary Number Cards (without Wild Cards)

Play with a partner.

1. Deal the cards facedown.
2. Both players turn over the top card.
3. The player with the larger number says "Me!" and takes the cards. If the cards are the same, both players turn over another card.
4. Keep turning over cards. Each time, the player with the larger number says "Me!" and takes the cards.
5. The game is over when there are no more cards to turn over.

More Ways to Play

- The player with the **smaller** number says "Me!"
- Play with 3 players.
- Play with the Wild Cards. A Wild Card can be any number.

© Pearson Education 1

Sessions 2.4, 2.5, 2.6, 2.7 Unit 1 M17

▲ Resource Masters, M17

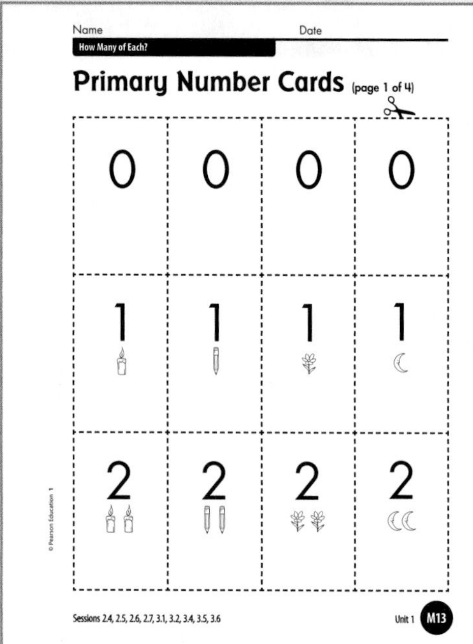
Name Date

How Many of Each?

Primary Number Cards (page 1 of 4)

0	0	0	0
1	1	1	1
2	2	2	2

© Pearson Education 1

Sessions 2.4, 2.5, 2.6, 2.7, 3.1, 3.2, 3.4, 3.5, 3.6 Unit 1 M13

▲ Resource Masters, M13

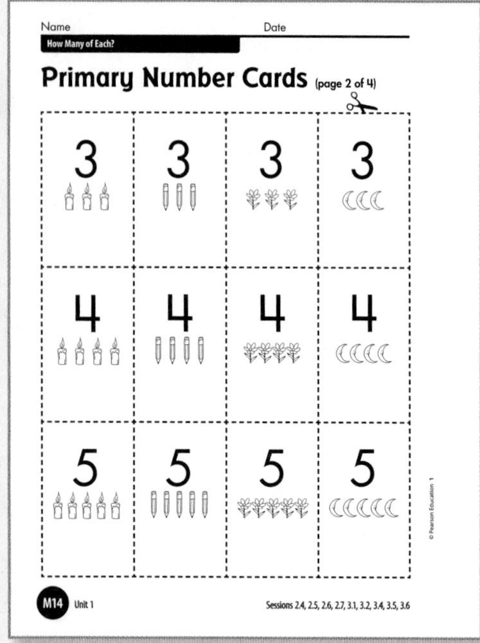
Name Date

How Many of Each?

Primary Number Cards (page 2 of 4)

3	3	3	3
4	4	4	4
5	5	5	5

© Pearson Education 1

M14 Unit 1 Sessions 2.4, 2.5, 2.6, 2.7, 3.1, 3.2, 3.4, 3.5, 3.6

▲ Resource Masters, M14

ONGOING ASSESSMENT: Observing Students at Work

Students are counting and comparing numbers up to 10. Some may be using number combinations and relationships to find the totals.

- **Do students count each dot or object to find the total?** Do they group them in some way? Do they "just know" any totals?
- **What strategies do students use for determining which card shows the larger number?** Do they "just know" which number is larger?

DIFFERENTIATION: Supporting the Range of Learners

Intervention If there are students having trouble with these games, spend some time assessing what it is they are struggling with. Do they recognize the number on the card? Can they count the dots or objects? Do they know how to compare the results of such counts? Can they visually compare obviously different amounts (e.g., 3 and 9) and say which is more? It may help some students to build cube towers for each number and then compare the two towers.

PAIRS

2C Mystery Boxes

For complete details about this activity, see Session 2.3 pages 66–68.

Remind students to hand in completed copies of Mystery Boxes (M8) so that you can prepare charts of the data for the discussion at the end of Session 2.5.

PAIRS

2D Staircases

For complete details about this activity, see Session 2.2 pages 61–63.

Ask two students to save their completed staircases for you to use during the discussion.

3 DISCUSSION

Counting Forward and Back

15 MIN CLASS

Math Focus Points for Discussion

- Developing an understanding of how the quantities in the counting sequence are related: each number has 1 more or 1 less than the number before or after it.

To begin, organize the steps of one Staircase so that one or two of the steps are out of order. Ask students what they notice.

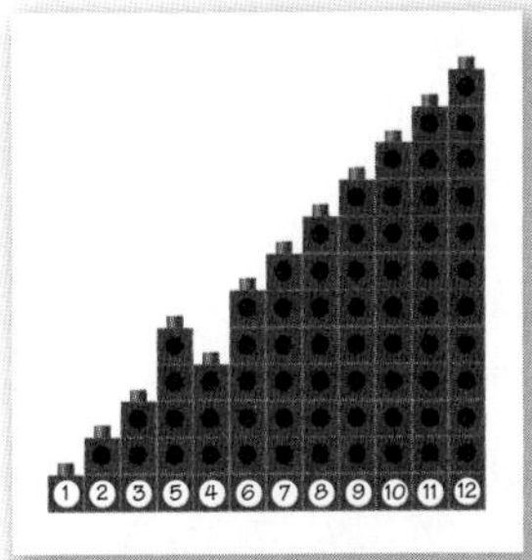

What do you mean I made a mistake? Where? How do you know? How could we fix it? How can you tell when the steps are correct?

Notice how students respond. Is it the visual nature of the steps that helps them see the errors? The number labels in the wrong order? Can students articulate that each step should have one more cube in it than the previous one? Or that each step has the cubes for the last step plus 1 more cube?

Next, show a set of steps students commonly build during these sessions: from 1 to 12 and back down to 1 again.

I saw many children build something like this. What does this set of steps show?

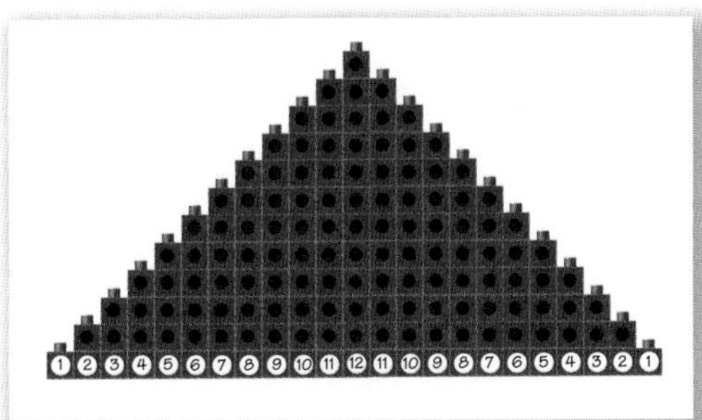

If students do not notice that each step has one more in it until you get to 12 and that then each step has one less than the previous, point this out to them.❷

Professional Development

❷ **Dialogue Box:** Discussing Staircases, pp. 226–227

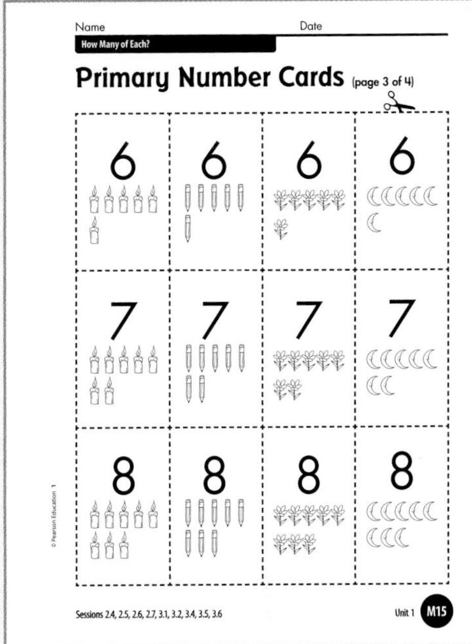

Name Date

How Many of Each?

Primary Number Cards (page 3 of 4)

6	6	6	6
7	7	7	7
8	8	8	8

Sessions 2.4, 2.5, 2.6, 2.7, 3.1, 3.2, 3.4, 3.5, 3.6 Unit 1 M15

▲ Resource Masters, M15

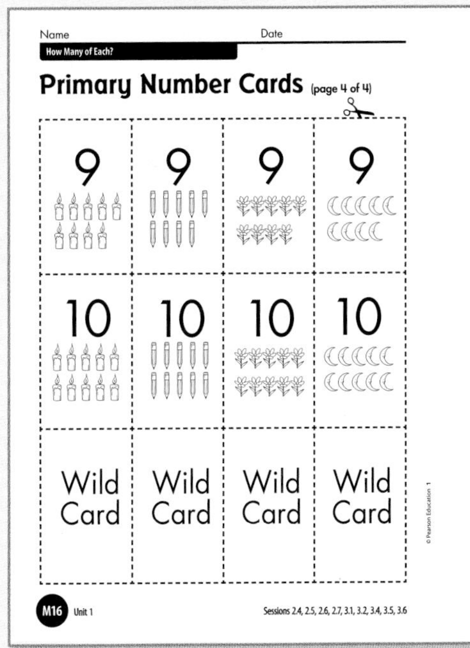

Name Date

How Many of Each?

Primary Number Cards (page 4 of 4)

9	9	9	9
10	10	10	10
Wild Card	Wild Card	Wild Card	Wild Card

M16 Unit 1 Sessions 2.4, 2.5, 2.6, 2.7, 3.1, 3.2, 3.4, 3.5, 3.6

▲ Resource Masters, M16

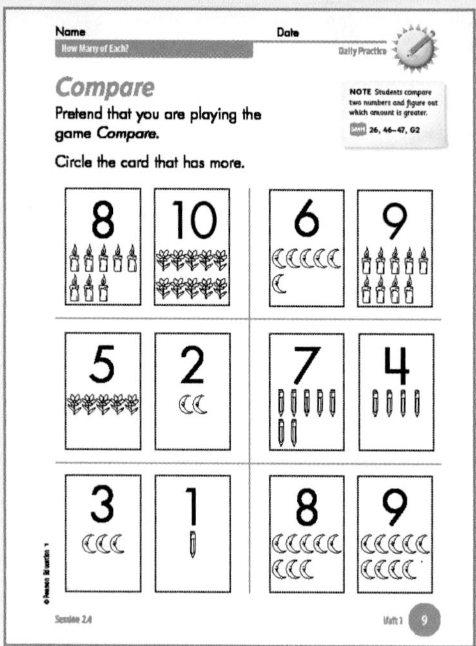
Name Date

How Many of Each?

Daily Practice

Compare

Pretend that you are playing the game *Compare.*

Circle the card that has more.

NOTE Students compare two numbers and figure out which amount is greater.

SMH 26, 46–47, G2

8 10 | 6 9

5 2 | 7 4

3 1 | 8 9

Session 2.4 Unit 1 9

▲ Student Activity Book, p. 9

Do you see that when you count, each number has 1 more? So each step or tower has to have 1 more cube. So the 5 tower has 1, 2, 3, 4, 5 cubes. And the one next to it has 1, 2, 3, 4, 5 cubes, plus 1 more cube. 6 cubes. 6 is 1 *more than* 5.

This discussion offers a good opportunity to introduce the idea of counting back. Count several times up to 12 and back down to 1, together as a class. Counting back can be a challenging task for first graders, so starting with a visual image of the quantities and labels that show the numbers can help.

4 SESSION FOLLOW-UP
Daily Practice

Daily Practice: For reinforcement of this unit's content, have students complete *Student Activity Book* page 9.

Student Math Handbook: Students and families may use *Student Math Handbook* pages 21–23 and G2, G3 for reference and review. See pages 243–252 in the back of this unit.

Counting Backward

Math Focus Points

- Practicing the rote counting sequence forward and backward, from 1 to 30
- Comparing two quantities up to 10 to see which is larger
- Counting a set of objects by 1s

Today's Plan		Materials
1 ACTIVITY *Start With/Get To:* Counting Backward	10 MIN CLASS	• Materials from Session 2.1, p. 54
2 MATH WORKSHOP Which Is More? 2A Mystery Boxes 2B *Compare Dots* 2C *Compare*	30 MIN	2A • Materials from Session 2.3, p. 65 2B • Materials from Session 2.4, p. 71 • M18–M20 (as needed; optional)* 2C • Materials from Session 2.4, p. 71
3 DISCUSSION Mystery Boxes	20 MIN CLASS	• Chart: "Mystery Box Data"*
4 SESSION FOLLOW-UP Daily Practice and Homework		• *Student Activity Book,* pp. 10–12 • *Student Math Handbook,* pp. 6–8, 26 • M13–M16*; M17* • M21–M22, Family Letter* • Envelope or folder (1 per student; optional)

*See *Materials to Prepare,* p. 53.

Classroom Routines

Morning Meeting Follow your daily *Morning Meeting* routine.

Math Note

① **Counting** Some students think that *counting* requires starting with 1; others will be familiar with counting backward. *Start With/Get To* will provide practice with this rote sequence over the course of the year.

10 MIN CLASS

ACTIVITY

1 *Start With/Get To:* Counting Backward

Begin this session by introducing a new variation of *Start With/Get To.*

Today we are going to learn a different way to do *Start With/Get To.* Usually we *start with* 1, and we choose a number to *get to.* Today we're going to do the opposite; we're going to choose a number to *start with,* and we're going to *get to* 1.

Ask a student to choose a *start with* number card from the basket, say the number, and help you find and mark it on the number line.

We marked [15] as our *start with* number. We're going to *start with* [15] and *get to* 1. Can we do that? Can we start counting with a bigger number? Let's try it.

Count together as a class, slowly pointing to each number on the number line as you say it. Ask whether this sequence sounds familiar to anyone. Some students will recall the discussion at the end of Session 2.4 in which you counted backward together as a class. Repeat the activity as time allows.①

30 MIN

MATH WORKSHOP

2 Which Is More?

Let students know that at the end of Math Workshop today, you will have a discussion about Mystery Boxes. Any students who need to complete this choice should do so today.

PAIRS

2A Mystery Boxes

For complete details about this activity, see Session 2.3, pages 66–68.

Remind students to hand in completed copies of *Student Activity Book* page 7 or Mystery Boxes (M8) so that their data will be included in the charts used for the discussion at the end of this session.

PAIRS

2B *Compare Dots*

For complete details about this activity, see Session 2.4, pages 72–73.

During Math Workshop, students work on different activities that focus on the same math ideas.

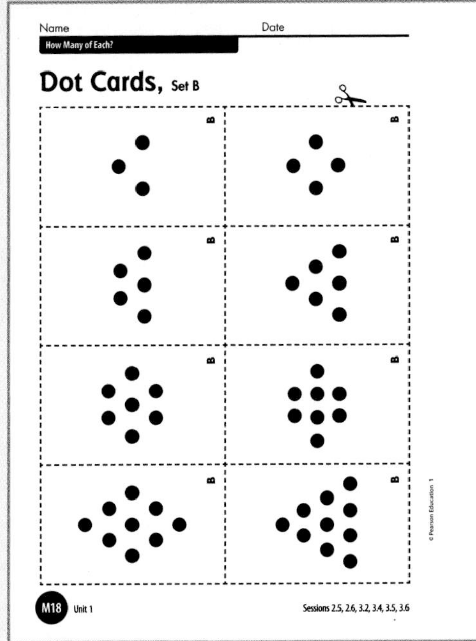
Name Date

How Many of Each?

Dot Cards, Set B

© Pearson Education 1

M18 Unit 1 Sessions 2.5, 2.6, 3.2, 3.4, 3.5, 3.6

▲ Resource Masters, M18; T7

DIFFERENTIATION: Supporting the Range of Learners

To keep this activity going, students can play the same game with Dot Cards Set B (M18) and Dot Cards Set C (M19), which show different arrangements of the same numbers. Dot Cards Set D (M20) involves working with larger numbers.

PAIRS

2C Compare

For complete details about this activity, see Session 2.4, pages 72–73.

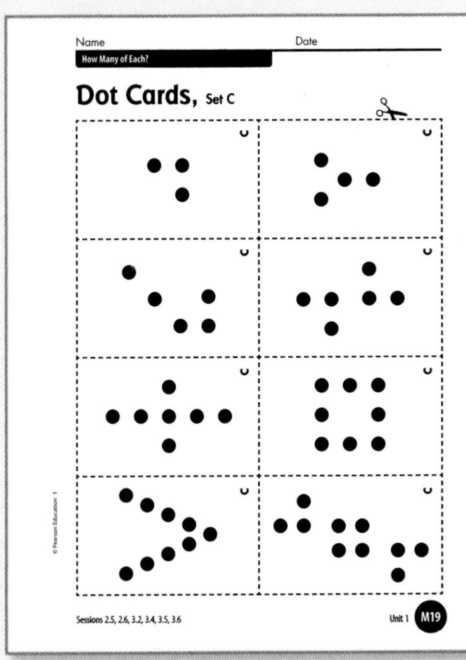
Name Date

How Many of Each?

Dot Cards, Set C

© Pearson Education 1

Sessions 2.5, 2.6, 3.2, 3.4, 3.5, 3.6 Unit 1 M19

▲ Resource Masters, M19

20 MIN CLASS

DISCUSSION

3 Mystery Boxes

Math Focus Points for Discussion

- Developing strategies for accurately counting a set of objects by 1s

Post the chart you prepared showing students' Mystery Box data, and explain that the chart shows how many objects students thought were in each box.

The main focus of this discussion is how many objects are in the Mystery Boxes. Because the information is organized as a chart, spend a few minutes discussing students' observations about the data. If students are interested, come back to this at another time, but be sure to spend the majority of time discussing counting.

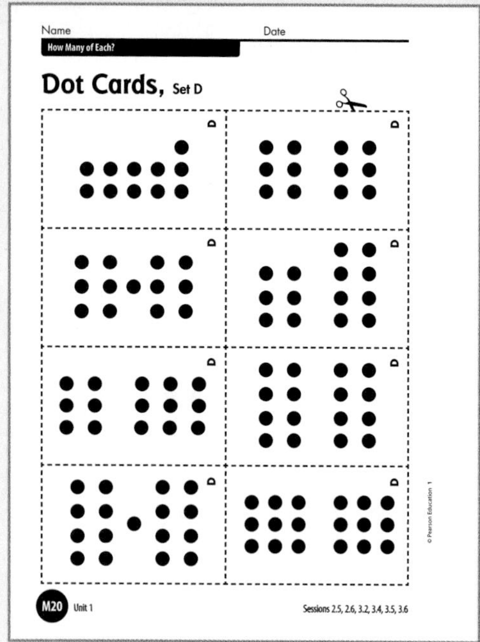
Name Date

How Many of Each?

Dot Cards, Set D

M20 Unit 1

Sessions 2.5, 2.6, 3.2, 3.4, 3.5, 3.6

© Pearson Education 1

▲ Resource Masters, M20

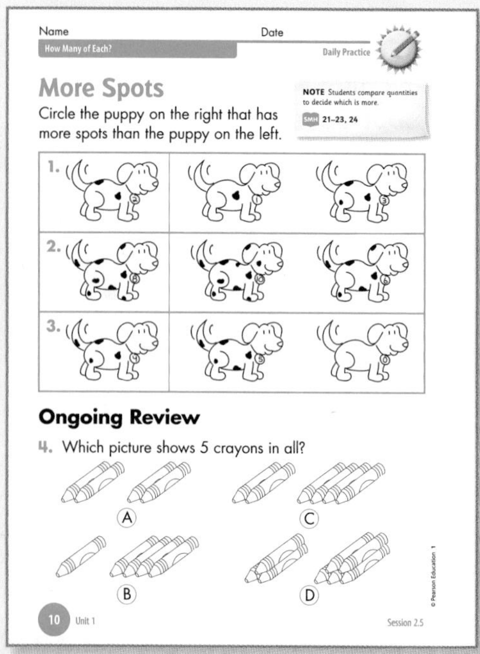
Name Date

How Many of Each? Daily Practice

More Spots

Circle the puppy on the right that has more spots than the puppy on the left.

NOTE Students compare quantities to decide which is more.

SMH 21–23, 24

1.

2.

3.

Ongoing Review

4. Which picture shows 5 crayons in all?

(A) (B) (C) (D)

10 Unit 1

Session 2.5

© Pearson Education 1

▲ Student Activity Book, p. 10

Mystery Box Data						
A Buttons	B Clothespins	C Cubes	D Bears	E Shells	F Keys	G Pennies
20	17	16	13	14		17
19	17	16	13	14		17
20	18	16	13	13		17
22	18	16	13	14		
	15	16		14		
	18			15		
				14		

Explain how to read the chart.

This column shows how many [buttons] people thought were in Box [A]. How many people investigated Box [A]? (4) How do you know?

Look at the data, all the information we collected about Mystery Boxes. What do you notice about our data?

Students might say:

"Lots of kids counted things in Box E."

"Box A had the most things in it."

"There are different numbers for Box B."

Ask questions that explore students' abilities to read and interpret data.

Because of the size of the quantities, there will probably be disagreements about how many items are in each box. This is where you should focus the discussion. Be sure to talk about strategies for counting accurately, as well as common counting errors such as these:

- Skipping or repeating numbers
- Making mistakes with the sequence
- Skipping or double-counting objects

- Not saying one number name for each object
- Not having a system for keeping track of what has been counted and what remains to be counted

Model accurate counting strategies using the objects from one of the boxes.❷

Also, if the materials in the boxes are to be used for a specific purpose, this offers the chance to highlight the importance of accurate counting.

The [clothespins] in Box [B] are going to become [pins] that we use when we collect data. Each of you will need to have one. Were there the correct number in the box, or did I put in too many or too few? How can we decide which of these numbers shows how many [pins] were really in the box?

Have several volunteers count them, using the strategies modeled above and do a final count together.

SESSION FOLLOW-UP

Daily Practice and Homework

Daily Practice: For reinforcement of this unit's content, have students complete *Student Activity Book* page 10.

Homework: Have students play *Compare* with someone at home. Each student will need a deck of Primary Number Cards (M13–M16) and a copy of the game directions for *Compare* (M17). Tell students that the person with whom they play should help them record the results of the game on *Student Activity Book* pages 11–12.

You might also want to send home an envelope or folder for storing these and any other math information and materials that will go home in the future. Encourage students to keep their cards in a special place at home because they will be using them for other games throughout the school year.

Student Math Handbook: Students and families may use *Student Math Handbook* pages 6–8 and 26 for reference and review. See pages 243–252 in the back of this unit.

Family Letter: Send home copies of Family Letter (M21–M22).

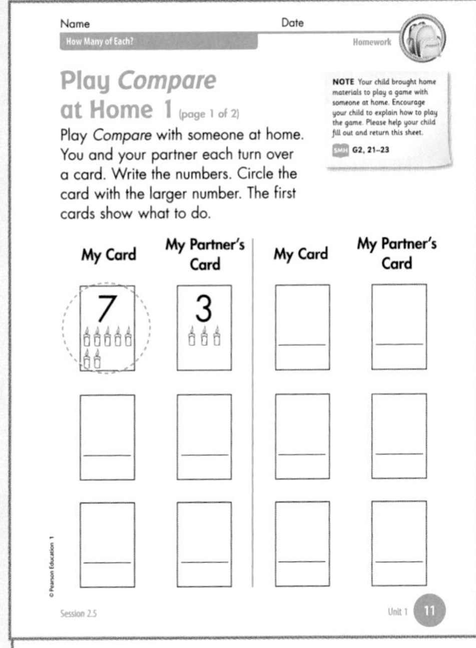

Name Date

How Many of Each? Homework

Play *Compare* at Home 1 (page 1 of 2)

Play *Compare* with someone at home. You and your partner each turn over a card. Write the numbers. Circle the card with the larger number. The first cards show what to do.

NOTE Your child brought home materials to play a game with someone at home. Encourage your child to explain how to play the game. Please help your child fill out and return this sheet.

SMH G2, 21–23

My Card	My Partner's Card	My Card	My Partner's Card
7	3		

Session 2.5 Unit 1 11

▲ Student Activity Book, pp. 11–12

Professional Development

❷ **Dialogue Box:** Counting What's in a Mystery Box, p. 228

Assessment: Counting 20 and Quick Images

Math Focus Points

- Developing and analyzing visual images for quantities up to 10
- Counting a set of objects up to 20 by 1s
- Comparing two quantities up to 20 to see which is larger

Vocabulary

image

Today's Plan		Materials
1 ACTIVITY *Quick Images*	20 MIN CLASS	• T2 • Counters
2 ASSESSMENT ACTIVITY *Counting 20*	10 MIN INDIVIDUALS	• M23* • Countable materials (optional)*
3 MATH WORKSHOP Which Is More? 3A *Compare Dots* 3B *Compare*	30 MIN	3A • Materials from Session 2.4, p. 71 For variation, use M18–M20, (from Session 2.5) 3B • Primary Number Cards (1 deck per student) (from Session 2.4)
4 SESSION FOLLOW-UP Daily Practice		• *Student Activity Book,* p. 13 • *Student Math Handbook,* pp. 6–8, 21–23, 26, 31; G2, G3

*See *Materials to Prepare,* p. 53.

Classroom Routines

Start With/Get To: Get To 1 As you did in Session 2.5, explain that you will *get to* 1. Ask a volunteer to mark the number 1 on the number line. Choose a card to determine what number you will *start with.* Ask students what number is shown on the card and where that number is on the class number line. Mark the number, and then as a class, count from the *start with* number backward to 1. Use the number line to keep track of the count.

ACTIVITY

1 Quick Images

Quick Images is the third, and final, yearlong routine in first grade. This activity will be done two or three times a week.❶

Students will need to be seated so that they can see the image projected, work with counters, and draw pictures of the image they see. Distribute counters, pencil, and paper to each student.

Today we're going to learn another activity that we'll be doing all year. It is called *Quick Images*. An image is another name for a picture. We'll be looking at some pictures, or images, of dots. We call it *Quick Images* because you'll get to see the picture for only a short time. Then I'll cover it up, and you will try to make a copy of the picture you saw. We'll do one together first, so you can see how the activity goes.

Choose a transparency of a card from Dot Cards, Set A (T2) showing either 5 or 6 dots. Before turning on the overhead projector, tell the students where the dot image will appear, and remind them to look carefully because they will not have long to get the picture in their minds. To help students concentrate on the image, they should not draw anything or use counters while the image is visible.

OK. Hands in your laps. No pencils or counters when I'm showing the image. Here it is.

Show the dot pattern for a little longer than 5 seconds for this first time, and then cover it. (Usually show the image for about 5 seconds.)❷

Now use the counters or pencil and paper to make a copy of what you saw.

If some students are concerned that they cannot recall the figure exactly, assure them that they will have another chance to see the picture and to revise their work.

When students have completed their first attempts at representing the image, explain that you are going to show it again. Encourage students to study the picture carefully while it is visible.

Hands in your laps. Here comes the picture again. Look carefully.

Show the image for another 5 seconds. Then let students revise their arrangement of counters or create new drawings.

When students are finished, show the image while you ask students to explain how they remembered what they saw.

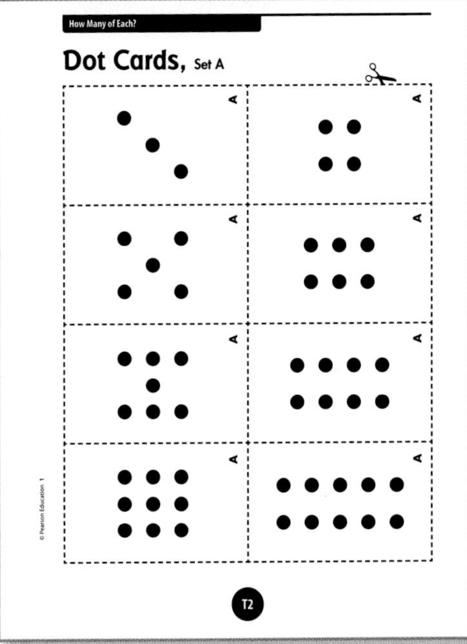

▲ Transparencies, T2

Professional Development

❶ **Part 4: Classroom Routines** in *Implementing Investigations in Grade 1:* Quick Images

Teaching Note

❷ **Timing** You may need to adjust the amount of time you flash the image. If you show the image for too long, you will see students simply copying the image from the screen, rather than building from their mental image; if you show it too briefly, they will not have time to form a mental image and will not be sure what to draw or build.

Teaching Note

❸ **Dialogue Box:** Seeing Dot Images, p. 229

When you first saw the dots, what did you remember that helped you make your drawing?

Students might say:

"I counted 5 dots."

"The dots made an X."

Reassure students that it can be difficult to tell the number of dots or to remember how they are arranged when they have seen the picture only briefly. Tell them that class will begin with *Quick Images* for the next several days, so they will have time to practice and continue to get better at this.

Repeat the activity, using other transparency Dot Cards, Set A (T2). If you began with the 6-dot card, you might next show the 4-dot or the 7-dot card. If you use related images, some students may begin relating visual and number patterns. Follow these steps each time:

- Briefly show the image.
- Students make a copy of the dot pattern, using counters or pencil and paper.
- Show the picture again briefly.
- Students revise their work.
- With the image showing, volunteers share how many dots they saw in the picture, how the dots were arranged, and how they remembered.

Encourage students to talk about revisions they made in their work and to explain how they remembered the picture. They can show their counters or copy their drawings on the overhead, or you can demonstrate on the transparency of the image.❸

Quick Images helps students develop visual images of numbers.

ASSESSMENT ACTIVITY
Counting 20

10 MIN INDIVIDUALS

This is an opportunity for you to assess how well your students are doing with counting to 20.

In math class we've been doing a lot of counting, and we've been thinking and talking about strategies for counting accurately. Today, everyone is going to work on a counting activity on his or her own.

Show Assessment: Counting 20 (M23) to students, and explain the task.

You need to draw exactly 20 circles on this sheet. You'll want to remember everything we've said about careful counting. Remember to double-check and make sure that you really have 20. I'll be walking around and asking whether you are sure that you have 20 and how you know.

ONGOING ASSESSMENT: Observing Students at Work

Students count and represent a set of exactly 20 objects.④

- **Do students draw exactly 20 circles?** What errors do you notice in their counting?
- **How do students keep track of their count?** Do they need to keep recounting from 1 to see how many circles they have? Do any students use groups (of 2, 4, 5, 10)?

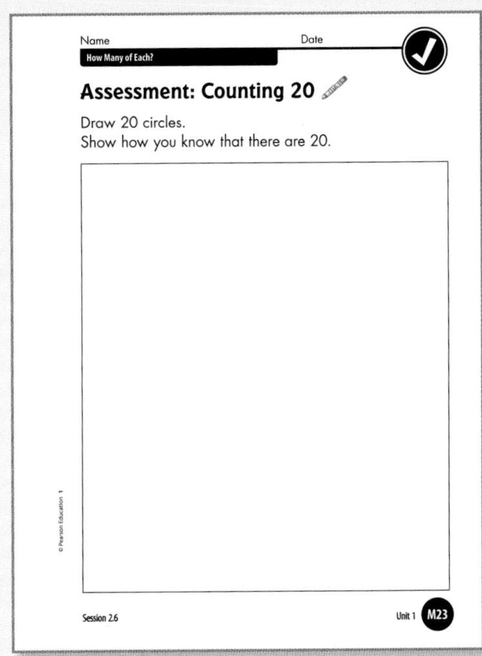

Name Date

How Many of Each?

Assessment: Counting 20

Draw 20 circles.
Show how you know that there are 20.

Session 2.6 Unit 1 M23

▲ Resource Masters, M23

Professional Development

④ **Teacher Note:** Assessment: Counting 20, pp. 194–197

- **Do students double-check?** Do they label their drawings as proof that they have 20?

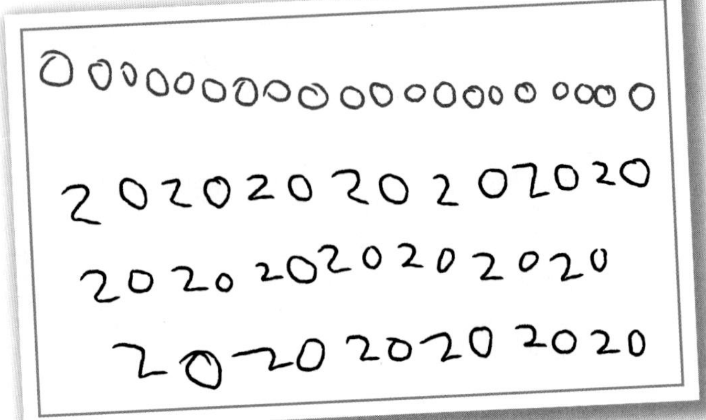

Sample Student Work

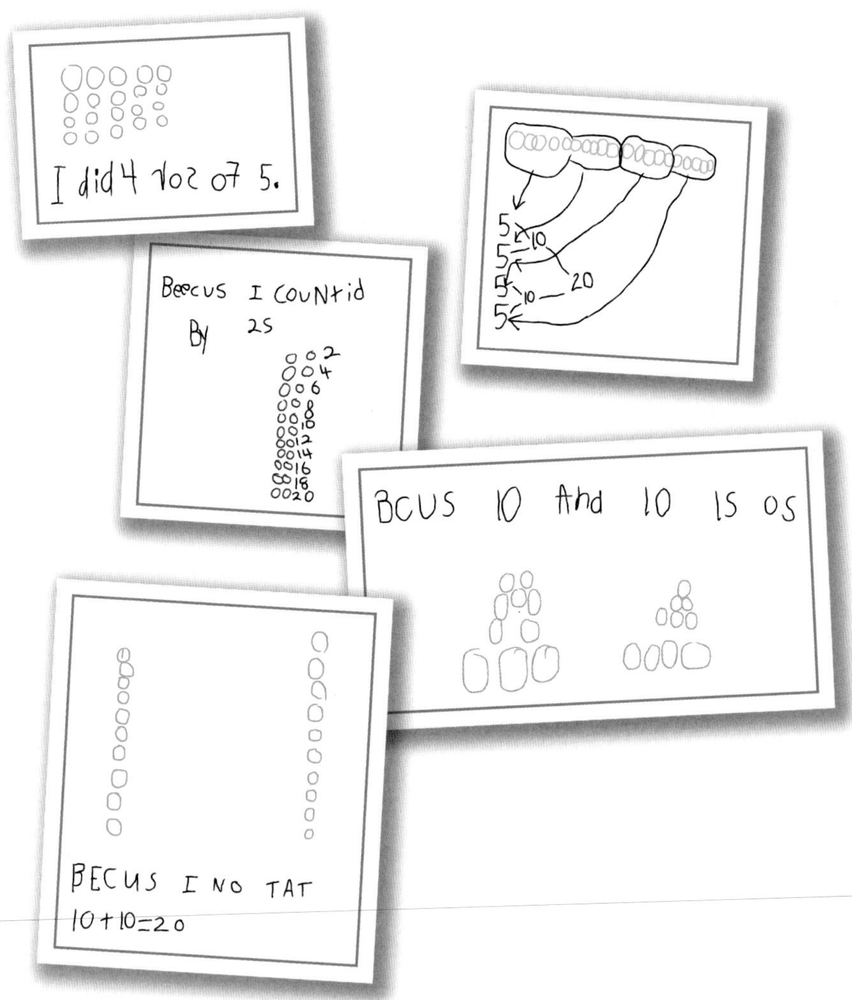

Sample Student Work

DIFFERENTIATION: Supporting the Range of Learners

Intervention After students have attempted the task, check in one on one or in a small group with students who seemed unable to complete it successfully. Establish how many circles they *can* accurately draw. (Can they draw 10? 15?) Then assess their counting with actual objects. Some students find this easier. Place a bin of materials before them and ask them to count out 20 (or fewer). Then place more than 20 items in front of them, and ask them to count 20 (or fewer). 5 6

30 MIN

MATH WORKSHOP

Which Is More?

In Math Workshop, students continue playing *Compare Dots* or *Compare* with a partner.

PAIRS

3A Compare Dots

For complete details about this activity, see Session 2.4, pages 72–73. For variation, pairs can play the game with Dot Cards, Sets B, C, or D (M18–M20).

PAIRS

3B Compare

For complete details about this activity, see Session 2.4, pages 72–73.

SESSION FOLLOW-UP

4 Daily Practice

Daily Practice: For reinforcement of this unit's content, have students complete *Student Activity Book* page 13.

Student Math Handbook: Students and families may use *Student Math Handbook* pages 6–8, 21–23, 26, 31 and G2, G3 for reference and review. See pages 243–252 in the back of this unit.

Professional Development

5 **Teacher Note:** Counting Is More Than 1, 2, 3, p. 192

6 **Teacher Note:** Observing Students as They Count, p. 193

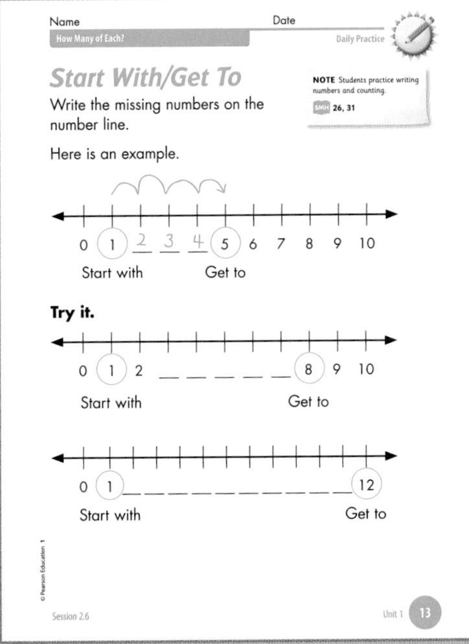

Name Date

How Many of Each? Daily Practice

Start With/Get To

Write the missing numbers on the number line.

NOTE Students practice writing numbers and counting.

SMH 26, 31

Here is an example.

0 (1) 2 3 4 (5) 6 7 8 9 10

Start with Get to

Try it.

0 (1) 2 ___ ___ ___ ___ ___ (8) 9 10

Start with Get to

0 (1) ___ ___ ___ ___ ___ ___ ___ ___ ___ ___ (12)

Start with Get to

© Pearson Education 1

Session 2.6 Unit 1 13

▲ Student Activity Book, p. 13

Ordering Numbers

Math Focus Points

- Connecting number names and written numbers to the quantities they represent
- Introducing standard notation for comparing quantities (greater than, less than, and equal to)
- Ordering 2 set of numbers up to 12

Vocabulary

greater than
less than
equal to

Today's Plan			Materials
ACTIVITY 1 Introducing Ordering Numbers	15 MIN	CLASS	• *Student Activity Book*, p. 14 • Primary Number Cards (1 deck; from Session 2.4) • Connecting cubes (class set)
ACTIVITY 2 Ordering Numbers	30 MIN	PAIRS	• *Student Activity Book*, p. 14 • Primary Number Cards (1 deck; from Session 2.4) • Connecting cubes (about 40 per pair)
DISCUSSION 3 Comparing and Ordering Numbers	15 MIN	CLASS	• Primary Number Cards (1 deck per class) • Dot Cards, Set A (1 deck; from Session 2.4; optional)
SESSION FOLLOW-UP 4 Daily Practice and Homework			• *Student Activity Book,* pp. 15–16 • *Student Math Handbook,* pp. 43, 44–45 • Primary Number Cards (1 deck per student; sent home in Session 2.5); M17 (1 per student; sent home in Session 2.5)

Classroom Routines

Quick Images: Dot Cards **Show a transparency of the 5 from Dot Cards Set B (T7). Follow the basic *Quick Images* activity. Ask students to determine the total number of dots. Repeat with the 6 and then the 9. For a full write-up of this routine, see *Part 4: Classroom Routines* in *Implementing Investigations in Grade 1: Quick Images.***

ACTIVITY

Introducing *Ordering Numbers*

To introduce this activity, you will need a bin of connecting cubes and a deck of Primary Number Cards (M13–M16).

Remember when we built staircases? We built a cube tower, or step, for every number from 1 through 12, and then we put them in order. Today we're going to build more steps, but this time we're going to build only part of the staircase.

Ask volunteers to randomly choose four cards from your deck of Primary Number Cards. After each card is chosen, ask students what number is on the card and how many cubes should be in a step for that card.

[Jacinta] picked a [4]. How many cubes should be in her step? How about the card that [Edgar] chose? How many cubes would [Edgar] need?

Build a step for each number. Once you have built them, ask students how they would put those steps in order, from the one with the fewest cubes to the one with the most cubes.

Students might say:

"Pick the smallest step and put that first."

"Look at the numbers. One is not there, so look for 2, then 3."

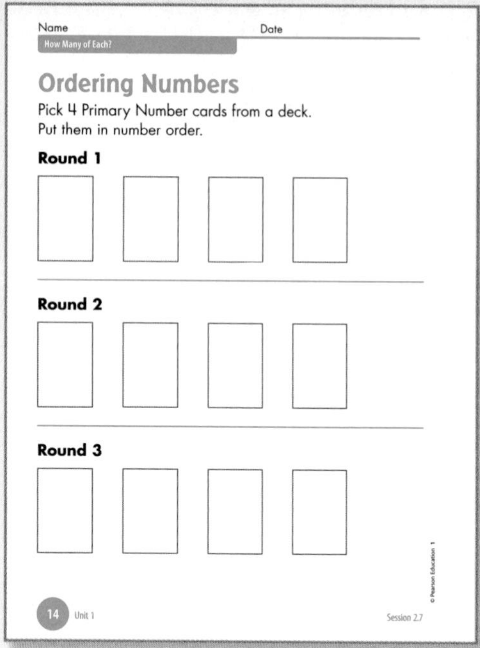
Name Date

How Many of Each?

Ordering Numbers

Pick 4 Primary Number cards from a deck.
Put them in number order.

Round 1

Round 2

Round 3

© Pearson Education 1

14 Unit 1 Session 2.7

▲ **Student Activity Book, p. 14**

Ask several students to share their strategies. Then put the steps in order, placing the correct number card beside each step.

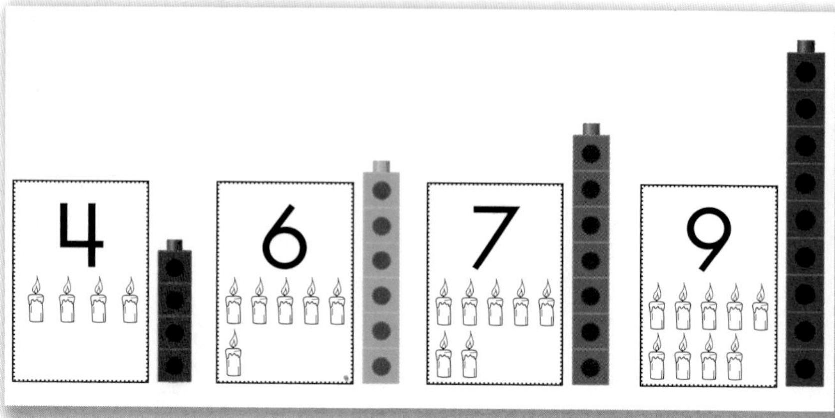

Some students will place the steps in a row with no gaps; others will want to leave spaces or holes to represent the missing numbers in the sequence (e.g., 5 and 8).

Explain that students will record their work by writing the numbers in order on *Student Activity Book* page 14.

2 ACTIVITY

Ordering Numbers

30 MIN PAIRS

Students deal out four cards and figure out how to put them in order. Students can work together, but each student should record on his or her own copy of *Student Activity Book* page 14.

This game helps students learn to compare and order numbers.

ONGOING ASSESSMENT: Observing Students at Work

Students are identifying numbers, putting them in order, and recording their work.

- **Do students recognize the number on the card?** Do they count the items to figure out the number?
- **How do students put the numbers in order?** Do they work only with the numbers? Do they build cube towers and order them by comparing lengths?
- **Can students accurately record from least to most?**

As you observe, look for one student who uses towers and another who uses only the cards to solve this problem to inform the discussion at the end of this session.

DIFFERENTIATION: Supporting the Range of Learners

Extension As students finish, they can continue with Ordering Numbers or they can play *Compare* or *Compare Dots* with a partner. See Session 2.4, pages 72–73, for complete details about these games.

DISCUSSION

15 MIN CLASS

3 Comparing and Ordering Numbers

Math Focus Points for Discussion

- Introducing standard notation for comparing quantities (greater than, less than, equal to)

Begin the discussion by talking about the comparison of two numbers, as in *Compare*. This will provide the opportunity to introduce the standard notation for greater than, less than, and equal to.[1]

You've been playing a lot of games that involve comparing two numbers to see which is more or which is less. Mathematicians have some special words and symbols that they use to show this.

Let's play a round of *Compare* [or *Compare Dots*] and see how they work.

Deal two cards. Ask students which card has more and how they know.

Professional Development

[1] **Teacher Note:** Introducing Notation, Part 1, pp. 198–199

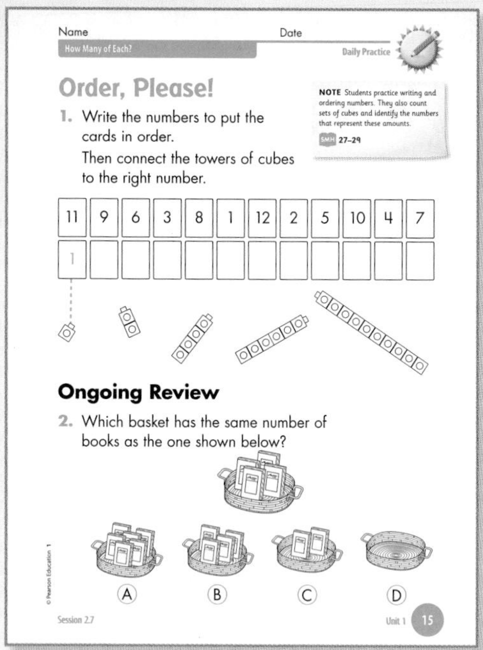
Name Date

How Many of Each? Daily Practice

Order, Please!

NOTE Students practice writing and ordering numbers. They also count sets of cubes and identify the numbers that represent these amounts.

SMH 27–29

1. Write the numbers to put the cards in order.

   Then connect the towers of cubes to the right number.

11	9	6	3	8	1	12	2	5	10	4	7
1											

Ongoing Review

2. Which basket has the same number of books as the one shown below?

   Ⓐ Ⓑ Ⓒ Ⓓ

© Pearson Education 1

Session 2.7 Unit 1 15

▲ Student Activity Book, p. 15

[8] is *more than* [3]. A mathematician might say [8] is *greater than* [3], or [3] is *less than* [8]. If they were going to write that down, it would look like this:

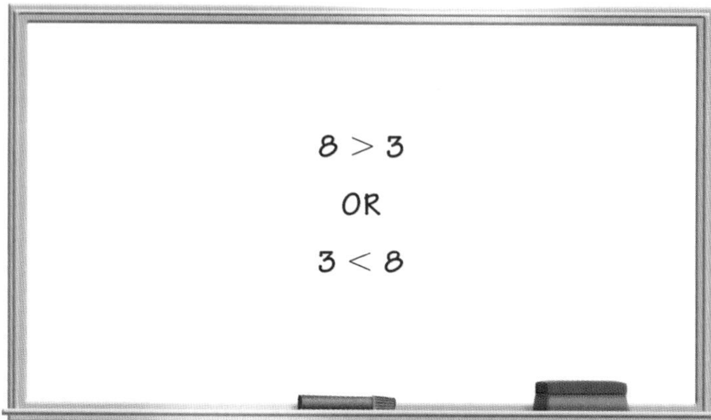

Ask students whether they have seen these symbols before. Spend a few minutes talking about ways to remember what these symbols mean and how they are written. Keep in mind that it is not the intent to have all students use these symbols. The symbols are being introduced as one way to record comparisons of two numbers.

Students might say:

"It's like an arrow pointing to the smaller number."

"The big part is near the big number."

Let's deal another pair of cards. Now we have a [4] and a [6]. Let's try the mathematician words and symbols with these two numbers.

Try this example with students. Then use another example in which both numbers are the same so that you can introduce the equal sign.

What happens if we deal two more cards, and we get a 5 and a 5? Is one number greater than the other? Less than the other? In this situation we use this symbol. It's called the equal sign, and it means that what is on either side is the same.

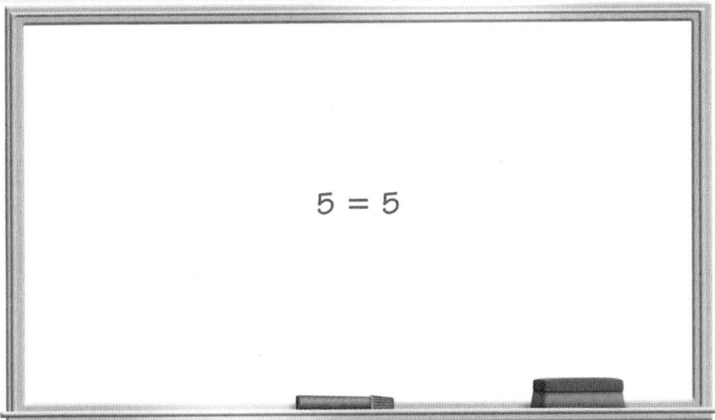

Students' understanding and use of such notation will develop over time through experience seeing, talking about, and using such symbols and language.

If there is time, spend a few minutes discussing students' strategies for ordering 4 numbers, or cube towers, as in Ordering Numbers.

Students might say:

"I looked at the number cards and put them in order. Then I copied the numbers onto the sheet."

"I used cubes and made towers for each number. Then I put them in order from shortest to tallest."

4 SESSION FOLLOW-UP
Daily Practice and Homework

Daily Practice: For reinforcement of this unit's content, have students complete *Student Activity Book* page 15.

Homework: Students play *Compare* with someone at home. They should already have at home the materials they need: a deck of Primary Number Cards (M13–M16) and a copy of the game directions (M17). Tell students that the person with whom they play should help them record the results of the game on *Student Activity Book* page 16.

Student Math Handbook: Students and families may use *Student Math Handbook* pages 43–45 for reference and review. See pages 243–252 in the back of this unit.

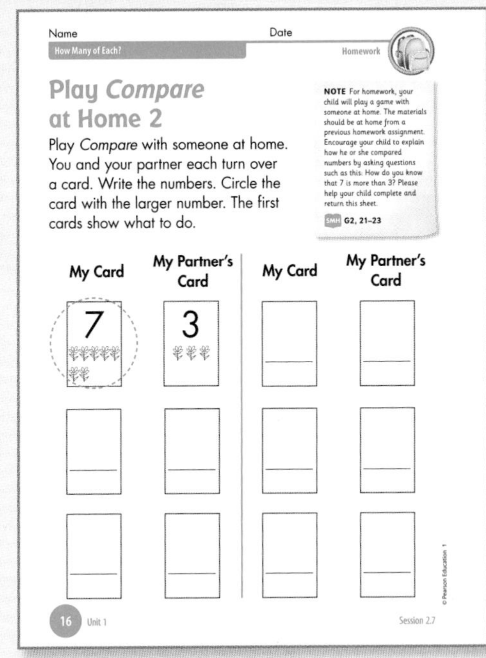

Name Date

How Many of Each? Homework

Play *Compare* at Home 2

Play *Compare* with someone at home. You and your partner each turn over a card. Write the numbers. Circle the card with the larger number. The first cards show what to do.

NOTE For homework, your child will play a game with someone at home. The materials should be at home from a previous homework assignment. Encourage your child to explain how he or she compared numbers by asking questions such as this: How do you know that 7 is more than 3? Please help your child complete and return this sheet.

SMH G2, 21–23

My Card	My Partner's Card	My Card	My Partner's Card
7	3		

16 Unit 1 Session 2.7

▲ Student Activity Book, p. 16

Mathematical Emphases

Counting and Quantity Developing strategies for accurately counting a set of objects by ones

Math Focus Points

- Connecting number names and written numbers to the quantities they represent

Counting and Quantity Developing an understanding of the magnitude and position of numbers

Math Focus Points

- Comparing two quantities up to 20 to see which is larger
- Developing an understanding of how the quantities in the counting sequence are related: each number has 1 more or 1 less than the number before or after it

Whole Number Operations Making sense of and developing strategies to solve addition problems with small numbers

Math Focus Points

- Visualizing and retelling the action in an addition situation
- Modeling the action of an addition problem with counters or drawings
- Finding the total of two or more quantities up to a total of 20 by counting all, counting on, or using number combinations
- Seeing that adding the same two numbers (e.g., 4 and 3) results in the same total, regardless of context (e.g., number cubes, cards, objects)

INVESTIGATION 3

Whole Number Operations Using manipulatives, drawings, tools, and notation to show strategies and solutions

Math Focus Points

- Using the number line as a tool for counting
- Introducing standard notation (+ and =) for representing addition situations
- Recording a solution to a problem

Combining

SESSION 3.1 p. 100	Student Activity Book	Student Math Handbook	Professional Development: Read Ahead of Time
Double Compare and Double Compare Dots Students play *Double Compare* and *Double Compare Dots,* variations of games learned earlier in this unit. Students compare two pairs of cards to see which pair shows more objects or dots. The session ends with the whole class solving several story problems together.	17	6–8, 21–23; G6, G7	• **Teacher Note:** *Double Compare:* Strategies for Combining and Comparing, pp. 201–203; Adapting Story Problems, p. 200
SESSION 3.2 p. 107			
Five-in-a-Row Students play a new game called *Five-in-a-Row,* a variation on the game *Bingo.* A Math Workshop focused on combining and comparing numbers follows. The session ends with the whole class solving more story problems.	18–20	21–23, 33–37; G6, G7, G9	• **Dialogue Box:** An Addition Story Problem Aloud, pp. 230–231
SESSION 3.3 p. 112			
Addition Story Problems Students solve addition story problems as a class. Then each child individually solves an addition story problem and records his or her solution strategy to share with the class.	21–22	33–37, 44–45	• **Teacher Notes:** Discussing Story Problems, pp. 206–207; Recording Strategies for a Combining Problem, pp. 204–205; Introducing Notation Part 1, pp. 198–199 • **Dialogue Box:** Discussing Addition Strategies, pp. 232–233

Classroom Routines See page 20 for an overview.

Morning Meeting

- Daily Schedule
- Pocket monthly calendar and yearlong calendar
- Weather chart for this month and yearlong weather chart

Start With/Get To

- A basket
- M6–M7 Start With/Get To cards, numbers 1–30
- Clothespins (2)
- Class number line

Quick Images

- T2, T7, Dot Cards, Sets A and B Cut apart.

Materials to Gather	Materials to Prepare
• **Dot Cards, Set A** (1 deck per pair; from Session 2.4) • **Primary Number Cards** (1 deck per pair; from Session 2.4) • **Counters** (20 per pair) • **Connecting cubes** (as needed; optional)	• **M24, *Double Compare Dots*** Make copies. (as needed) • **M25, *Double Compare*** Make copies. (as needed)
• **T8, *Five-in-a-Row* Gameboard A** (optional) • **Dot cubes** (2 per pair); **counters** (about 20 per pair); **chart paper** (optional) • **Homework materials: Primary Number Cards** (1 deck per student; sent home in Session 2.5) • **Materials for *Double Compare*** See Session 3.1. • **Materials for *Double Compare Dots*** See Session 3.1. • **Dot Cards, Sets B, C, D** (as needed; from Session 2.5; optional)	• **M25, *Double Compare*** Make copies. (1 per student for homework) • **M26, *Five-in-a-Row* Gameboard A** Make copies. You may wish to make copies on cardstock and laminate the gameboards. (1 per pair or group) • **M27, *Five-in-a-Row*** Make copies. (as needed) • **Chart paper** Make a large chart-paper display showing *Five-in-a-Row* Gameboard A. (optional)
• **Cubes or counters** (as needed) • **Chart paper** (optional)	• **Chart paper** Write the story problem from *Student Activity Book* page 21 on chart paper.

Overhead Transparency

Combining, *continued*

SESSION 3.4 p. 119	Student Activity Book	Student Math Handbook	Professional Development: Read Ahead of Time
Roll and Record Students learn a new game called *Roll and Record* that involves combining two amounts and recording the total. A Math Workshop focuses on combining two amounts. The session ends with the whole class solving more story problems.	23–26	21–23, 33–37; G6, G7, G9, G19	
SESSION 3.5 p. 126			
More Addition Story Problems Students solve another addition story problem on paper. Math Workshop continues to focus on combining games and is followed by a discussion about the story problem the students solved.	27–29	26, 31, 33–37; G6, G7, G9, G19	
SESSION 3.6 p. 131			
Assessment: Double Compare and Combining Games Students complete an assessment based on the game *Double Compare.* The session ends with a discussion about strategies for combining.	31	33–37; G6, G7, G9, G19	• **Teacher Note:** Assessment: *Double Compare*, pp. 208–210 • **Dialogue Box:** Is It *Always* 11?, pp. 234–235
SESSION 3.7 p. 137			
How Many in All? Students solve a story problem about a growing group of objects (e.g., Ms. E. packed 1 apple, 2 oranges, 3 bananas, and so on for a picnic).	32	33–37, 46–47	• **Dialogue Box:** How Many in All?, pp. 236–238

Materials to Gather	Materials to Prepare
• **Materials for *Five-in-a-Row*** See Session 3.2. • **T9, *Roll and Record* Recording Sheet** (Overhead Transparency) • **Materials for *Double Compare Dots* and *Double Compare*** See Session 3.1.	• **M28, *Roll and Record* Recording Sheet** Make copies. (as needed) • **M29, *Roll and Record*** Make copies. (as needed) • **M30–M31, *Five-in-a-Row* Gameboards B and C** Make copies. You may wish to make copies on cardstock and laminate the gameboards. (1 per pair or group; optional)
• **Chart paper** (optional); **cubes or counters** (optional) • **Materials for *Double Compare Dots* and *Double Compare*** See Session 3.1. • **Materials for *Five-in-a-Row*** See Session 3.2. • **M26, M30–M31, Gameboards A, B, and C** (1 per pair or group; from Sessions 3.2, 3.4) • **Materials from *Roll and Record*** See Session 3.4.	• **Chart paper** Write the story problem from *Student Activity Book* page 27 on chart paper or write it on the board.
• **Materials for *Five-in-a-Row*** See Session 3.2. • **Materials for *Roll and Record*** See Session 3.4. • **Materials for *Double Compare Dots* and *Double Compare*** See Session 3.1. • **Primary Number Cards** (1 deck per class; from Session 2.4) • **Dot cubes** (2 per class); **assorted counters** (as needed)	• **M32, Assessment: *Double Compare*** Make copies. (1 per student)
• **Children's book with a number pattern that increases by one** (optional) such as ***Rooster's Off to See the World*** or ***The Very Hungry Caterpillar,*** **both by Eric Carle** See alternative suggestions on page 138. • **Counters or cubes** (as needed) • **Chart paper**	• **Story problem with a number pattern that increases by one** Instead of using one of the literature selections suggested for this session, you may create your own story about a growing group of objects, such as this: For a picnic, Mrs. E. packed 1 apple, 2 oranges, 3 bananas, and so on. Follow the mathematical structure $1 + 2 + 3 + 4 + 5$. (optional)

Overhead Transparency

Double Compare and Double Compare Dots

Math Focus Points

- Finding the total of two or more quantities up to a total of 20 by counting all, counting on, or using number combinations
- Comparing two quantities up to 20 to see which is larger
- Visualizing and retelling the action in an addition situation
- Modeling the action of an addition problem with counters or drawings

Vocabulary

more
fewer

Today's Plan		Materials
1 ACTIVITY **Introducing *Double Compare* and *Double Compare Dots***	15 MIN CLASS	• Dot Cards, Set A and Primary Number Cards (from Session 2.4)
2 MATH WORKSHOP **Comparing Numbers** 2A *Double Compare* 2B *Double Compare Dots*	30 MIN	2A • Primary Number Cards (from Session 2.4) • Counters; connecting cubes (optional) • M25* 2B • Dot Cards, Set A (from Session 2.4) • M24*
3 ACTIVITY **Introducing Story Problems Aloud**	15 MIN CLASS	• Cubes and counters
4 SESSION FOLLOW-UP **Daily Practice**		• *Student Activity Book,* p. 17 • *Student Math Handbook,* pp. 6–8, 21–23; G6, G7

*See *Materials to Prepare,* p. 97.

Classroom Routines

Start With/Get To: Get To 1 **Choose a *start with* number. Ask students to find and mark the number on the class number line. As a class, count together, from this number, backward to 1.**

1

ACTIVITY

Introducing *Double Compare Dots* and *Double Compare*

Because students have recently played *Compare Dots* and *Compare,* the introduction of these variations should go fairly quickly. Gather students together for a demonstration game of each.

Today we're going to learn two new games. One is called *Double Compare Dots,* and the other is called *Double Compare.* They are like the games we learned the other day, *Compare Dots* and *Compare.*

In these new games, each player turns over two cards instead of one. Then partners compare to see who has more dots. The one with more dots says "Me." Let's try a round of *Double Compare Dots.*

Ask your volunteers to each turn over two dot cards. Students can deal half the deck to each player or leave the deck whole and draw cards from the top.

Look at the cards [Sacha] has. Now look at the cards [Leah] has. Who has more dots? How do you know?

Give students a few moments to think about it. Then ask several students to explain how they know who has more.

Players compare two pairs of cards to decide which pair shows the larger number.

Algebra Note

① **Teacher Note:** *Double Compare:* Strategies for Combining and Comparing, pp. 201–203

Students might say:

"I counted all the dots and saw that Leah has more."

"I saw that they both have a card with 3 dots, so I compared the other two cards."

Although many students will count all the dots and compare totals, some will use other strategies, such as seeing and using groups of dots that are the same.

If the totals are the same, players flip their next 2 cards. The player with the larger total says "Me." The game is over when players have turned over all their cards.

Now let's try a round of *Double Compare.* The rules are the same; it's just the cards that are different.

Ask two volunteers to each turn over two Primary Number Cards.

What numbers did [Teo] turn over? [Tamika?] [Teo] has a [7] and a [4]. [Tamika] has a [4] and an [8]. Who has more? How do you know?

Give students a few moments to think about it, and then ask several to explain how they know which pair of cards shows the larger total.①

Students might say:

"They both have a 4, but Tamika has an 8, and 8 is more than 7, so Tamika has more."

"Teo has 11 and Tamika has 12. Tamika has more."

Again, the player with the larger total says "Me." If the totals are the same, players flip their next 2 cards. The game is over when players have turned over all their cards.

MATH WORKSHOP

Comparing Numbers

30 MIN

Pairs of students play two new games that focus on combining and comparing numbers up to 20.

2A Double Compare

PAIRS

Pairs of students play *Double Compare.* Each player turns over two cards. Together the students decide which pair of cards shows the larger total. Have available copies of *Double Compare* (M25) as needed.

ONGOING ASSESSMENT: Observing Students at Work

Students are combining and comparing numbers up to 20.

- **Do students need to count the objects on the card to figure out what number they have?** Do they recognize the numbers on the cards?
- **How do students compare the two pairs of cards?** Do they find the total of each pair? How? Do they count all? Count on? Use facts they know? Do they "just know" any pairs?
- **Do students use strategies that do not rely on finding the totals, such as comparing the amounts on individual cards?**

DIFFERENTIATION: Supporting the Range of Learners

Intervention If there are students who are having trouble counting the amounts on the cards accurately, they can play with only the cards 1 through 6.

Intervention Students who are struggling with knowing which pair of cards has more might find it helpful to build and compare cube towers.

2B Double Compare Dots

PAIRS

Pairs of students play *Double Compare Dots.* Each player turns over two cards. Together the students decide which pair of cards shows more dots in all. Have available copies of *Double Compare Dots* (M24) as needed.

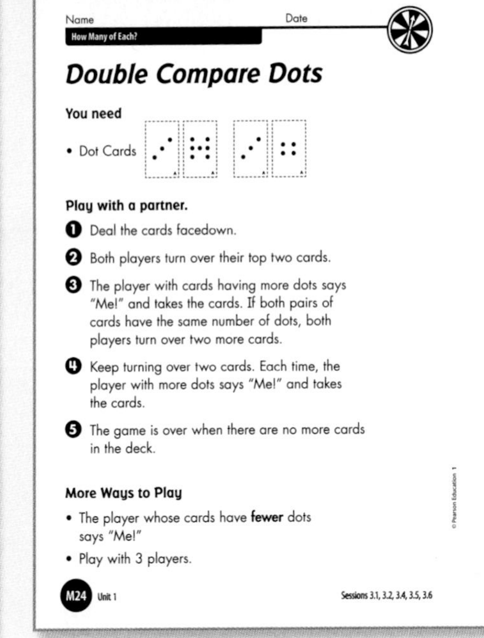

Name Date

How Many of Each?

Double Compare Dots

You need

- Dot Cards

Play with a partner.

1. Deal the cards facedown.
2. Both players turn over their top two cards.
3. The player with cards having more dots says "Me!" and takes the cards. If both pairs of cards have the same number of dots, both players turn over two more cards.
4. Keep turning over two cards. Each time, the player with more dots says "Me!" and takes the cards.
5. The game is over when there are no more cards in the deck.

More Ways to Play

- The player whose cards have **fewer** dots says "Me!"
- Play with 3 players.

© Pearson Education 1

M24 Unit 1 Sessions 3.1, 3.2, 3.4, 3.5, 3.6

▲ Resource Masters, M24

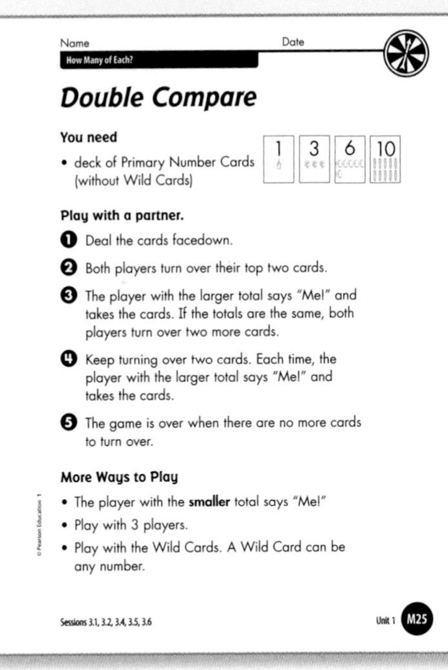

Name Date

How Many of Each?

Double Compare

You need

- deck of Primary Number Cards (without Wild Cards)

Play with a partner.

1. Deal the cards facedown.
2. Both players turn over their top two cards.
3. The player with the larger total says "Me!" and takes the cards. If the totals are the same, both players turn over two more cards.
4. Keep turning over two cards. Each time, the player with the larger total says "Me!" and takes the cards.
5. The game is over when there are no more cards to turn over.

More Ways to Play

- The player with the **smaller** total says "Me!"
- Play with 3 players.
- Play with the Wild Cards. A Wild Card can be any number.

© Pearson Education 1

Sessions 3.1, 3.2, 3.4, 3.5, 3.6 Unit 1 M25

▲ Resource Masters, M25

Differentiation

❷ **English Language Learners** Story problems present special challenges for English Language Learners, who may understand the underlying math concepts but not the language of the problem. If English Language Learners cannot easily follow the story problems, meet with a small group and review the problems, using real-life objects, manipulatives, or simple drawings to represent with them quantities that are added (or subtracted) in each story. You can also preview some story problems to build English Language Learners' confidence, and to support their participation in upcoming discussions.

Professional Development

❸ **Teacher Note:** Adapting Story Problems, p. 200

ONGOING ASSESSMENT: Observing Students at Work

Students are becoming familiar with visual images of the numbers up to 10 and with combining and comparing numbers up to 20. See the questions above in *Double Compare.*

DIFFERENTIATION: Supporting the Range of Learners

See the suggestions above for *Double Compare.*

3 ACTIVITY

15 MIN CLASS

Introducing Stories Problems Aloud

Story problems are introduced in this session and occur regularly throughout the remainder of this unit. For the first few sessions, students solve story problems as a whole class. Later in the Investigation, they solve problems individually on paper. Take this opportunity to establish the routine for story problems done as a whole group. Have a collection of counters or cubes available for modeling and solving the problems.❷

Tell a story problem like the one that follows. You might change the context of the problem to make it more familiar or interesting to your students, but it is important to keep the numbers small and the structure the same so that students can focus on making sense of the story problem: visualizing the quantities, the sequence of actions, and the result.❸

I'm going to tell a story, and I want you to try to see it in your minds as I tell it. The other day I went to the supermarket because I wanted to buy some fruit. I walked around the fruit and vegetable area in the market until I found the bananas.

I picked up one bunch of bananas. I counted them. There were 4 bananas in the bunch. I decided I needed some more. So I picked up 2 more bananas.

What happened in the story?

Ask several students to tell what they remember about the story: What happened first? Then what happened? Even if one student tells the story correctly, ask a few more students to tell it as well. The focus is on visualizing the sequence and action of the story, not on retelling it *exactly* as you did.

Some students may anticipate a question at the end of the story, such as, "How many bananas in all did I pick up?" Remind students that for now you are interested only in what they remember about the story and how they are thinking about it; you are not looking for an answer.

Next, ask students whether there were more than or fewer than 4 bananas at the end of the story.

So first, I had 4 bananas. At the end of the story, did I have **more** than 4 or **fewer** than 4 bananas? How do you know?

After students have shared their ideas about this question, ask them to actually solve the problem and model it using cubes or counters.

Students might say:

"More. I pictured a bunch of 4 bananas and a smaller bunch of 2 next to it."

"I know that 4 and 2 more has to be more than just 4."

So if I had 4 bananas, and then I took 2 more, how many bananas did I buy?

Ask a few students to share their strategy for figuring out the total.

Let's use the cubes to show what happened in this story. I had 4 bananas. [Show a tower of 4 cubes.] Then I took 2 more. [Show a tower of 2.] How many did I buy in all?

Some students will count all the cubes in each tower. Some will snap them together and count them all, and some might count on from 4 (or 2).

Students use cubes to model the action of a story problem.

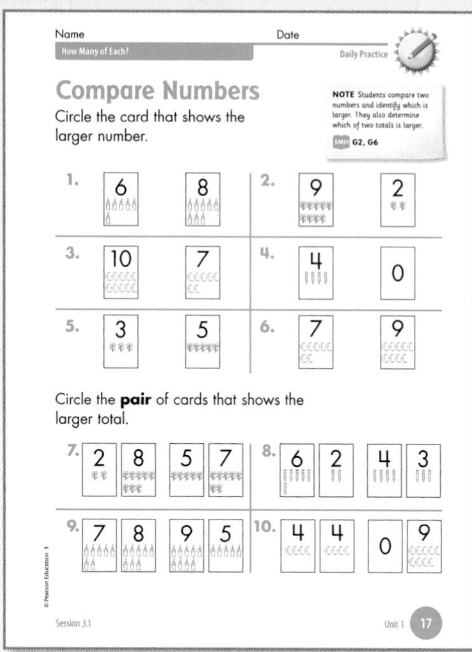

Name Date

How Many of Each? Daily Practice

Compare Numbers

Circle the card that shows the larger number.

NOTE Students compare two numbers and identify which is larger. They also determine which of two totals is larger.

SMH G2, G6

1. 6 8
2. 9 2
3. 10 7
4. 4 0
5. 3 5
6. 7 9

Circle the **pair** of cards that shows the larger total.

7. 2 8 5 7
8. 6 2 4 3
9. 7 8 9 5
10. 4 4 0 9

© Pearson Education 1

Session 3.1 Unit 1 17

▲ Student Activity Book, p. 17

If there is time, try one more story problem with the class.

Pretty soon we ran out of bananas at my home. The next time I was at the store, I bought some more bananas. This time I picked up one bunch that had 6 bananas. Then I picked up 2 more bananas. Try to see this story in your mind. Who can tell me what happened?

Again, ask students to put the story in their own words, and then tell you whether there would be more than or fewer than 6 bananas at the end of the story.

Can you use the cubes to show us what happened?

How would you figure out how many bananas there are in all?

4 SESSION FOLLOW-UP Daily Practice

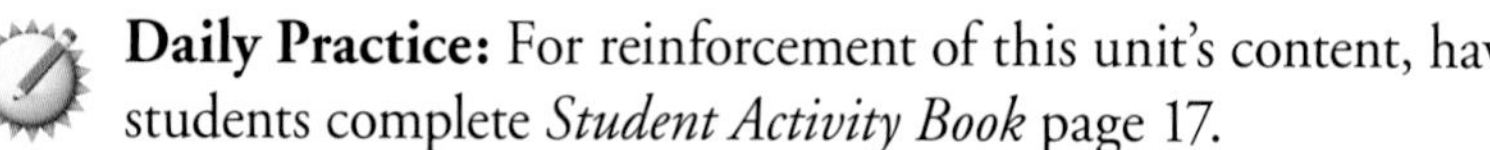

Daily Practice: For reinforcement of this unit's content, have students complete *Student Activity Book* page 17.

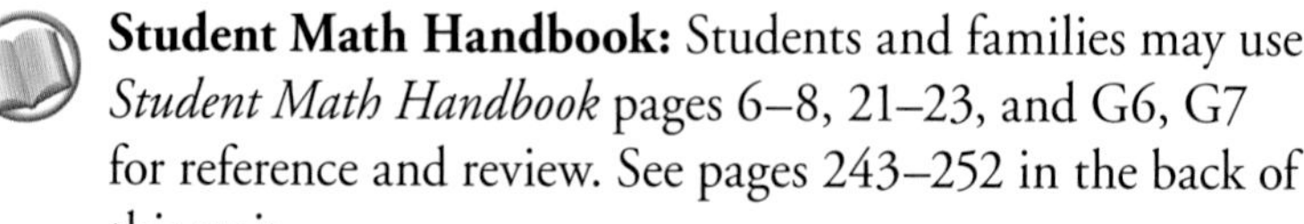

Student Math Handbook: Students and families may use *Student Math Handbook* pages 6–8, 21–23, and G6, G7 for reference and review. See pages 243–252 in the back of this unit.

Five-in-a-Row

Math Focus Points

- Connecting number names and written numbers to the quantities they represent
- Finding the total of two or more quantities up to a total of 20 by counting all, counting on, or using number combinations
- Comparing two quantities up to 20 to see which is larger

Vocabulary

sum
plus

Today's Plan			Materials
1 ACTIVITY **Introducing *Five-in-a-Row***	15 MIN	CLASS	• T8 • Dot cubes; counters
2 MATH WORKSHOP **Combining and Comparing Numbers** 2A *Five-in-a-Row* 2B *Double Compare* 2C *Double Compare Dots*	30 MIN		2A • M26*; M27* • Dot cubes; counters 2B • Materials from Session 3.1, p. 100 2C • Materials from Session 3.1, p. 100 • Dot Card Sets, B, C, D (from Session 2.5; optional)
3 ACTIVITY **More Story Problems Aloud**	15 MIN	CLASS	• Cubes or counters (optional); chart paper (optional)
4 SESSION FOLLOW-UP **Daily Practice and Homework**			• *Student Activity Book,* pp. 18–20 • M25*; Primary Number Cards (from Session 2.5) • *Student Math Handbook,* pp. 21–23, 33–37; G6, G7, G9

*See *Materials to Prepare,* p. 97.

Classroom Routines

Quick Images: Dot Cards Show transparencies of the 3- and 4-dot cards from Dot Cards Set B (T7) at the same time. Follow the basic *Quick Images* activity. Ask students to determine the total number of dots. Repeat with the 3- and 4-dot cards from Dot Cards Set A (T2) and compare the arrangement.

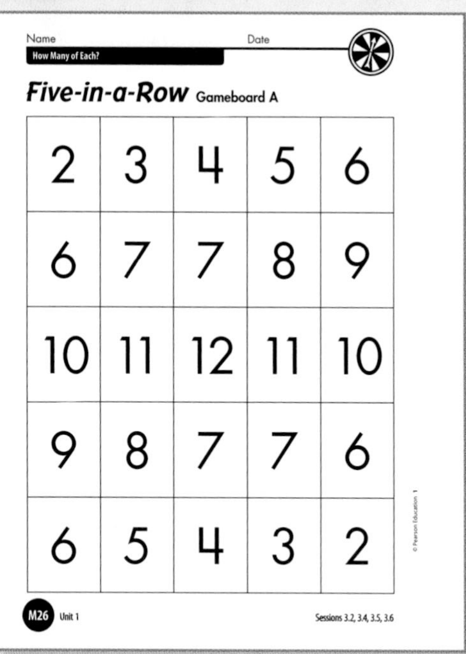

Name Date

How Many of Each?

Five-in-a-Row Gameboard A

2	3	4	5	6
6	7	7	8	9
10	11	12	11	10
9	8	7	7	6
6	5	4	3	2

M26 Unit 1 Sessions 3.2, 3.4, 3.5, 3.6

▲ Resource Masters, M26; T8

ACTIVITY

Introducing *Five-in-a-Row*

Introduce *Five-in-a-Row* by playing a demonstration game. Display a transparency of *Five-in-a-Row* Gameboard A (T8), or a chart-paper version for display. The object of this game is to mark five squares in a row *horizontally*, *vertically*, or *diagonally*.

Roll two dot cubes, and draw the dot arrangements you rolled on the board or on chart paper. Ask students what numbers you rolled and how many dots there are altogether.

[Richard] said I rolled a [2] and a [5]. How many dots is that altogether? What's the **sum** of [2] and [5]? How do you know? Who has another way they know that [5] **plus** [2] is [7]?

After you have agreed upon the total, ask a volunteer to find that number on your gameboard. He or she can place a counter on any square that matches the sum. (If you are using a chart-paper gameboard, draw an X in the box to show where the counter is placed.)

As they play Five-in-a-Row, *students combine numbers and think strategically.*

Roll the dot cubes again, record your rolls, and ask students to find the total. Before placing the next counter, explain that the goal of the game is to mark five squares in a row going across, up and down, or corner to corner. Encourage students to think about where they could place the counter to help them get five in a row.

Continue playing for a few more rolls of the dot cubes until you think everyone understands how to play. Make sure that students understand that they can cover only one square on each turn. Explain that when there is more than one square with their number, they can choose where to put their marker. If they cannot make a move (for example, the sum of the cards is 7 but all the 7s are covered), they should roll again.

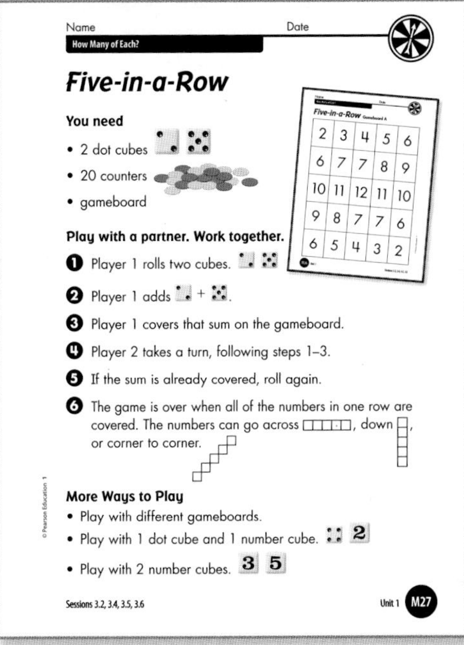

Name Date

How Many of Each?

Five-in-a-Row

You need

- 2 dot cubes
- 20 counters
- gameboard

Play with a partner. Work together.

1. Player 1 rolls two cubes.
2. Player 1 adds.
3. Player 1 covers that sum on the gameboard.
4. Player 2 takes a turn, following steps 1–3.
5. If the sum is already covered, roll again.
6. The game is over when all of the numbers in one row are covered. The numbers can go across, down, or corner to corner.

More Ways to Play

- Play with different gameboards.
- Play with 1 dot cube and 1 number cube.
- Play with 2 number cubes.

Sessions 3.2, 3.4, 3.5, 3.6 Unit 1 M27

▲ Resource Masters, M27

MATH WORKSHOP

Combining and Comparing Numbers

30 MIN

Students play games focused on combining and comparing numbers, and on connecting quantities to the number names and written numbers.

2A Five-in-a-Row

PAIRS GROUPS

Students play *Five-in-a-Row,* in pairs or small groups. The object is to get five markers in a row—horizontally, vertically, or diagonally—by covering the sum of two numbers rolled. Have available copies of *Five-in-a-Row* (M27) as needed.

ONGOING ASSESSMENT: Observing Students at Work

Students are combining single-digit numbers and connecting the written numbers and number names to the quantities they represent.

- **How do students total their rolls?** Do they count every single dot? Use counters? Count on from one number? Do they "just know" some number combinations? Can they quickly add 1 or 2? Do any students use number combinations they know to figure out those they do not know?
- **How do students determine which squares to cover?** Are they beginning to think strategically about which squares will help them get 5 in a row?

Story Problem Routine

1. Tell students a story. Encourage them to visualize the action in the story.
2. Ask several students to retell the story after they have heard it. (Or, several students can each tell one part of the story. Occasionally, you might have each student retell the story to a partner.)
3. After retelling each story, ask whether the end result in each case will be more or less than the amount you started with.
4. Ask students to share strategies for solving the problem, including modeling the problem with cubes or counters.
5. Model methods of recording on chart paper or the board.

Professional Development

1 **Dialogue Box:** An Addition Story Problem Aloud, pp. 230–231

2B *Double Compare*

PAIRS

For complete details about this activity, see Session 3.1, pages 101–103.

DIFFERENTIATION: Supporting the Range of Learners

Extension Students ready for more of a challenge can play *Triple Compare,* where players each turn over 3 cards and compare the totals.

2C *Double Compare Dots*

PAIRS

For complete details about this activity, see Session 3.1, pages 101–103.

DIFFERENTIATION: Supporting the Range of Learners

Extension Students who are ready for more variation can play *Double Compare Dots* with Dot Cards, Sets B or C (M18–M19). Students ready for an even greater challenge can play *Double Compare Dots* with Dot Cards, Set D (M20) or *Triple Compare Dots,* where players each turn over three cards and compare the totals.

ACTIVITY 3 More Story Problems Aloud

15 MIN CLASS

Present one of these story problems, following the *Story Problem Routine* you introduced in Session 3.1. Expand the routine by modeling ways to record students' strategies on paper.

Here are two problems you might use or adapt:

Nicky and Toshi were on a rock hunt. Nicky found 4 beautiful smooth rocks. Toshi found 5 rocks that were very round. How many rocks did they find?

Isabel, Libby, and Vic went to the park. Isabel saw 3 birds sitting in a tree. Libby saw 2 dogs being taken for walks, and Vic saw 3 squirrels in the bushes. How many animals did they see in the park?

As students share their thinking today, model ways to record students' strategies. 1

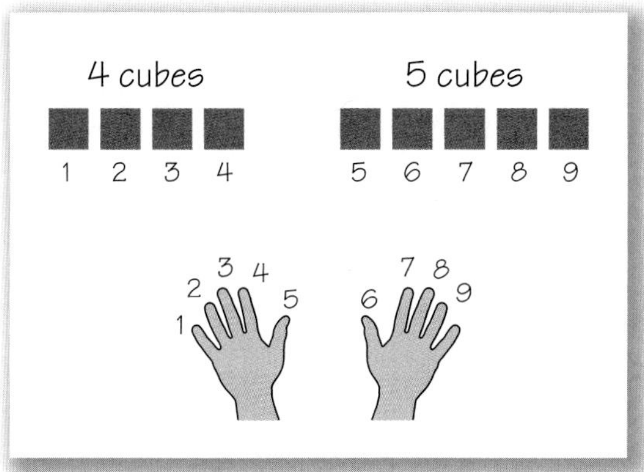

SESSION FOLLOW-UP
Daily Practice and Homework

Daily Practice: For reinforcement of this unit's content, have students complete *Student Activity Book* page 18.

Homework: Students play *Double Compare* with someone at home. Each student will need a copy of the game directions for *Double Compare* (M25). Students should already have at home a deck of Primary Number Cards (M13–M16). Tell students that the person with whom they play should help them record the results of the game on *Student Activity Book* pages 19–20.

Student Math Handbook: Students and families may use *Student Math Handbook* pages 21–23, 33–37; G6, G7, G9 for reference and review. See pages 243–252 in the back of this unit.

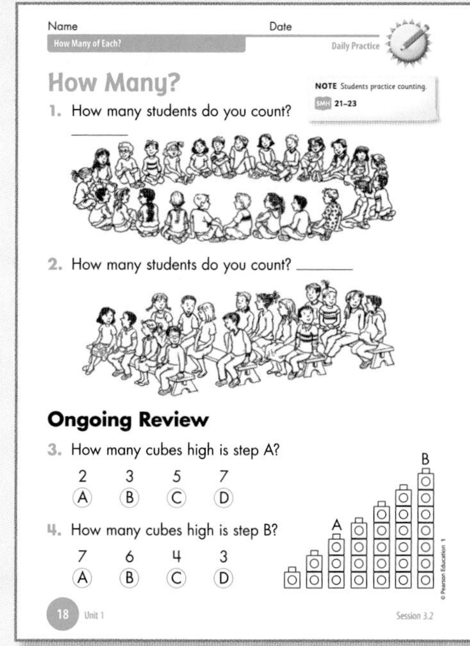

Name Date

How Many of Each? Daily Practice

How Many?

NOTE Students practice counting.

SMH 21–23

1. How many students do you count? ______

2. How many students do you count? ______

Ongoing Review

3. How many cubes high is step A?

2	3	5	7
(A)	(B)	(C)	(D)

4. How many cubes high is step B?

7	6	4	3
(A)	(B)	(C)	(D)

© Pearson Education 1

18 Unit 1 Session 3.2

▲ Student Activity Book, p. 18

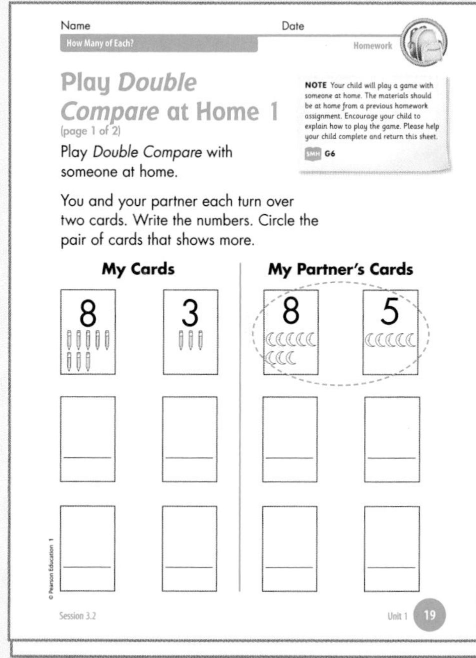

Name Date

How Many of Each? Homework

Play *Double Compare* at Home 1
(page 1 of 2)

NOTE Your child will play a game with someone at home. The materials should be at home from a previous homework assignment. Encourage your child to explain how to play the game. Please help your child complete and return this sheet.

SMH G6

Play *Double Compare* with someone at home.

You and your partner each turn over two cards. Write the numbers. Circle the pair of cards that shows more.

My Cards		My Partner's Cards	
8	3	8	5

© Pearson Education 1

Session 3.2 Unit 1 19

▲ Student Activity Book, pp. 19–20

Addition Story Problems

Math Focus Points

- Visualizing and retelling the action in an addition situation
- Modeling the action of an addition problem with counters or drawings
- Finding the total of two or more quantities up to a total of 20 by counting all, counting on, or using number combinations
- Introducing standard notation (+ and =) for representing addition situations

Vocabulary

equal
plus
add
equation

Today's Plan		Materials
ACTIVITY 1 **More Addition Stories**	15 MIN CLASS	• Cubes or counters; chart paper (optional)
ACTIVITY 2 **Solving an Addition Story Problem**	30 MIN INDIVIDUALS	• *Student Activity Book,* p. 21 • Chart paper*; cubes or counters
DISCUSSION 3 **Sharing Strategies**	15 MIN CLASS	• *Student Activity Book,* p. 21 • Chart: "How Many Pencils?" (from Activity 2); cubes or counters; chart paper (optional)
SESSION FOLLOW-UP 4 **Daily Practice and Homework**		• *Student Activity Book,* p. 22 • *Student Math Handbook,* pp. 33–37, 44–45

*See *Materials to Prepare,* p. 97.

Classroom Routines

Start With/Get To: Get To 1 Choose a *start with* number. Ask students to find and mark the number on the class number line. As a class, count together from this number backward to 1.

ACTIVITY

More Addition Stories

15 MIN CLASS

Present several story problems, following the *Story Problem Routine* on page 110. Here are two related problems to use or adapt:

Leah and Diego were working together at the art table. Diego had 3 crayons, and Leah had 3 crayons. How many crayons did they have altogether?

Leah and Diego are still working together at the art table. Diego still has 3 crayons, but now Leah has 4 crayons. How many crayons do they have altogether?

Present the stories separately. After students have discussed and shared strategies for each, ask them to think about whether one can help solve the other. If no students comment on the connection between the two problems above, bring it to their attention.❶

So I noticed that in the first problem you solved $3 + 3$ and in the second problem you solved $3 + 4$. Do you notice anything similar about these two problems?❷

Students might say:

"3 and 3 is 6. 4 is 1 more than 3. So 3 and 4 is 7, 1 more than 6."

ACTIVITY

Solving an Addition Story Problem

30 MIN INDIVIDUALS

Post the problem from *Student Activity Book* page 21 that you prepared on chart paper. Then read the problem aloud.

How Many Pencils?

I was cleaning the classroom.

I found 5 pencils on the floor.

I found 6 pencils under the window.

How many pencils did I find?

Teaching Note

❶ **Number Relationships** Many students may not yet see relationships between such problems. At this point in time, pose the question as a way of gathering information about what your students may know or realize about how these problems and numbers are related. Students will continue to work with and think about these ideas throughout Grades 1 and 2.

Algebra Note

❷ **Looking for the Generalization** If students are able to use one problem to solve another, encourage them to think about and verbalize the generalization underneath it—that if 1 is added to one addend, the total increases by 1.

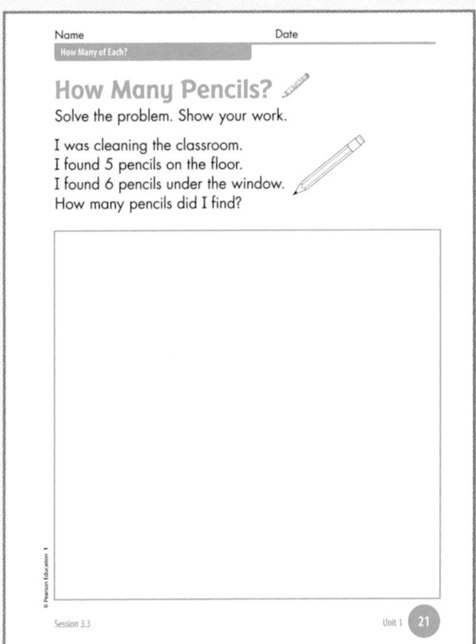

Name Date

How Many of Each?

How Many Pencils?

Solve the problem. Show your work.

I was cleaning the classroom.
I found 5 pencils on the floor.
I found 6 pencils under the window.
How many pencils did I find?

© Pearson Education 1

Session 3.3 Unit 1 21

▲ Student Activity Book, p. 21

I was cleaning the classroom. I found 5 pencils on the floor. I found 6 pencils under the window. How many pencils did I find?

Ask two or three students to retell the story in their own words. Keep the emphasis on retelling the story, and insist that no one anticipate the answer at this point.

Encourage students to solve this problem in whatever way makes sense to them, including using cubes, counters, counting on their fingers, or drawing pictures. Students should work individually, but encourage them to discuss their strategies with one another.

Keep track of how you solved the problem, and write down or draw on paper how you solved it so that someone else can understand exactly what you did. You can use numbers, pictures, and/or words. When we come back together, we'll share some of your strategies.

Students solve story problems and record their work.

ONGOING ASSESSMENT: Observing Students at Work

Students solve a problem about combining two amounts, and record their solutions.

- **Can students remember and make sense of the sequence of actions in the story?**
- **How do students solve the problem?** Can they explain their strategies? Do they get the right answer?
- **How do students record their work?** Do they use numbers? Pictures? Words? Equations? Does their work accurately reflect the strategy they used to solve the problem?

As you observe, make note of some approaches you see, so that you can encourage students with different approaches to share their work with the whole class in the next part of the session.[3]

DIFFERENTIATION: Supporting the Range of Learners

Intervention Reread the problem with students who are having difficulty getting started, and encourage them to tell the story in their own words. Have them model the problem with actual pencils.

Extension You can write a related story problem with larger numbers on a sheet of paper for students who solve this problem easily and record their strategies clearly. For example, *I found 11 pencils on the floor. Then I found 9 more under the window. Now how many did I have?*

Keep in mind that recording may be difficult for many students. The goal is for children to record in a way that helps someone else understand their solution. Help them figure out ways to write or draw about what they did. As students see a variety of recording methods, they will begin to understand what it means to record their thinking. However, this will take time.[4]

Sample Student Work

Professional Development

[3] **Teacher Note:** Discussing Story Problems, pp. 206–207

[4] **Teacher Note:** Recording Strategies for a Combining Problem, pp. 204–205

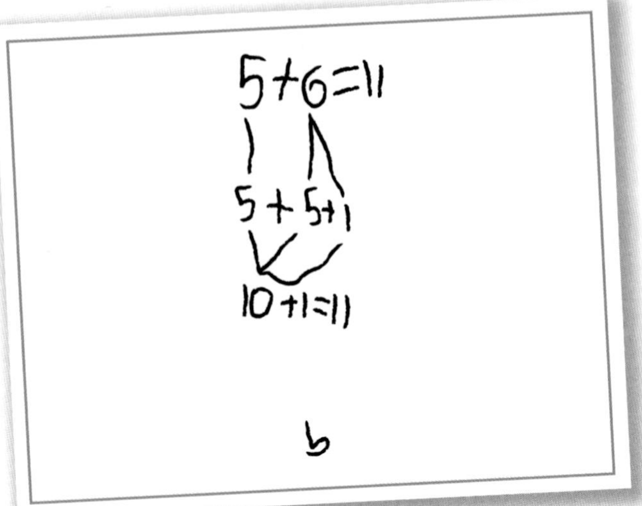

Sample Student Work

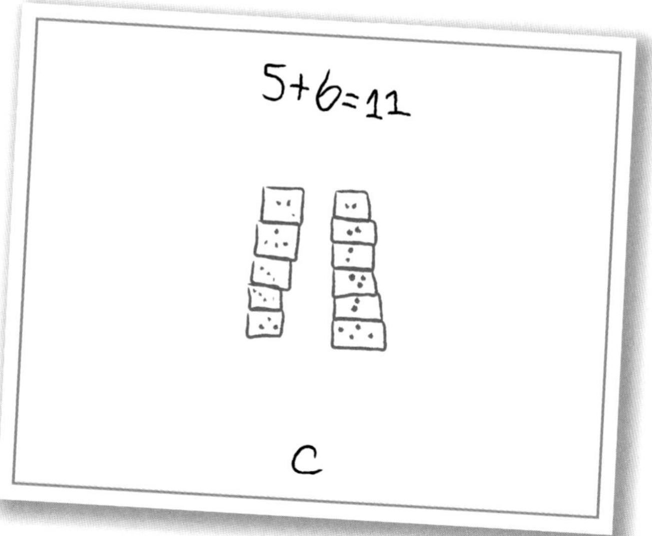

Sample Student Work

DISCUSSION

3 Sharing Strategies

Math Focus Points for Discussion

- Finding the total of two or more quantities up to a total of 20 by counting all, counting on, or using number combinations
- Introducing standard notation (+ and =) for representing addition situations

Gather the group together to share strategies for solving the problem on *Student Activity Book* page 21 and recording the work. Post the chart "How Many Pencils?" and have cubes or counters available for students who want to use them to demonstrate.

Ask volunteers to explain how they solved the pencil problem. As students share their approaches, record each on the board or on chart paper. Label each method with a letter or number, or by using a different color.

After several students have shared their approaches, ask:

Does anyone have a way that is different from one of the ways I've listed here?❺

If no one in your class has used addition equations and you do not find an opportunity to introduce it as you record students' strategies, model it for the class at the end of this activity. Write $6 + 5 = 11$ on the board or on chart paper, and ask students to revisit what the = symbol means. (Students first saw the equal sign formally in Session 2.7.)

We talked about this symbol the other day, and I've seen some children using it. Who remembers something about this symbol that they'd like to share?

Students might say:

"The numbers on both sides are the same in all."

"It means the 5 and 6 is the same as the 11. The equal sign means they are even."

Spend some time talking about the rest of the equation you have written. Point to the appropriate number(s) in the equation as you talk about it with students.

We said that 6 pencils and 5 more pencils makes 11. What I've written here is one way to show that 6 and 5 is the same amount, or is **equal** to, 11. This symbol is called **plus**. It tells you to *combine* those numbers, or to put them together, or to **add** them. 6 plus 5 equals 11. If you have 6 pencils, and you take 5 more pencils, you have 11 pencils total. The whole thing is called an **equation**.❻

Professional Development

❺ **Dialogue Box:** Discussing Addition Strategies, pp. 232–233

❻ **Teacher Note:** Introducing Notation, Part 1, pp. 198–199

Teaching Note

❼ **Strategies** This is a way of validating all students' approaches while also giving you a sense of what kinds of strategies are being used in your class as a whole. Note that comparing and contrasting different strategies can be challenging for students, particularly early in the year. Many students will think their strategy is different if, for example, they drew cubes or lines instead of pencils. Their ability to compare and contrast will develop over the course of the year, as they have repeated opportunities to do so.

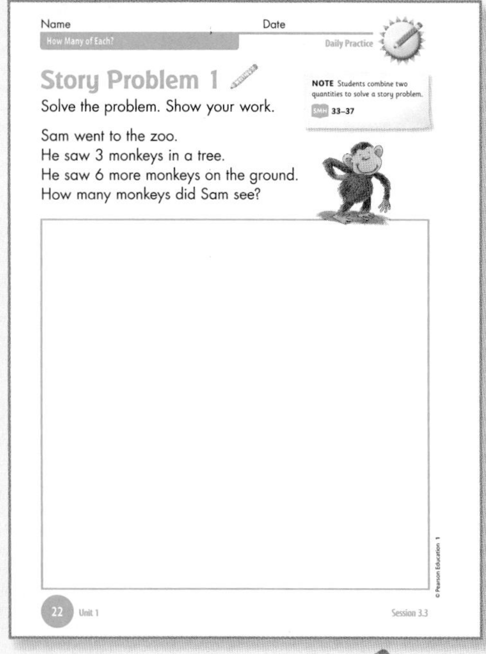
Name Date

How Many of Each? Daily Practice

Story Problem 1

Solve the problem. Show your work.

NOTE Students combine two quantities to solve a story problem.

SMH 33–37

Sam went to the zoo.
He saw 3 monkeys in a tree.
He saw 6 more monkeys on the ground.
How many monkeys did Sam see?

© Pearson Education 1

22 Unit 1 Session 3.3

▲ **Student Activity Book, p. 22**

When you have recorded several different strategies, ask students to look at their approach and decide which of the ones you have recorded is closest to their own. Ask students to raise hands to indicate which approach they used.

[Tamika] drew 6 pencils [cubes, lines], then drew 5 pencils [cubes, lines], and then *counted all* of the pencils. Raise your hand if you drew both groups and then *counted all* of them. [Libby] knew that there were 6 pencils and *counted on* from 6: 7, 8, 9, 10, 11. Who else *counted on* to solve this problem?❼

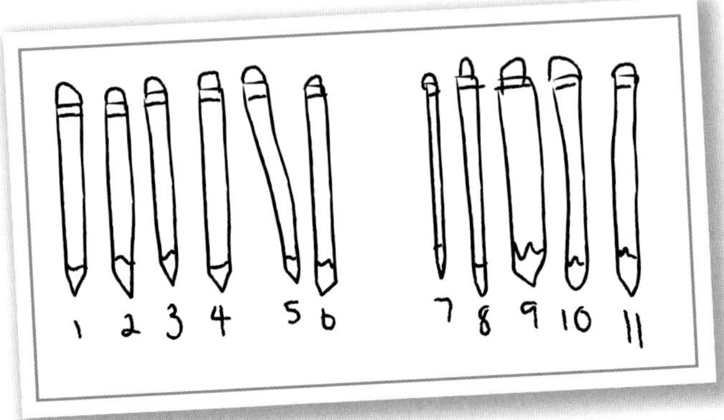

Sample Student Work

SESSION FOLLOW-UP

4 Daily Practice and Homework

Daily Practice: For reinforcement of this unit's content, have students complete *Student Activity Book* page 22.

Homework: Students complete *Student Activity Book* page 22.

Student Math Handbook: Students and families may use *Student Math Handbook* pages 33–37, 44–45, for reference and review. See pages 243–252 in the back of this unit.

Roll and Record

Math Focus Points

- Connecting number names and written numbers to the quantities they represent
- Finding the total of two or more quantities up to a total of 20 by counting all, counting on, or using number combinations
- Visualizing and retelling the action in an addition situation
- Modeling the action of an addition problem with counters or drawings

Today's Plan		Materials
1 ACTIVITY Introducing *Roll and Record*	15 MIN CLASS	• T9 • Dot cubes
2 MATH WORKSHOP Combining Games 2A *Roll and Record* 2B *Five-in-a-Row* 2C *Double Compare* 2D *Double Compare Dots*	30 MIN	2A • *Student Activity Book,* p. 23 • M28*; M29* • Dot cubes; counters (optional) 2B • Materials from Session 3.2, p. 107 • M30–M31* (optional) 2C • Materials from Session 3.1, p. 100 2D • Materials from Session 3.1, p. 100
3 ACTIVITY More Addition Stories	15 MIN CLASS	• Cubes or counters; Chart paper (optional)
4 SESSION FOLLOW-UP Daily Practice and Homework		• *Student Activity Book,* pp. 24–26 • *Student Math Handbook,* pp. 21–23, 33–37, G6, G7, G9, G19 • M25 (sent home in Session 3.2) • Primary Number Cards (sent home in Session 2.5)

*See *Materials to Prepare,* p. 99.

Classroom Routines

Morning Meeting Review **Follow your daily *Morning Meeting* Routine. During *Calendar*, review the days of the week, noting which days are school days and which are weekend days. Discuss that there are 7 days in the week, 5 school days and 2 weekend days. Use an equation to represent this information: $5 + 2 = 7$.**

Teaching Note

➊ **Writing Numerals** *Roll and Record* is an opportunity for students to practice writing numerals to record mathematical information. Correct numeral formation should be addressed as part of the handwriting curriculum.

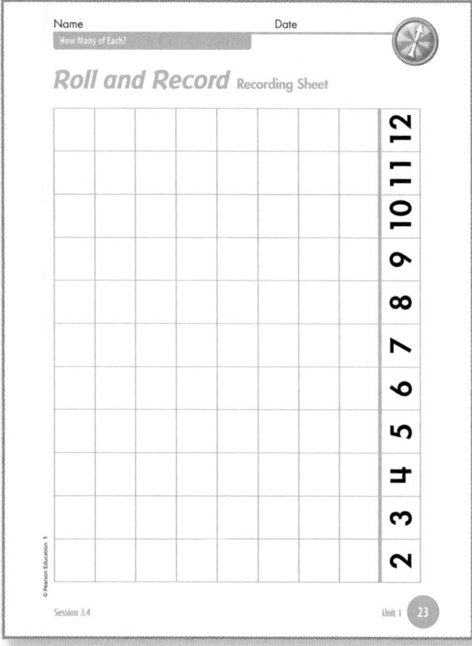

Name Date

How Many of Each?

Roll and Record Recording Sheet

2	3	4	5	6	7	8	9	10	11	12

© Pearson Education 1

Session 3.4 Unit 1 23

▲ Student Activity Book, p. 23; Resource Masters, M28; T9

ACTIVITY

Introducing *Roll and Record*

15 MIN CLASS

Introduce *Roll and Record* by playing a round or two with the class.

Today we are going to learn a new game called *Roll and Record.* Each pair will need two dot cubes and a recording sheet to play this game.

I am going to roll two dot cubes. How many dots do you see on both cubes? How did you figure that out?

The teacher demonstrates rolling the dot cubes.

Students might say:

"I counted the dots on one cube, and then I kept going with the other. There are 6 dots."

"I know there are 4 dots on one and 2 dots on the other. That's 6."

Everyone agrees that there are [six] dots. So now I am going to write a [6] on my recording sheet. Where do you think I will write a [6]? How did you figure that out?

Display the transparency of *Roll and Record* Recording Sheet (T9). Model how to record the total you rolled in the correct column, counting from 1 to the total rolled as one way to find the correct number.➊

The teacher models how to record.

Tell students that they will play alone or in pairs, but each player needs to record on his or her own recording sheet. That way, every student will practice writing numbers.

Ask a volunteer to roll the dot cubes a few more times, and model ways to find and record the total. Do this enough times that students can see where the first number is written in a column, as well as what happens when a number is rolled for a second time in the same column.

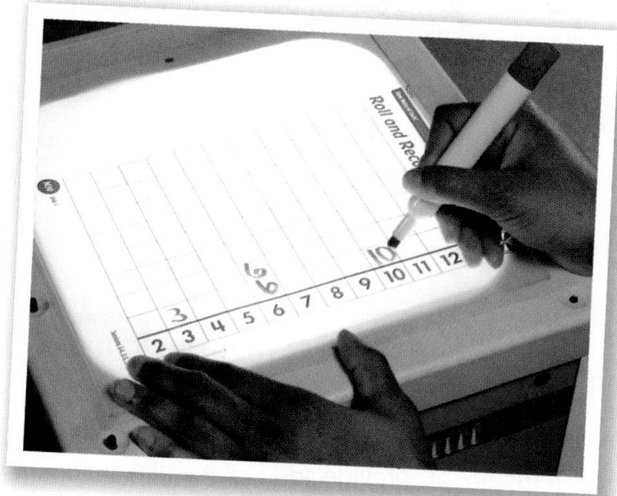

The teacher models recording a second number in the same column.

This game is a race. It's not a race with your partner; it's a race with the numbers. It's a race to see which number gets to the top first.

The game is over when one of the columns is completely filled.

Algebra Note

❷ **Building on the Known** When students use something known to solve an unknown, encourage students to articulate the generalization that underlies their strategy. For example, if 1 is added to one addend, the total increases by 1. Some students might explain, "5 is 1 more than 4, so I added 1 to 8 and got 9."

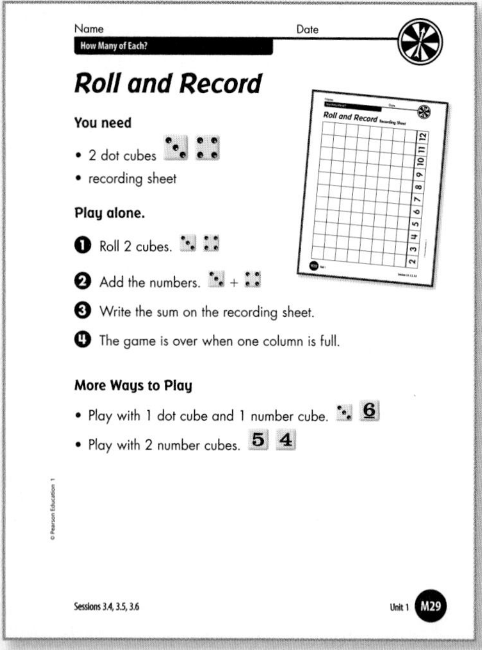
Name Date

How Many of Each?

Roll and Record

You need

- 2 dot cubes
- recording sheet

Play alone.

1. Roll 2 cubes.
2. Add the numbers.
3. Write the sum on the recording sheet.
4. The game is over when one column is full.

More Ways to Play

- Play with 1 dot cube and 1 number cube.
- Play with 2 number cubes.

Sessions 3.4, 3.5, 3.6 Unit 1 M29

▲ Resource Masters, M29

MATH WORKSHOP

Combining Games

30 MIN

As you circulate among these choices, keep track of the different strategies students are using to combine two numbers. You will want each of these strategies represented in the discussion at the end of Session 3.6. They will probably include counting all, counting on, "just knowing," and using something known (e.g., $4 + 4$) to solve an unknown (e.g., $4 + 5$).❷

2A *Roll and Record*

PAIRS INDIVIDUALS

Students play *Roll and Record* as you demonstrated. The game is over when one column is filled. Have available copies of *Roll and Record* (M29) as needed.

ONGOING ASSESSMENT: Observing Students at Work

Students count and combine small amounts, practice writing the numbers, and connect number names and written numbers to the quantities they represent.

- **How do students determine the total number of dots?** Do they count them all? Count on? Use their fingers? Use a number combination they "just know"?
- **How do students decide which number to write?** Do they recognize the numbers 2–12? Do they count up on a number line? Can they reproduce the numerals accurately? Which numbers and/or numerals are most problematic for students?

DIFFERENTIATION: Supporting the Range of Learners

Intervention Encourage students who are having difficulty writing the numbers to use the examples provided on *Student Activity Book* page 23 to help them. Also, provide additional number writing instruction and practice during handwriting sessions. Students having difficulty combining two amounts accurately can model the problem by taking a counter for each dot.

2B *Five-in-a-Row*

PAIRS GROUPS

For complete details about this activity, see Session 3.2, pages 108–109.

DIFFERENTIATION: Supporting the Range of Learners

Extension Students can play on *Five-in-a-Row* Gameboards B and C (M30–M31) for variation.

2C *Double Compare*

PAIRS

For complete details about this activity, see Session 3.1, pages 101–103.

2D *Double Compare Dots*

PAIRS

For complete details about this activity, see Session 3.1, pages 101–103.

Math Workshop is a time when students work on similar math ideas as they play a variety of games.

Name Date

How Many of Each?

Five-in-a-Row Gameboard B

12	11	10	9	8
7	7	6	5	4
3	2	2	3	4
5	6	6	7	7
8	9	10	11	12

M30 Unit 1 Sessions 3.4, 3.5, 3.6

▲ Resource Masters, M30

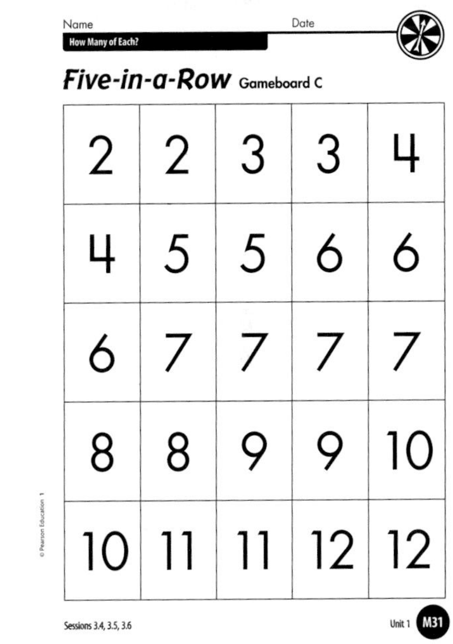

Name Date

How Many of Each?

Five-in-a-Row Gameboard C

2	2	3	3	4
4	5	5	6	6
6	7	7	7	7
8	8	9	9	10
10	11	11	12	12

Sessions 3.4, 3.5, 3.6 Unit 1 M31

▲ Resource Masters, M31

Story Problem Routine

1. Tell students a number story. Encourage them to visualize the action in the story.
2. Ask several students to retell the story after they have heard it. (Or several students can each tell one part of the story. Occasionally, you might have each student retell the story to a partner.)
3. After retelling each story, ask whether the end result in each case will be more or less than the amount you started with.
4. Ask students to share strategies for solving the problem, including modeling the problem with cubes or counters.
5. Model methods of recording on chart paper or the board.

Algebra Note

❸ **Relationships** If students can see a connection between the two problems, encourage them to articulate what is the same and what is different.

ACTIVITY

3 More Addition Stories

15 MIN CLASS

Present several story problems, following the *Story Problem Routine.* Here are two related problems to use or adapt.

Yesterday during indoor recess, I counted 4 children in the block area and 4 children at the art table. How many children did I count?

Today during indoor recess, I counted 4 children in the block area and 5 children at the art table. How many children did I count?

Note that in these two problems, the numbers are closely related. Present the stories separately, but after students have discussed and shared strategies for each, ask them about the relationship between the two problems. If students do not comment on this, you might suggest it yourself:

I noticed that in the first problem you solved $4 + 4 = 8$ and in the second problem you solved $4 + 5 = 9$. Do you notice anything similar about these two problems?❸

Many students may not yet see relationships between such problems. At this point in time, pose the question as a way of gathering information about what your students may know or realize about how these problems and numbers are related. Students will continue to work with and think about these ideas throughout first and second grade.

SESSION FOLLOW-UP

Daily Practice and Homework

Daily Practice: For reinforcement of this unit's content, have students complete *Student Activity Book* page 24.

Homework: Students play *Double Compare* with someone at home. They should already have at home the materials they need: a deck of Primary Number Cards (M13–M16) and a copy of the game directions for *Double Compare* (M25). Tell students that the person with whom they play should help them record the results of the game on *Student Activity Book* pages 25–26.

Student Math Handbook: Students and families may use *Student Math Handbook* pages 21–23, 33–37 and G6, G7, G9, G19 for reference and review. See pages 243–252 in the back of this unit.

Name Date

How Many of Each? Daily Practice

Make a Dot Picture

NOTE Students find ways to organize sets of dots so that they are easy to count.

SMH 21–23

1. Circle the dot pictures that you think are easiest to remember.

Draw each number of dots in a way that is easy to remember.

2. Show 7 dots.
3. Show 10 dots.
4. Show 5 dots.
5. Show 8 dots.

Ongoing Review

6. Which cube tower shows 6?

Ⓐ Ⓑ Ⓒ Ⓓ

24 Unit 1 Session 3.4

© Pearson Education 1

▲ Student Activity Book, p. 24

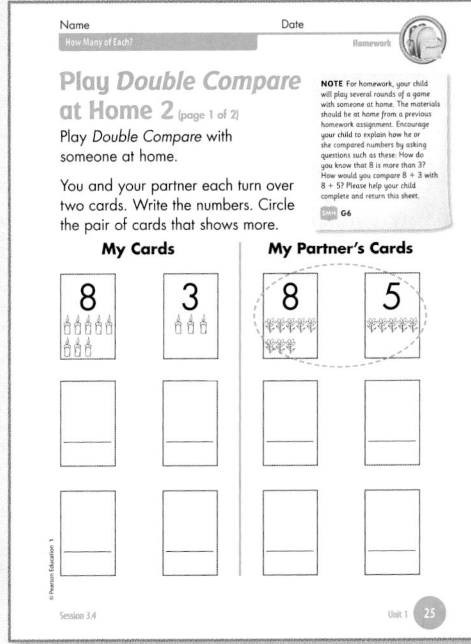

Name Date

How Many of Each? Homework

Play *Double Compare* at Home 2 (page 1 of 2)

Play *Double Compare* with someone at home.

You and your partner each turn over two cards. Write the numbers. Circle the pair of cards that shows more.

NOTE For homework, your child will play several rounds of a game with someone at home. The materials should be at home from a previous homework assignment. Encourage your child to explain how he or she compared numbers by asking questions such as these: How do you know that 8 is more than 3? How would you compare 8 + 3 with 8 + 5? Please help your child complete and return this sheet.

SMH G6

My Cards		My Partner's Cards	
8	3	8	5

© Pearson Education 1

Session 3.4 Unit 1 25

▲ Student Activity Book, p. 25

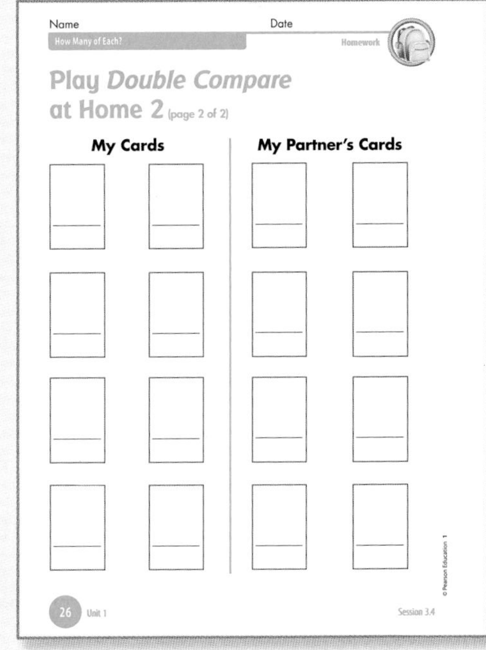

Name Date

How Many of Each? Homework

Play *Double Compare* at Home 2 (page 2 of 2)

My Cards | My Partner's Cards

© Pearson Education 1

26 Unit 1 Session 3.4

▲ Student Activity Book, p. 26

More Addition Story Problems

Math Focus Points

- Visualizing and retelling the action in an addition situation
- Modeling the action of an addition problem with counters or drawings
- Finding the total of two or more quantities up to a total of 20 by counting all, counting on, or using number combinations
- Introducing standard notation (+ and =) for representing addition situations

Vocabulary

counting all
counting on

Today's Plan		Materials
1 ACTIVITY **Solving an Addition Story Problem**	20 MIN INDIVIDUALS	• *Student Activity Book*, p. 27 • Chart paper (optional)*
2 MATH WORKSHOP **Combining Games** 2A *Roll and Record* 2B *Five-in-a-Row* 2C *Double Compare* 2D *Double Compare Dots*	20 MIN	2A • Materials from Session 3.4, p. 119 2B • Materials from Session 3.2, p. 107 • M30–M31 (from Session 3.4; optional) 2C • Materials from Session 3.1, p. 100 2D • Materials from Session 3.1, p. 100 • Dot Cards, Sets A–D (from Session 2.6; optional)
3 DISCUSSION **Sharing Strategies**	20 MIN CLASS	• Cubes or counters; chart: "How Many Cupcakes?"; (from Activity 1); chart paper (optional)
4 SESSION FOLLOW-UP **Daily Practice and Homework**		• *Student Activity Book,* pp. 28–29 • *Student Math Handbook,* pp. 26, 31, 33–37; G6, G7, G9, G19

*See *Materials to Prepare,* p. 99.

Classroom Routines

Quick Images: Dot Cards Show transparencies of the 5- and 6-dot cards from Dot Cards Set B (T7) at the same time. Follow the basic *Quick Images* activity. Ask students to determine the total number of dots. Repeat with the 5- and 6-dot cards from Dot Cards Set A (T2) and compare the arrangements.

1 ACTIVITY

20 MIN INDIVIDUALS

Solving an Addition Story Problem

Explain to students that today they will individually solve a story problem on paper and that the class will discuss it at the end of math class. As students finish recording their work, they transition into a Math Workshop, in which all the addition, or combining, games they have learned so far are available.

Post the problem from *Student Activity Book* page 27 on chart paper or the board.

Rosa and Max went to the bake sale.

Rosa bought 7 cupcakes.

Max bought 6 cupcakes.

How many cupcakes did they buy?

Read the problem aloud to students, and ask several students to retell the story in their own words. Students use numbers, pictures, words, and/or equations to record their work on *Student Activity Book* page 27.

ONGOING ASSESSMENT: Observing Students at Work

Students solve a problem about combining two groups, and record their work.❶

- **Can students remember and make sense of the sequence of actions in the story?**
- **How do students solve the problem?** Do they count all? Count on? Use a number fact (6 + 6) they know?
- **Do they get the right answer?** Can they explain their strategies?
- **How do students record their work?** Do they use numbers? Pictures? Words? Equations? Does their work accurately reflect the strategy they used to solve the problem?

Name Date

How Many of Each?

How Many Cupcakes?

Solve the problem. Show your work.

Rosa and Max went to the bake sale.
Rosa bought 7 cupcakes.
Max bought 6 cupcakes.
How many cupcakes did they buy?

Session 3.5 Unit 1 27

▲ Student Activity Book, p. 27

Professional Development

❶ **Teacher Note:** Recording Strategies for a Combining Problem, p. 204

Sample Student Work

MATH WORKSHOP

Combining Games

20 MIN

As you circulate among these choices, keep track of the different strategies students are using to combine two numbers. You will want each of these strategies represented in the discussion at the end of Session 3.6. They will probably include counting all, counting on, just knowing, and using something known (e.g., 3 + 3) to solve an unknown (e.g., 3 + 4).

2A Roll and Record

PAIRS INDIVIDUALS

For complete details about this activity, see Session 3.4, pages 120–122.

2B Five-in-a-Row

PAIRS GROUPS

For complete details about this activity, see Session 3.2, pages 108–109.

2C Double Compare

PAIRS

For complete details about this activity, see Session 3.1, pages 101–103.

2D Double Compare Dots

PAIRS

For complete details about this activity, see Session 3.1, pages 101–103.

DISCUSSION

3 Sharing Strategies

Math Focus Points for Discussion

- Finding the total of two or more quantities up to a total of 20 by counting all, counting on, or using number combinations
- Introducing standard notation (+ and =) for representing addition situations

In much the same way you did at the end of Session 3.3, gather the students to share strategies for solving the problem about cupcakes and recording their solutions. Have counters available for students who want to use them to demonstrate.

Ask volunteers to explain how they solved the problem. As students share their approaches, record each on the board or on chart paper. Label each method with a letter or number or by using a different color, but also continue naming strategies by the math involved; for example, counting all, counting on, and using what you know. For strategies in which it is appropriate, use and revisit addition notation and the meaning of the + and = symbols.❷ ❸

Students might say:

"I started with 7 and counted 6 more with my fingers."

"I know that 6 and 6 is 12. 7 is one more than 6, so it's 13."

"I counted out 6 cubes and 7 cubes. Then I counted them all together."

After several students have shared their approaches, ask:

Does anyone have a way that is different from one of the ways I've written here?

Professional Development

❷ **Teacher Note:** Discussing Story Problems, pp. 206–207

❸ **Dialogue Box:** Discussing Addition Strategies, pp. 232–233

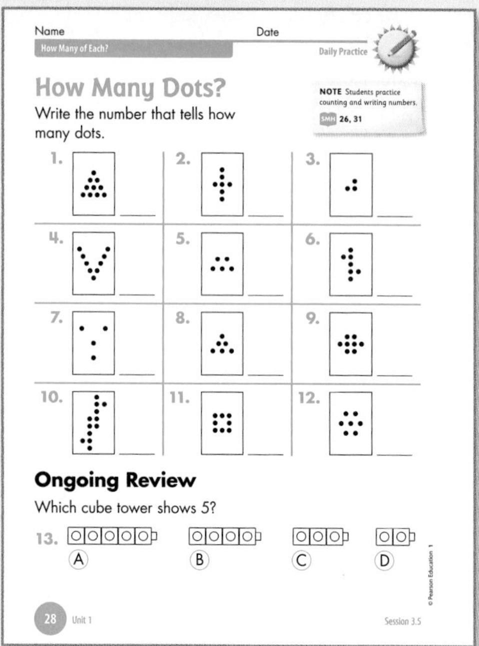
Name Date

How Many of Each?

Daily Practice

How Many Dots?

Write the number that tells how many dots.

NOTE Students practice counting and writing numbers.

SMH 26, 31

1. 2. 3.

4. 5. 6.

7. 8. 9.

10. 11. 12.

Ongoing Review

Which cube tower shows 5?

13. Ⓐ Ⓑ Ⓒ Ⓓ

© Pearson Education 1

28 Unit 1 Session 3.5

▲ Student Activity Book, p. 28

Name Date

How Many of Each?

Homework

Apples and Oranges

Solve the problem. Show your work.

NOTE This problem is about combining two numbers. Encourage your child to find his or her own way to solve the problem and record the work.

SMH 46–47

I went to the store to buy some fruit. I bought 5 apples and 4 oranges. How many pieces of fruit did I buy?

© Pearson Education 1

Session 3.5 Unit 1 29

▲ Student Activity Book, p. 29

When you have recorded several different strategies, ask students to look at their approach and decide which of the ones you have recorded is closest to their own. Students can raise their hands to indicate which approach they used.

As students share strategies, they see different ways to solve a problem and to record solutions.

SESSION FOLLOW-UP

4 Daily Practice and Homework

Daily Practice: For reinforcement of this unit's content, have students complete *Student Activity Book* page 28.

Homework: On *Student Activity Book* page 29, students solve an addition story problem for homework. Remind students that in addition to the answer, you need to see how they figured it out. They should use numbers, but they can also use words, pictures, equations, or a combination to show their solution strategies.

Student Math Handbook: Students and families may use *Student Math Handbook* pages 26, 31, 33–37 and G6, G7, G9, G19 for reference and review. See pages 243–252 in the back of this unit.

Assessment: Double Compare and Combining Games

Math Focus Points

- Comparing two quantities up to 20 to see which is larger
- Finding the total of two or more quantities up to a total of 20 by counting all, counting on, or using number combinations
- Seeing that adding the same two numbers (e.g., 4 and 3) results in the same total, regardless of context (e.g., number cubes, cards, objects)

Vocabulary

combine

Today's Plan		Materials
1 ASSESSMENT ACTIVITY *Double Compare*	10 MIN INDIVIDUALS	• M32*
2 MATH WORKSHOP Combining Games 2A *Roll and Record* 2B *Five-in-a-Row* 2C *Double Compare* 2D *Double Compare Dots*	30 MIN	2A • Materials from Session 3.4, p. 119 2B • Materials from Session 3.2, p. 107 • M30–M31 (from Session 3.4; optional) 2C • Materials from Session 3.1, p. 100 2D • Materials from Session 3.1, p. 100 • M11, M18–M19 (from Session 2.6; optional)
3 DISCUSSION Strategies for Combining	20 MIN CLASS	• Primary Number Cards (from Session 2.4) • Dot cubes; counters; chart paper
4 SESSION FOLLOW-UP Daily Practice		• *Student Activity Book*, p. 31 • *Student Math Handbook*, pp. 33–37; G6, G7, G9, G19

*See *Materials to Prepare*, p. 99.

Classroom Routines

Start With/Get To: Start With 1 **Choose a *get to* number. Asks students to find and mark the number on the class number line. As a class, count together, from 1 to the *get to* number.**

Name Date

How Many of Each?

Assessment: *Double Compare*

Which pair of cards shows more?
Circle the cards.

6 5 4 9

Show how you know.

© Pearson Education 1

M32 Unit 1 Session 3.6

▲ Resource Masters, M32

ASSESSMENT ACTIVITY

1 Double Compare

Tell students you are going to give them a problem to solve on their own so that you can get a sense of how they are growing in their abilities to combine and compare numbers.➊

Show students a copy of Assessment: *Double Compare* (M32), and explain the directions.

Encourage students to not only circle the pair of cards that shows more, but also show how they figured it out.➋

ONGOING ASSESSMENT: Observing Students at Work

Students combine and compare numbers up to 14.

- **Do students circle the correct pair of cards?**
- **How do they figure out which pair shows more?** Do they total each pair and compare? Do they use another strategy?
- **For students who find the total of each pair of cards, what strategy do they use?** Do they count all? Count on? Use another strategy?
- **How do students show their thinking?** Do they number the objects? Record the totals? Write about their strategy?

DIFFERENTIATION: Supporting the Range of Learners

Intervention Showing how they solved the problem is often a challenge for beginning first graders. Students' first attempts may not show you *how* they solved the problem. For example, they may only circle the pair of cards they think has more, record only one or both totals, or write sentences such as "I counted" or "9 and 4 is 13" or "because 4 and 9 makes a bigger number than 6 and 5."

Teaching Note

➊ **Assessing the Benchmarks** This assessment asks students to compare two pairs of numbers and tell which pair is larger. Depending on how students solve it, this problem addresses Benchmark 2 and can also provide information about Benchmarks 1 and 3.

Professional Development

➋ **Teacher Note:** Assessment: *Double Compare,* pp. 208–210

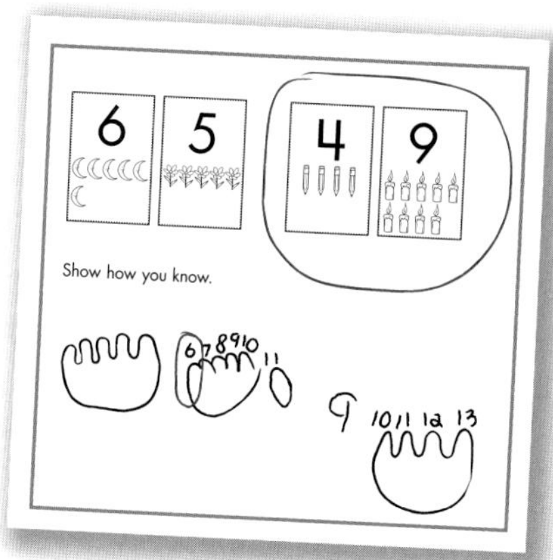

Sample Student Work

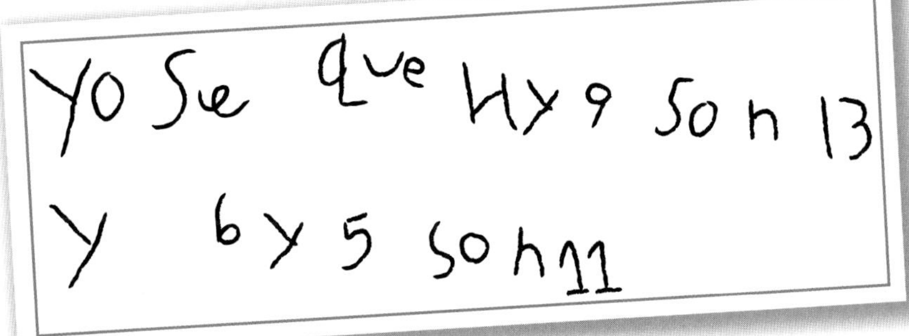

Sample Student Work

Translation: I know that 4 and 9 is 13 and 6 and 5 is 11.

As you circulate and observe students at work, encourage students to explain and record *how* they figured out which pair of cards showed more. For example, you might ask, "How did you decide to circle 4 and 9?" or "You say you counted. Can you show me *how* you counted?" or "Can you tell me how you figured out that 6 and 5 is 11, and that 4 and 9 is 13?" or "I see your work for only this pair of cards. Did you figure out how many this student had [6 + 5]?" Students can add their ideas to their paper, or you can take dictation for students who are unable to record their response.

Another thing to be on the lookout for is students who are solving a different problem than the one posed on the assessment page. For example, some students add all four numbers, compare 65 and 49, or circle the larger card in each pair (i.e., the 6 in the left-hand pair and the 9 in the right-hand pair). Reread the directions with these students to clarify what the problem is asking.

As students finish the assessment, they transition into a Math Workshop in which all of the addition games are available.

MATH WORKSHOP

Combining Games

30 MIN

As you circulate among these choices, keep track of the different strategies students are using to combine two numbers. You will want each of these strategies represented in the discussion at the end of this session. They will probably include counting all, counting on, just knowing, and using something known (e.g., 3 + 3) to solve an unknown (e.g., 3 + 4).

2A Roll and Record

PAIRS INDIVIDUALS

For complete details about this activity, see Session 3.4, pages 120–122.

2B Five-in-a-Row

PAIRS GROUPS

For complete details about this activity, see Session 3.2, pages 108–109.

2C Double Compare

PAIRS

For complete details about this activity, see Session 3.1, pages 101–103.

Observing students as they play math games gives you a chance to see how they are combining and comparing numbers.

2D Double Compare Dots

PAIRS

For complete details about this activity, see Session 3.1, pages 101–103.

DISCUSSION

3 Strategies for Combining

Math Focus Points for Discussion

- Finding the total of two or more quantities up to a total of 20 by counting all, counting on, or using number combinations
- Seeing that adding the same two numbers (e.g., 4 and 3) results in the same total regardless of context (e.g., number cubes, cards, objects)

Bring two dot cubes, a deck of Primary Number Cards (M13–M16), and a collection of counters to this discussion about strategies students have been using to combine two numbers.

We've been working a lot lately on ways to **combine**, or add 2 numbers together. When we roll two number cubes and find out how many dots there are, that's one time we've been adding numbers. Many kids add the 2 numbers together when they play *Double Compare.* And we've been solving story problems about combining two numbers together.

Let's talk about how you are combining numbers. Let's think first about these dot cubes. I rolled a [4] and a [3]. Who can tell us how they would figure out how many dots there are altogether?

Ask a student or two to share their strategy for combining [4] and [3]. Have cubes or counters available to model students' strategies as they share them.[3]

Students might say:

"I counted all of the dots. 1, 2, 3, 4, 5, 6, 7."

"I started with 4 and went on 5, 6, 7."

"I just know that 4 + 3 is 7."

Professional Development

3 **Dialogue Box:** Discussing Addition Strategies, pp. 232–233

Algebra Note

4 **It's 1 More** You might find that more students are using or experimenting with the idea that if they add 1 to one addend, the total increases by 1. Those who have been using the idea for a while might now be able to verbalize it more clearly. Some students might also use a variation of the idea: "$4 + 4 = 8$ and 3 is one less than 4, so I took one away from 8 to get 7." (If you subtract 1 from one addend, the total decreases by 1.)

Professional Development

5 **Dialogue Box:** Is It *Always* 11?, pp. 234–235

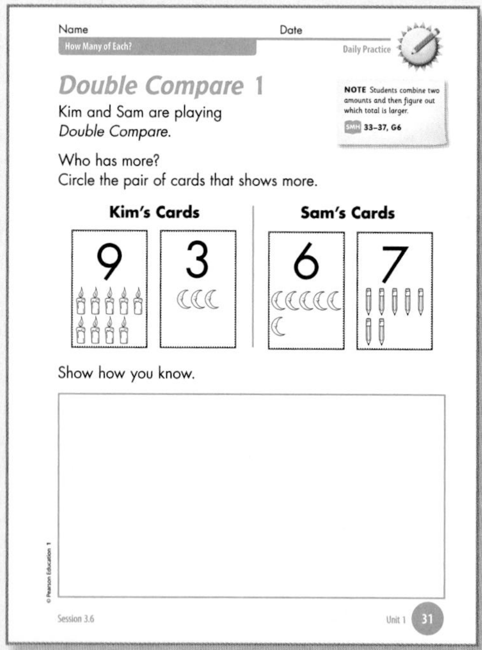

Name Date

How Many of Each? Daily Practice

Double Compare 1

Kim and Sam are playing *Double Compare.*

NOTE Students combine two amounts and then figure out which total is larger.

SMH 33–37, G6

Who has more?
Circle the pair of cards that shows more.

Kim's Cards		Sam's Cards	
9	3	6	7

Show how you know.

© Pearson Education 1

Session 3.6 Unit 1 31

▲ Student Activity Book, p. 31

Other students may use what they know about $3 + 3$ or $4 + 4$ to solve $4 + 3$. 4

As students share strategies, record one of each example strategy on a sheet of chart paper that can become a reference in your classroom this year.

Also ask students about other situations, or contexts that use the same numbers. For each, ask a student or two to share how they would solve the problem.

What do you get if you play *Double Compare* and you flip over a 4 and a 3?

What about a story problem? I bought 4 red apples and 3 green apples. How many apples did I buy?

How about this hand in *Double Compare Dots?* [Show a card with 4 objects and a card with 3 objects.]

For some students, $4 + 3$ is a new problem to be solved each time they see it.

Students might say:

"The numbers are the same. It's just what we are counting that's different."

Other students may be ready to claim that not only is $4 + 3$ always 7, but $3 + 4$ is *also* always 7. Encourage all students to explain their thinking and to use cubes to model their thinking and strategies, but do not expect all students to make meaningful sense of these ideas the first time you discuss them. These ideas will be revisited throughout the first grade curriculum. 5

SESSION FOLLOW-UP

Daily Practice

Daily Practice: For reinforcement of this unit's content, have students complete *Student Activity Book* page 31.

Student Math Handbook: Students and families may use *Student Math Handbook* pages 33–37 and G6, G7, G9, G19 for reference and review. See pages 243–252 in the back of this unit.

How Many in All?

Math Focus Points

- Finding the total of two or more quantities up to a total of 20 by counting all, counting on, or using number combinations
- Developing an understanding of how the quantities in the counting sequence are related: each number is 1 more or 1 less than the number before or after it
- Recording a solution to a problem

Today's Plan			Materials
ACTIVITY 1 Story About Many Groups	20 MIN	CLASS	• *Rooster's Off to See the World, The Very Hungry Caterpillar,* or another story problem with a number pattern that increases by one (optional)*; chart paper
ACTIVITY 2 Finding How Many in All?	25 MIN	INDIVIDUALS	• Cubes or counters
DISCUSSION 3 How Many in All?	15 MIN	CLASS	
SESSION FOLLOW-UP 4 Daily Practice			• *Student Activity Book,* p. 32 • *Student Math Handbook,* pp. 33–37, 46–47

*See *Materials to Prepare,* p. 99.

Classroom Routines

Quick Images: Dot Cards **Show transparencies of both 4-dot cards from Dot Cards Set A (T2) and Dot Cards Set B (T7) at the same time. Follow the basic *Quick Images* activity. Ask students to determine the total number of dots. Repeat with both 4-dot cards and one of the 3-dot cards.**

Teaching Note

➊ **Using Children's Literature** Any of the following books may be used for this activity: *Rooster's Off to See the World,* and *The Very Hungry Caterpillar,* both by Eric Carle; *1 Hunter* by Pat Hutchin, *One Gorilla* by Atsuko Morozumi; *My Little Sister Ate One Hare* by Bill Grossman, *P Bear's New Year's Party* by Paul Owen Lewis, *Dinner at the Panda Palace* by Stephanie Calmenson. You may also create your own story with the mathematical structure 1 + 2 + 3 + 4 + 5.

20 MIN CLASS

ACTIVITY

1 A Story About Many Groups

Read the first half of the story you have chosen to the class.➊ The story should begin with 1 animal, character, or thing. Then, a group of 2 joins the first lone [animal], followed by groups of 3, 4, and 5. The second half of the story can continue the pattern upward to 10, or reverse it and return to 1. As you read or tell the story, you might pause once or twice to ask students what they think happens next.

First there was 1 rooster. Then, 2 cats came. What do you think might happen next? Why do you think so? After 4 fish came, what do you think happened next?

Accept several responses. Some students will attend to the numerical information in the story as they make predictions, and others will connect with the different parts of the story (e.g., where the journey might take them, what someone could make with all that fruit).

Stop reading when you are halfway through the story—when the group of 5 [animals] has joined the groups of 1, 2, 3, and 4. Ask a volunteer to summarize the story so far and record the information on chart paper.

Students might say:

"There was a group of 5, a group of 4, a group of 3, a group of 2, and 1 all alone."

When you have agreement that there are groups of 1, 2, 3, 4, and 5 animals, characters, or things, present the problem.

That's quite a few [animals, things]! Today you'll be figuring out how many that is altogether. You will also find a way to show on paper how you figured it out.

Story books with number themes help reinforce the classroom learning.

25 MIN INDIVIDUALS

ACTIVITY

2 Finding How Many in All

Students should work individually, but encourage them to share with one another their strategies for solving the problem (1 + 2 + 3 + 4 + 5) and recording their work.

Sample Student Work

Professional Development

❷ **Dialogue Box:** How Many in All?, pp. 236–238

ONGOING ASSESSMENT: Observing Students at Work

Students combine several small amounts and record their work.

- **How do students represent the number in each group?** Do they use manipulatives? Pictures? Numbers? Words? Some combination of these? Do they arrange the groups in order?
- **How do students find the total number of [animals]?** Do they count by 1s? Combine the numbers in each group? Use counters or their fingers? Use the pattern in the numbers?
- **How do students record their solution strategy?** With numbers? Pictures? Words? Tallies? Equations? A combination?

Circulate to observe how students approach the problem and to offer support as needed. Note children who solved the problem and recorded their work in different ways to use in the end of session discussion.

3 DISCUSSION

How Many in All?

15 MIN CLASS

Math Focus Points for Discussion

- Finding the total of two or more quantities up to a total of 20 by counting all, counting on, or using number combinations
- Recording a solution to a problem

When everyone has found a solution, gather students together with their papers to share some of their solutions. Students should share how they kept track of the groups *and* how they found the total.❷

How did you find the total number of animals?

Students might say:

"I counted out each animal with a different color cube. Then, I put them together and counted them all."

"I drew pictures of the animals. Then I counted them."

"I wrote it out with numbers. First, I wrote one 1 and two 2s. Then, I added three 3s . . . until I was done."

Did anyone else find a solution that way? Did anyone find the solution a different way?

This problem might give you an opportunity to model a longer equation for students, one with more than two addends.❸

$$1 + 2 + 3 + 4 + 5 = 15$$

Finish reading the story to students at the end of this discussion or during story time.

SESSION FOLLOW-UP

Daily Practice

Daily Practice: For reinforcement of this unit's content, have students complete *Student Activity Book* page 32.

Student Math Handbook: Students and families may use *Student Math Handbook* pages 33–37 and 46–47 for reference and review. See pages 243–252 in the back of this unit.

Teaching Note

❸ **Recording** Treat equations as just one of the many good ways of recording that students have used. For young students, finding a way to record their thinking and their solutions is an important part of making sense of problems. At this point in the year, it is critical not to emphasize one particular recording method over the others.

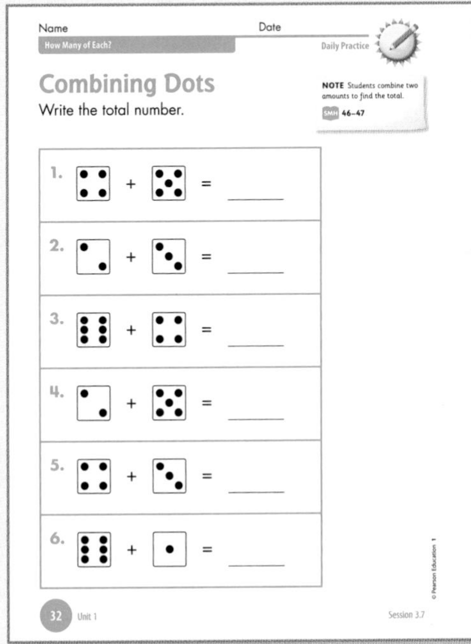

Name Date

How Many of Each? Daily Practice

Combining Dots

Write the total number.

NOTE Students combine two amounts to find the total.

SMH 46–47

1. + = ____

2. + = ____

3. + = ____

4. + = ____

5. + = ____

6. + = ____

32 Unit 1 Session 3.7

▲ Student Activity Book, p. 32

INVESTIGATION 4

Mathematical Emphases

Number Composition Composing numbers up to 10 with two addends

Math Focus Points

- Finding and exploring relationships among combinations of numbers up to 10
- Recording combinations of two numbers that make a certain total
- Solving a problem with multiple solutions
- Solving a problem in which the total and one part are known

Whole Number Operations Making sense of and developing strategies to solve addition problems with small numbers

Math Focus Points

- Visualizing and retelling the action in an addition situation
- Modeling the action of an addition problem with counters or drawings
- Finding the total of two or more quantities up to a total of 20 by counting all, counting on, or using number combinations

Whole Number Operations Using manipulatives, drawings, tools, and notation to show strategies and solutions

Math Focus Points

- Using the number line as a tool for counting
- Introducing standard notation (+ and =) for representing addition situations
- Recording a solution to a problem
- Representing number combinations with numbers, pictures and/or words

Composing Numbers

SESSION	Student Activity Book	Student Math Handbook	Professional Development: Read Ahead of Time
SESSION 4.1 p. 148 **Seven Peas and Carrots** Students solve a problem in which they determine one or more combinations of peas and carrots they could have to make 7 in all. This is the first of several How Many of Each? problems students will solve over the course of this year.	33–34	46–47	• **Teacher Notes:** About How Many of Each? Problems, pp. 211–212; Common Issues That Typically Arise with How Many of Each?, pp. 213–214; When the Teacher Records Students' Solutions, p. 215 • **Dialogue Box:** Observing Students at Work on Seven Peas and Carrots, pp. 239–241
SESSION 4.2 p. 154 **Three Towers** Students work with different combinations of one number as they build cube towers using two colors. Students record the number of each color in each tower.	35–36	33–37, 48–49; G25	• **Teacher Note:** Introducing Notation Part 1, pp. 198–199
SESSION 4.3 p. 161 **Heads and Tails** Students learn *Heads and Tails,* another activity focusing on number combinations. Math Workshop includes *Heads and Tails* and *Three Towers.* The session ends with a story problem aloud.	37–38	33–37; G13, G25	

Classroom Routines See page 20 for an overview.

Morning Meeting

- Pocket monthly calendar: Prepare and post the new monthly calendar at the appropriate time.
- Weather chart: Prepare and post a new monthly weather chart when needed.

Start With/Go To

- A basket
- M6–M7, *Start With/Get To* cards, numbers 1–30
- Clothespins (2)
- Class number line

Quick Images

- T2, T7, Dot Cards, Sets A and B
  Cut apart cards.

Materials to Gather	Materials to Prepare
• **Connecting cubes in 2 colors, green and orange** (7 of each color per class) • **Cubes or counters in 2 colors** (7 of each color per student or pair) • **Crayons or markers in same colors as cubes or counters** (1 of each color per student or pair) • **Paper plates** (1 per student; optional) • **Chart paper**	
• **T10, *Three Towers* Recording Sheet** • **Connecting cubes in 2 colors** (about 60 per pair) • **Dot cubes** (1 per pair) • **Crayons or markers in same colors as connecting cubes** (per pair) • **Chart paper** (optional)	• **M33, *Three Towers* Recording Sheet** Make copies. (as needed) • **M34, *Three Towers of 10*** Make copies. (as needed) • **Cube towers** Prepare 3 towers of 10 connecting cubes using blue and yellow in these patterns: *b b b b b y y y b b; b b b y y y y y y b; b b b b b y y y y y.*
• **T11, *Heads and Tails* Recording Sheet** • **Pennies** (at least 7 per pair) • **Cubes or counters** (as needed) • **Chart paper** • **Materials for *Three Towers of 10*** See Session 4.2.	• **M35, *Heads and Tails* Recording Sheet** Make copies. (as needed) • **M36, *Heads and Tails*** Make copies. (as needed)

Overhead Transparency

Composing Numbers, *continued*

	Student Activity Book	Student Math Handbook	Professional Development: Read Ahead of Time
SESSION 4.4 p. 167			
How Many Am I Hiding? Students learn and play *How Many Am I Hiding?* a new game that focuses on combinations of numbers. The session ends with a discussion about strategies for playing this game.	39–42	G14	
SESSION 4.5 p. 172			
Nine Peas and Carrots Students revisit a How Many of Each? problem, this time with 9 peas and carrots. They try to find more than one combination of peas and carrots.	43–45	46–47, 48–49	
SESSION 4.6 p. 177			
Combinations of Seven Students continue with activities that focus on breaking numbers into two smaller parts. The session ends with a discussion about combinations of 7.	47–48	44–45, 46–47; G13, G14, G25	• **Dialogue Box:** Sharing Combinations of Seven, p. 242
SESSION 4.7 p. 180			
End-of-Unit Assessment Students solve 2 problems as an End-of-Unit Assessment: one addition story problem and one How Many of Each? problem.	49	33–37, 46–47	• **Teacher Note:** End-of-Unit Assessment, pp. 216–223

Materials to Gather	Materials to Prepare
• **T12, *How Many Am I Hiding?* Recording Sheet** (Overhead Transparency) • **Connecting cubes** (10 per pair)	• **M36, *Heads and Tails*** Make copies. (1 per student for homework) • **M37, *How Many Am I Hiding?* Recording Sheet** Make copies. (as needed) • **M38, *How Many Am I Hiding?*** Make copies. (as needed) • **Cube towers** Make towers of 6 connecting cubes. (1 per student or pair)
• **Chart: "7 in all"** (from Session 4.1; optional) • **Cubes or counters in 2 colors** (9 of each color per student) • **Crayons or markers in same colors as cubes or counters** (1 of each color per student) • **Paper plates** (1 per student; optional) • **Chart paper**	
• **Materials for *Three Towers of 10*** See Session 4.2. • **T11, *Heads and Tails* Recording Sheet** (Overhead Transparency) (optional) • **Materials for *Heads and Tails*** See Session 4.3. • **Materials for *How Many Am I Hiding?*** See Session 4.4.	• **Chart paper** Make a chart-paper display of *Heads and Tails* Recording Sheet. (optional)
• **Counters** (20 per student)	• **M39–M40, End-of-Unit Assessment** Make copies. (1 per student)

Overhead Transparency

Seven Peas and Carrots

Math Focus Points

- Finding and exploring relationships among combinations of numbers up to 10
- Solving a problem with multiple solutions
- Recording a solution to a problem

Today's Plan		Materials
1 ACTIVITY **Introducing Seven Peas and Carrots**	15 MIN CLASS	• *Student Activity Book,* p. 33 • Chart paper; connecting cubes in 2 colors, green and orange
2 ACTIVITY **Solving Seven Peas and Carrots**	30 MIN INDIVIDUALS PAIRS	• *Student Activity Book,* p. 33 • Cubes or counters in 2 colors; paper plates; crayons or markers in same colors as cubes or counters
3 DISCUSSION **Sharing Solutions**	15 MIN CLASS	• *Student Activity Book,* p. 33 • Chart paper
4 SESSION FOLLOW-UP **Daily Practice**		• *Student Activity Book,* p. 34 • *Student Math Handbook,* pp. 46–47

Classroom Routines

Morning Meeting: How Many Now? **Follow your daily *Morning Meeting* Routine. As a variation to the *Attendance* routine, count the class when some students are missing at various times throughout the day. Discuss why this number is different than the attendance number determined during *Morning Meeting.* For a full write-up of this variation, see Part 4: Classroom Routines in *Implementing Investigations in Grade 1:* Morning Meeting.**

ACTIVITY

15 MIN CLASS

Introducing Seven Peas and Carrots

Begin by bringing a sheet of chart paper and cubes of two different colors (green and orange) to the meeting area. Gather students around you, and draw a large circle on the paper to represent a plate. Tell the following story to introduce How Many of Each? problems.❶ ❷

Last night I was really hungry. I bought some peas and some carrots and I mixed them up in a pot and I cooked them. When I was ready to eat, I took out my very special spoon and scooped some onto my plate. My spoon only holds 7 vegetables.

I want you to imagine that I scooped 7 vegetables onto my plate. Imagine that some of them are peas, and some of them are carrots. How many of each could I have? How many peas? How many carrots? Remember, I have 7 vegetables in all.

Write "7 in all" on the chart paper.

Accept two different student suggestions, and model them with cubes. If some students disagree with the solutions their classmates offer, ask them to explain their thinking, but keep the discussion brief and keep the focus on explaining the task clearly enough that students can find solutions on their own. Explain that there is more than one correct solution to this problem, and that students are to try to find solutions different from those just suggested. They will record their work on *Student Activity Book* page 33, using numbers, words, pictures, equations, or a combination of these.❸

Students find combinations of 7.

Math Note

❶ **How Many of Each? Problems** This peas-and-carrots problem is one example of a type of problem called How Many of Each? that students will solve throughout the school year. A basic How Many of Each? problem gives students 2 types of objects (such as peas and carrots) and a total number (in this case, 7). The students determine how many of each object they could have to make up the total.

Professional Development

❷ **Teacher Note:** About How Many of Each? Problems, pp. 211–212

Teaching Note

❸ **Recording** Because students are developing their own ways to record their work, it is best not to record these first suggested solutions. Seeing the teacher model a recording method can make it difficult for students to find their own methods. You will have a chance to discuss methods for recording at the end of this session, and again in Session 4.5.

Name Date

How Many of Each?

Seven Peas and Carrots

Solve the problem. Show your work.

I have 7 things on my plate.
Some are peas. Some are carrots.
How many of each could I have?
How many peas? How many carrots?

Session 4.1 Unit 1 33

▲ Student Activity Book, p. 33  

Teaching Note

④ **Addressing "Is this right?"** Often students will be eager to learn right away if their solution is correct. Instead of simply telling students when their solnution is correct, it is important to regularly ask students to explain the thinking behind an answer, whether correct or incorrect, and to encourage them to find ways to double-check solutions on their own.

ACTIVITY

2 Solving Seven Peas and Carrots

30 MIN INDIVIDUALS PAIRS

Whether students work alone or in pairs, encourage them to share their ideas.④ Have cubes or counters, perhaps in green and orange, available to help students model the problem. If students want to arrange cubes or counters on a "plate," they can draw a large circle on a sheet of paper or work on an actual paper plate.

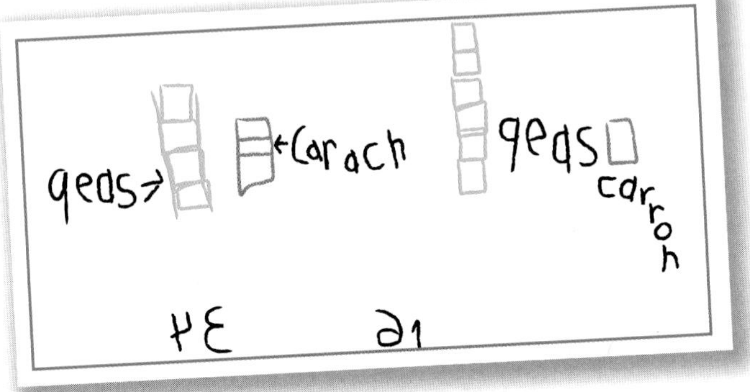

Sample Student Work

Sample Student Work

Sample Student Work

For this first experience, it is not necessary that each student find more than one solution. However, some students will begin to seek multiple solutions on their own, and many more will do the same over the course of the year as students work with a variety of problems that have many solutions.

ONGOING ASSESSMENT: Observing Students at Work

Students solve a complex problem, finding combinations of a number, and keeping track of and recording their work.⑤ ⑥

- **How do students approach, model, and solve the problem?** How do they record their work? Do they use manipulatives? Pictures? Numbers? Do they work mentally?
- **How do students count and keep track of the total number of peas and carrots (7)?** Of the number of peas and the number of carrots (the two subsets)?
- **Are students able to find at least one combination that is equal to 7?** Do they find more than one combination?

DIFFERENTIATION: Supporting the Range of Learners

Intervention If students are having difficulty getting started, have them use orange and green cubes to model the problem.

- Suppose that I had 6 carrots. How many peas would I need to have 7 in all?

Have students model this with cubes.

ELL Students will need to understand the phrase "how many" in order to solve How Many of Each? problems. English Language Learners will acquire this language through repeated modeling and practice. Think aloud as you model simple "how many" problems with assorted counters.

- How many buttons do I have? I have 1, 2, 3, 4, [5]. I have [5].

To develop English Language Learners' speaking skills, encourage pairs of students to ask and answer their own "how many" problems.

Professional Development

⑤ **Teacher Note:** Common Issues That Typically Arise with How Many of Each?, pp. 213–214

⑥ **Dialogue Box:** Observing Students at Work on Seven Peas and Carrots, pp. 239–241

Professional Development

7 **Teacher Note:** When the Teacher Records Students' Solutions, p. 215

3 DISCUSSION

Sharing Solutions

Math Focus Points for Discussion

- Solving a problem with multiple solutions
- Finding and exploring relationships among combinations of numbers up to 10

Call students together, and have them bring their copy of *Student Activity Book* page 33. Ask a volunteer to share one of the solutions she found. As the student holds up her paper and explains her solution, ask others to raise their hands if they got the same solution.

[Talisa] got 4 peas and 3 carrots. Did anyone else get that?

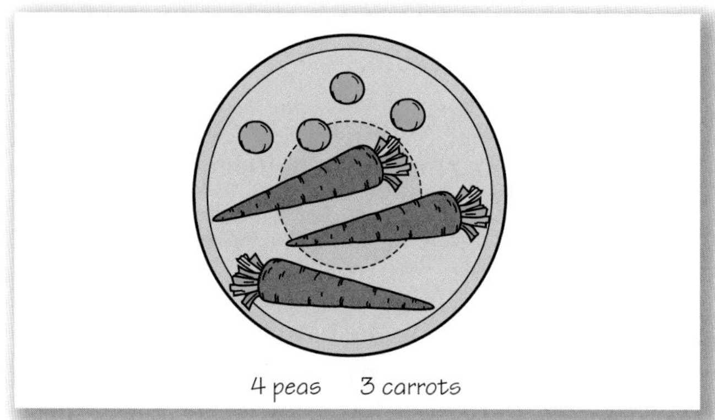

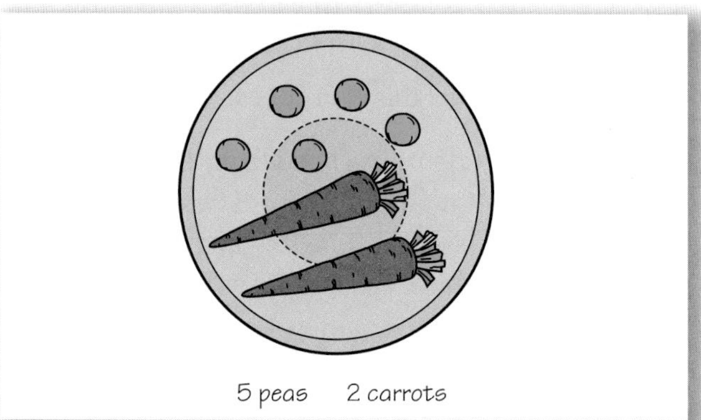

Because the focus of this discussion is on the combinations of 7 that students found rather than methods for recording, keep the recording method consistent for this discussion. Choose one of the ways you saw students using. Recording all the solutions given in one way can help students focus on which combinations have (and have not yet) been shared. 7

Did anyone find a *different* combination of 7 peas and carrots?

Accept and record a few more solutions. Note that sometimes students will see combinations like 4 peas and 3 carrots as different from 3 carrots and 4 peas. Encourage them to share *different* combinations than have been shared, perhaps by asking:

You shared a way with 4 peas. When I look at our posted list, I see that Talisa's solution used 4 peas. Can you find a way that used a different number of peas?

After several minutes, you may find that some students are still eager to share and are attentive, but others are beginning to find it difficult to remain engaged and focused. Before ending the discussion, acknowledge that there may be still other solutions. You might provide an opportunity later in the day for those students still eager to share to do so with a partner or in a smaller group or to individually add their solutions to your list.⑧

SESSION FOLLOW-UP

Daily Practice

Daily Practice: For reinforcement of this unit's content, have students complete *Student Activity Book* page 34.

Student Math Handbook: Students and families may use *Student Math Handbook* pages 46–47 for reference and review. See pages 243–252 in the back of this unit.

Teaching Note

⑧ **Saving Student Work** Students will revisit this activity several times in this unit and over the year. You might want to save students' work for this problem to compare with work on similar problems later in the unit and in the year.

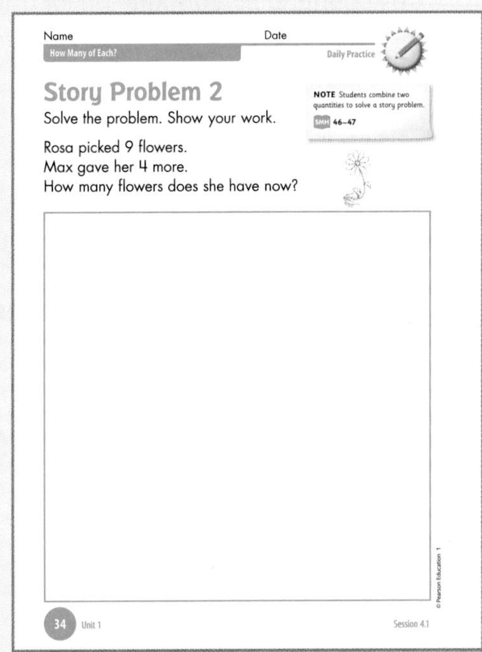

Name Date

How Many of Each? Daily Practice

Story Problem 2

Solve the problem. Show your work.

Rosa picked 9 flowers.
Max gave her 4 more.
How many flowers does she have now?

NOTE Students combine two quantities to solve a story problem.

SMH 46–47

34 Unit 1 Session 4.1

▲ Student Activity Book, p. 34

Three Towers

Math Focus Points

- Finding the total of two or more quantities up to a total of 20 by counting all, counting on, or using number combinations
- Finding and exploring relationships among combinations of numbers up to 10
- Using standard notation (+ and =) to represent addition situations

Vocabulary

symbols

Today's Plan			Materials
ACTIVITY **1 Introducing *Three Towers***	15 MIN	CLASS	• T10 • Connecting cubes in 2 colors; dot cube
ACTIVITY **2 Playing *Three Towers***	30 MIN	PAIRS	• *Student Activity Book,* p. 35 • M33*; M34* • Connecting cubes in 2 colors; dot cubes; crayons or markers in same colors as connecting cubes
DISCUSSION **3 *Three Towers***	15 MIN	CLASS	• Cube towers*; chart paper (optional)
SESSION FOLLOW-UP **4 Daily Practice**			• *Student Activity Book,* p. 36 • *Student Math Handbook,* pp. 33–37, 48–49; G25

*See *Materials to Prepare,* p. 145.

Classroom Routines

Quick Images: Dot Cards **Show transparencies of the 3-, 4-, and 5-dot cards from Dot Cards Set B (T7) at the same time. Follow the basic *Quick Images* activity. Ask students to determine the total number of dots. Repeat with the 4-, 5-, and 6-dot cards from Dot Cards Set A (T2) and compare the arrangements.**

ACTIVITY

1 Introducing *Three Towers*

To introduce the game, bring a dot cube and about 60 connecting cubes in two colors to the meeting area. Ask a volunteer to play a demonstration game with you.

We're going to learn a new game called *Three Towers.* You and your partner will work together to build three towers. Each tower needs to be the same number of cubes high. Today we're going to build towers of 10, so [Jacinta] and I will build 3 towers that are 10 cubes tall. To start, each player chooses a color.

Ask the student you are playing with to choose one of the two colors, and explain that you will use the cubes of the other color. Then demonstrate the first turn by rolling the dot cube.

We take turns rolling the dot cube. What number did I roll? [6] So how many cubes do I take? [6]

Make a stack of [6 yellow] cubes.

So I used my cubes to make a tower [6] cubes high. How many more cubes do we need to make a tower of 10?

Encourage students to share their strategies for figuring this out. Because this question may be challenging for many of your students, do not spend too much time on this conversation. Next, your student partner rolls the dot cube.

[Jacinta] rolled a 5. How many blue cubes does she take?

Remind students that they are working *together* on the same tower. Your partner shouldn't start a new tower after a roll; together you should finish the first tower and then begin the second once the first tower has 10.

Show the students how to put 4 blue cubes on top of the tower of 6 yellow cubes to make a complete tower of 10. Then start a new tower with the remaining blue cube.

Now we've finished one of our three towers of 10. We've also started our second tower, and so far it has 1 cube. Remember that we want to make towers of 10.

Continue playing until you have completed three towers, each 10 cubes high. You do not need to roll an exact number to finish the activity; set aside any extra cubes.

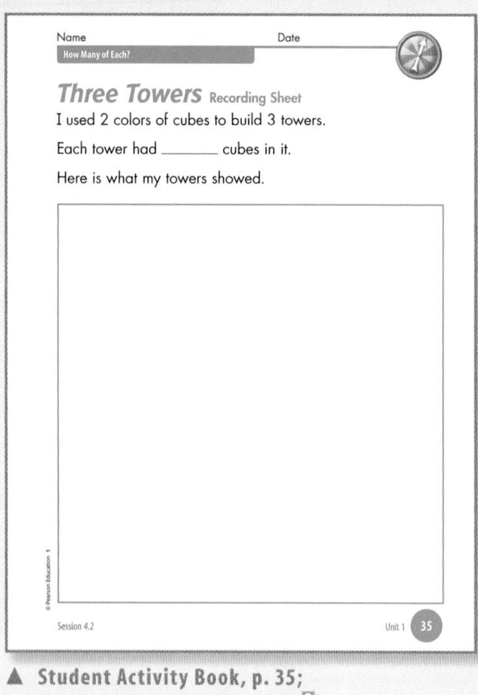
Name Date
How Many of Each?

Three Towers Recording Sheet

I used 2 colors of cubes to build 3 towers.

Each tower had ______ cubes in it.

Here is what my towers showed.

© Pearson Education 1

Session 4.2 Unit 1 35

▲ Student Activity Book, p. 35; Resource Masters, M33; T10

The last step is to find the number of cubes of each color in each tower. Choose a tower to start with, and count aloud as students count the number of each color with you. Repeat this count with each tower, and record the totals found for each tower on the board.

How many yellow cubes in this tower? There are 4 yellow cubes: 2 in the middle, and 2 at the top. How many blue cubes? Yes, there are 6 blue cubes: 1 at the bottom, and then this group of 5. So this tower of 10 cubes has 4 yellow cubes and 6 blue ones.

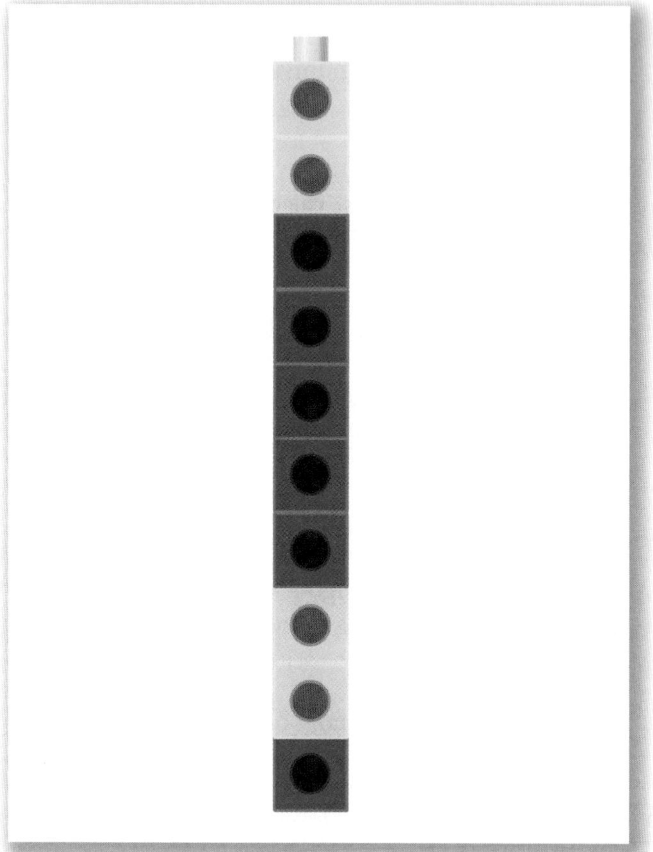

Both players will record what happened in their game, so both [Jacinta] and I would find a way to show how many of each color are in each tower.

Show *Student Activity Book* page 35 or *Three Towers* (T10), and explain to students that they will record what happens in their game on a sheet like this.

How might you show how many of each color are in this tower?

Some students will suggest drawing the towers at the end of the game. Others will use numbers with color or word labels (e.g., 4 yellow or 6 with a picture of a blue cube). Some will also use addition notation in their work.

ACTIVITY

Playing *Three Towers*

30 MIN PAIRS

Students now play *Three Towers* in pairs. Circulate as they play, and clarify the directions as necessary. Use this time to ask questions about the cubes: How many are in your tower so far? How many more do you need? Encourage students to add numbers to their work, showing the total of each color in each tower. Have available *Three Towers of 10* (M34) as needed.

ONGOING ASSESSMENT: Observing Students at Work

Students count, combine, and consider combinations of the number 10.

- **How do students decide how many cubes to take?** Do they count the dots? Just know the pattern?
- **How do students determine when a tower is complete or how many more they need to complete a tower?** Do they keep recounting from 1? Count on from the last total? Use number combinations they know?
- **How do students figure out the total number of each color in each tower?**
- **How do students record their work?**

Sample Student Work

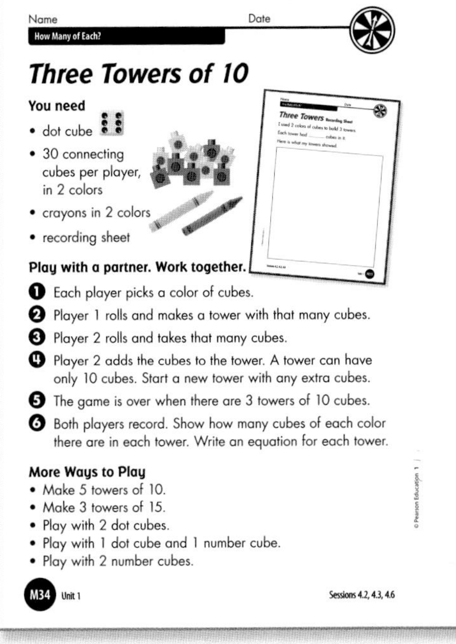

Name Date

How Many of Each?

Three Towers of 10

You need

- dot cube
- 30 connecting cubes per player, in 2 colors
- crayons in 2 colors
- recording sheet

Play with a partner. Work together.

1. Each player picks a color of cubes.
2. Player 1 rolls and makes a tower with that many cubes.
3. Player 2 rolls and takes that many cubes.
4. Player 2 adds the cubes to the tower. A tower can have only 10 cubes. Start a new tower with any extra cubes.
5. The game is over when there are 3 towers of 10 cubes.
6. Both players record. Show how many cubes of each color there are in each tower. Write an equation for each tower.

More Ways to Play

- Make 5 towers of 10.
- Make 3 towers of 15.
- Play with 2 dot cubes.
- Play with 1 dot cube and 1 number cube.
- Play with 2 number cubes.

M34 Unit 1 Sessions 4.2, 4.3, 4.6

▲ Resource Masters, M34

DIFFERENTIATION: Supporting the Range of Learners

Intervention Some students may benefit from building towers with fewer cubes in them (e.g., 3 towers of 6 or 8).

15 MIN CLASS

DISCUSSION

3 Three Towers

Math Focus Points for Discussion

- Using standard notation (+ and =) to represent addition situations

Bring to the discussion the cube towers you prepared.

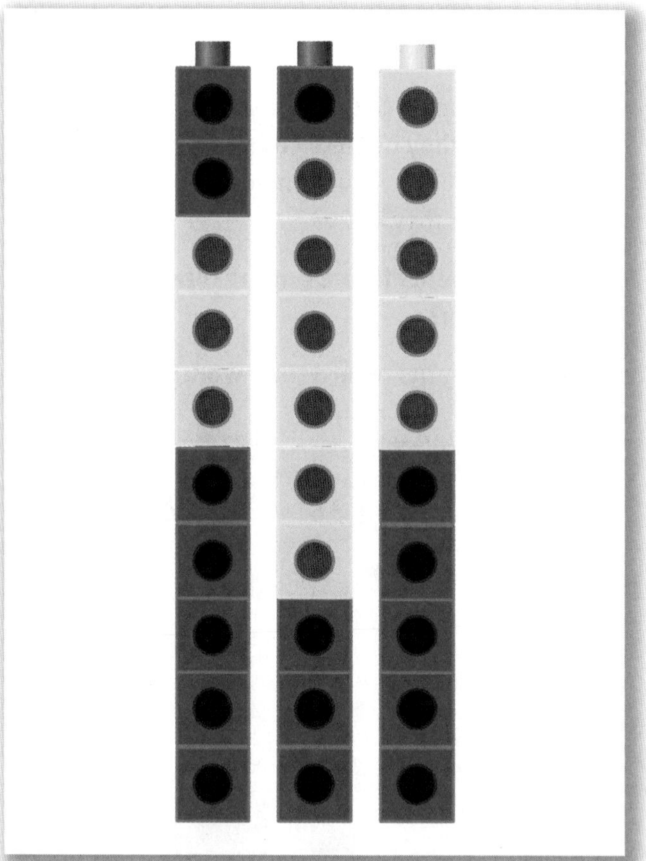

I watched you play *Three Towers* today. Here are the cube towers that one pair could have had at the end of the game. How many blue cubes were used for this first tower?

Students might say:

"I see 5 and then 2 more."

Encourage students to figure out how many blue cubes that makes altogether. Do the same for the yellow cubes.

How would you show the information about the first tower on paper? How would you show that the tower has seven blue cubes and three yellow cubes?

Use one of the methods students suggest; for example, sketching and coloring in a tower of ten cubes. Have students help you add labels that show the total of each color (7 and 3). Then use this opportunity to briefly revisit the meaning of addition notation, first introduced in Session 3.3.❶

We agreed that altogether there were 10 cubes. And we agreed that seven of the cubes were blue and three of them were yellow.

On the board or chart paper, write an equation.❷

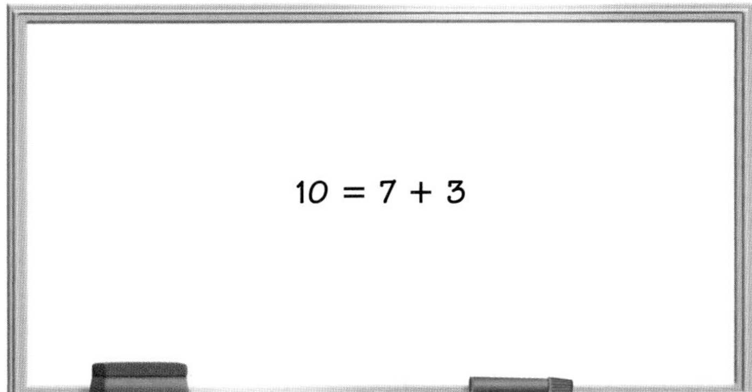

We have talked a little about these symbols, and I have seen children using them. Who remembers something about these symbols they would like to share? How does what I wrote connect to our tower? To our picture of the tower?

Point to the appropriate number(s) in the equation as you talk about it with students, keeping the focus on the action or relationship these symbols represent.

Professional Development

❶ **Teacher Note:** Introducing Notation, Part 1, pp. 198–199

Teaching Note

❷ **Notation** Some students think that writing the total followed by the equal sign is not an acceptable way to write an equation. They might think the equal sign means "the answer is coming now" or even "stop." Encourage students to think about whether what is on either side of the equal sign is the same. Continue to write equations in different ways.

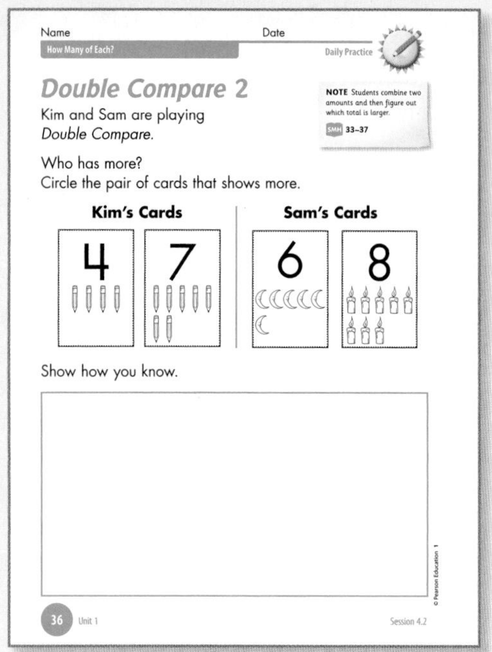

Name Date

How Many of Each? Daily Practice

Double Compare 2

NOTE Students combine two amounts and then figure out which total is larger.

SMH 33–37

Kim and Sam are playing *Double Compare.*

Who has more?
Circle the pair of cards that shows more.

Kim's Cards		Sam's Cards	
4	7	6	8

Show how you know.

36 Unit 1 Session 4.2

© Pearson Education 1

▲ Student Activity Book, p. 36

We said that there are 10 cubes altogether—7 blues and 3 yellows. What I've written here means that 10 is the same amount, or is *equal to,* 7 and 3. 7 *plus* 3 more *equals* 10. This symbol is called *plus,* it tells you to *combine* those numbers, to put them together, or to *add* them. What this *equation* says in words is that 10 is the same as 7 and 3.

Follow the same process for the other two towers. Record one of the towers in the reverse order (4 + 6 = 10), again talking through the notation, and providing lots of language around the use of the various symbols.

The teacher models how to represent addition problems with standard notation many times before first graders are expected to use it in their written work.

SESSION FOLLOW-UP

Daily Practice

Daily Practice: For reinforcement of this unit's content, have students complete *Student Activity Book* page 36.

Student Math Handbook: Students and families may use *Student Math Handbook* pages 33–37, 48–49 and G25 for reference and review. See pages 243–252 in the back of this unit.

SESSION 4.3

Heads and Tails

Math Focus Points

- Finding and exploring relationships among combinations of numbers up to 10
- Visualizing and retelling the action in an addition situation
- Modeling the action of an addition problem with counters or drawings
- Finding the total of two or more quantities up to a total of 20 by counting all, counting on, or using number combinations

Vocabulary

penny
cent
heads
tails

Today's Plan			Materials
1 ACTIVITY **Introducing *Heads and Tails***	15 MIN	CLASS	• M35* • T11 • Pennies
2 MATH WORKSHOP **Combinations of the Same Number** 2A *Heads and Tails* 2B *Three Towers*	30 MIN		2A • *Student Activity Book,* p. 37 • M35*; M36* • Pennies 2B • Materials from Session 4.2, p. 154 Use M33* in place of *Student Activity Book* p. 35 • Extra dot cubes and connecting cubes (optional)
3 ACTIVITY **More Story Problems Aloud**	15 MIN	CLASS	• Cubes or counters; chart paper (optional)
4 SESSION FOLLOW-UP **Daily Practice**			• *Student Activity Book,* p. 38 • *Student Math Handbook,* pp. 33–37, G13, G25

*See *Materials to Prepare,* p. 147.

Classroom Routines

Start With/Get To: Get To 1 Choose a *start with* number. Ask students to find and mark the number on the class number line. As a class, count together from this number backward to 1.

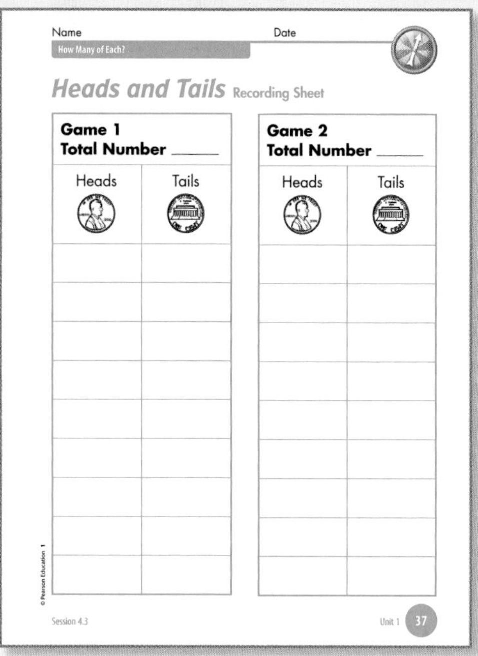
Name Date
How Many of Each?

Heads and Tails Recording Sheet

Game 1 Total Number ____	
Heads	Tails

Game 2 Total Number ____	
Heads	Tails

© Pearson Education 1
Session 4.3 Unit 1 37

▲ Student Activity Book, p. 37; Resource Masters, M35; T11

ACTIVITY

1 Introducing *Heads and Tails*

Spend a few minutes introducing and talking about pennies with students. Discuss their names (such as penny or cent), what they are used for, the names of the two sides, and strategies for remembering which side is heads and which is tails. Record the important information on a class chart that students can refer to as needed.

Penny

heads tails

What we know about it

Names

1 penny
1 cent 1¢
money
coin

It is money. It is a coin.

You buy things with it.
It is brown.
You throw a penny and make a wish.
It is round.
They have them at stores.
There are 2 sides.
There are pictures on it.
There is a different picture on each side.
Flip a coin—heads or tails.

Display the transparency of *Heads and Tails* Recording Sheet (T11).

Show students 7 pennies, and ask students how many there are. When students agree that there are 7, gather the pennies up in one hand.

I have 7 pennies that I'm going to drop. Let's see how many land facing heads up, and how many land facing tails up.

Drop the pennies, and ask how many landed heads up. Use the transparency to demonstrate filling in the *Heads and Tails* Recording Sheet (T11). Write 7 on the Total Number line, and have students help you fill in the top row for Game 1.

Heads and Tails Recording Sheet

Game 1 Total Number 7		Game 2 Total Number ____	
Heads	Tails	Heads	Tails
4	3		
5	2		

Repeat the game until students understand the procedure. Each time, write the numbers landing heads up and tails up on the transparency. Tell students that the game is over when all the rows of the recording sheet are filled. During Math Workshop, students will work alone or in pairs to play *Heads and Tails* with 7 pennies.

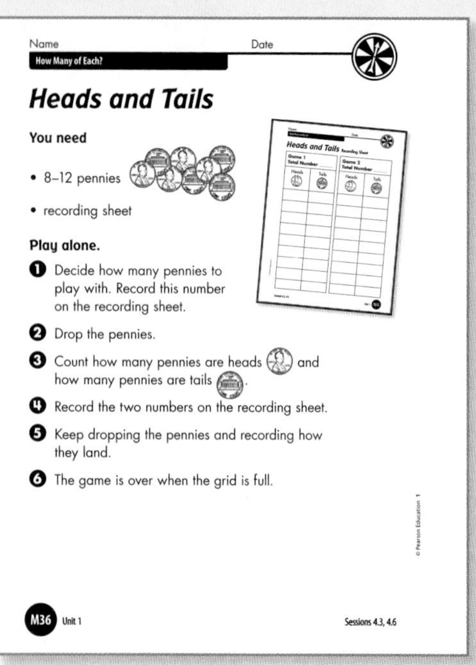

Name Date

How Many of Each?

Heads and Tails

You need

- 8–12 pennies
- recording sheet

Play alone.

1. Decide how many pennies to play with. Record this number on the recording sheet.
2. Drop the pennies.
3. Count how many pennies are heads and how many pennies are tails.
4. Record the two numbers on the recording sheet.
5. Keep dropping the pennies and recording how they land.
6. The game is over when the grid is full.

© Pearson Education 1

M36 Unit 1 Sessions 4.3, 4.6

▲ Resource Masters, M36

MATH WORKSHOP

2 Combinations of the Same Number

30 MIN

Students play the following two games, focused on different combinations for the same number. This work lays some of the groundwork for future experiences with the operations of addition and subtraction.

2A Heads and Tails

PAIRS

INDIVIDUALS

Students drop a set of pennies and record the number of heads and tails. They repeat the activity until they have completely filled a recording sheet. All students start by playing with seven pennies. Have available copies of *Heads and Tails* (M36) as needed.

ONGOING ASSESSMENT: Observing Students at Work

As they count and record numbers, students are beginning to think about different combinations of a number (e.g., 4 and 3 make 7, and so do 6 and 1, and 2 and 5).

- **How do students count the pennies?** Can they determine the numbers visually? Do they count each group, or do they use one of the numbers to find the other? Can they think that if there are 4 heads, and 4 and 3 is 7, there must be 3 tails?
- **Do students notice repeat combinations?** Combinations that do not equal their total number? Do they know how to use 0?
- **Can students accurately record the information?**
- **How accurate and legible are students' written numbers?** Is their ability improving over time?

DIFFERENTIATION: Supporting the Range of Learners

Intervention To check students' understanding of the relationship between the grid on their recording sheet and the way the pennies landed, choose one of the number pairs on their game grid and ask students to model it with pennies.

Extension Students who are ready can be challenged to find a combination of 7 not yet on their recording sheet. You can also have them play with more pennies.

Playing Heads and Tails *is another way for students to notice different combinations of the same number.*

2B Three Towers

PAIRS

For complete details about this activity, see Session 4.2, pages 155–157.

ONGOING ASSESSMENT: Observing Students at Work

- **Are any students using the addition notation introduced in Session 4.2 to record their work?** How accurately are students using addition notation?

DIFFERENTIATION: Supporting the Range of Learners

Extension Some students may be ready to play with two dot cubes and/or to make five towers. They can also think about the following questions: Have they found all the ways to make 10 with two numbers? Which ones are they missing? Can they build towers with 2 colors that show all the combinations of 10?

Story Problem Routine

1. Tell students a number story. Encourage them to visualize the action in the story.
2. Ask several students to retell the story after they have heard it. (Or several students can each tell one part of the story. Occasionally, you might have each student retell the story to a partner.)
3. After retelling each story, ask whether the end result in each case will be more or less than the amount you started with.
4. Ask students to share strategies for solving the problem, including modeling the problem with cubes or counters.
5. Model methods of recording on chart paper or on the board.

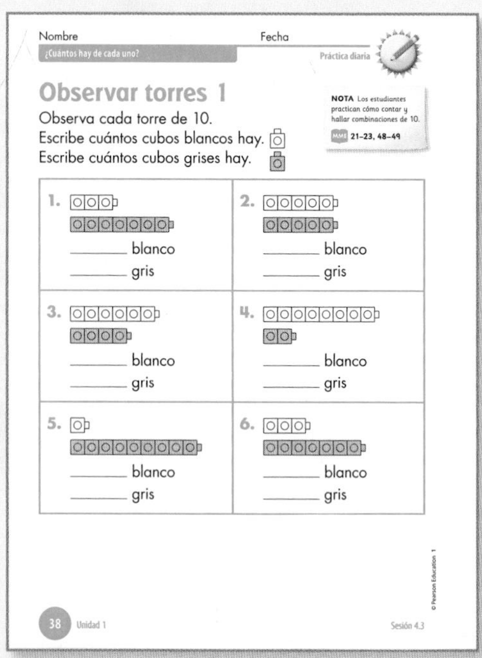

Nombre Fecha

¿Cuántos hay de cada uno? Práctica diaria

Observar torres 1

Observa cada torre de 10.
Escribe cuántos cubos blancos hay.
Escribe cuántos cubos grises hay.

NOTA Los estudiantes practican cómo contar y hallar combinaciones de 10.
SMH 21–23, 48–49

1. ______ blanco ______ gris
2. ______ blanco ______ gris
3. ______ blanco ______ gris
4. ______ blanco ______ gris
5. ______ blanco ______ gris
6. ______ blanco ______ gris

© Pearson Education 1

38 Unidad 1 Sesión 4.3

▲ Student Activity Book, p. 38

ACTIVITY

More Story Problems Aloud

15 MIN CLASS

Present several story problems, following the *Story Problem Routine.* Sometimes you can base story problems on the games students are playing or the activities they are doing.

Libby and Bruce were playing Heads and Tails. *They got 4 heads and 8 tails. How many pennies were they using?*

Neil and Danielle were playing Heads and Tails. *They got 5 heads and 7 tails. How many pennies were they using?*

SESSION FOLLOW-UP

Daily Practice

Daily Practice: For reinforcement of this unit's content, have students complete *Student Activity Book* page 38.

Student Math Handbook: Students and families may use *Student Math Handbook* pages 33–37 and G13, G25 for reference and review. See pages 243–252 in the back of this unit.

How Many Am I Hiding?

Math Focus Points

- Solving a problem in which the total and one part are known
- Finding and exploring relationships among combinations of numbers up to 10
- Recording combinations of two numbers that make a certain total

Vocabulary

total

Today's Plan			Materials
ACTIVITY **1** Introducing *How Many Am I Hiding?*	15 MIN	CLASS	• T12 • Connecting cubes
ACTIVITY **2** Playing *How Many Am I Hiding?*	30 MIN	PAIRS	• *Student Activity Book,* p. 39 • M37*; M38* • Connecting cubes
DISCUSSION **3** Strategies for *How Many Am I Hiding?*	15 MIN	CLASS	• 6-cube towers*
SESSION FOLLOW-UP **4** Daily Practice and Homework			• *Student Activity Book,* pp. 40–42 • M36* • *Student Math Handbook,* p. G14

*See *Materials to Prepare,* p. 149.

Classroom Routines

Quick Images: Dot Cards Show transparencies of the 3-, 4-, and 5-dot cards from Dot Cards Set B (T2) at the same time. Follow the basic *Quick Images* activity. Ask students to determine the total number of dots. Repeat with the 4-, 5-, and 6-cards from Dot Cards Set A (T7) and compare the arrangements.

Math Note

❶ **Breaking Numbers Apart** The game *How Many Am I Hiding?* offers a new experience with breaking numbers apart. In this game, students need to determine what part of a number (or total) is hidden or missing. This problem involves a total, or whole, made up of two parts—the number of cubes showing and the number of cubes hidden. Holding onto all of this information can be challenging. Provide cubes for students to use to model and solve the problem. Some students will use them, and others will use their fingers or work mentally.

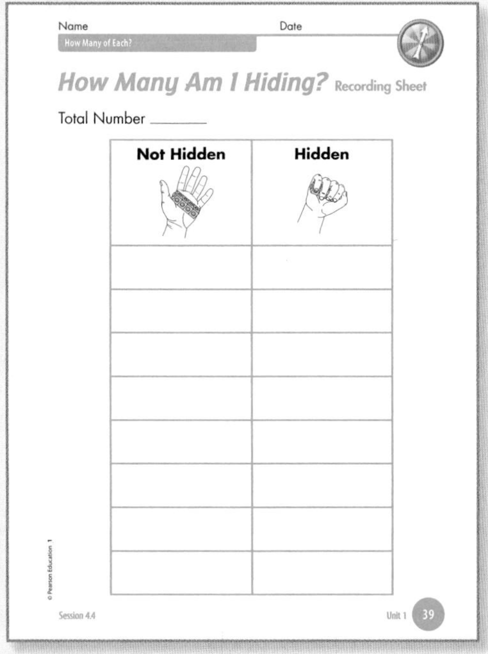
Name Date

How Many of Each?

How Many Am I Hiding? Recording Sheet

Total Number ______

Not Hidden	Hidden

Session 4.4 Unit 1 39

▲ Student Activity Book, p. 39; Resource Masters, M37;T12

ACTIVITY 1

15 MIN CLASS

Introducing *How Many Am I Hiding?*

To introduce the game *How Many Am I Hiding?*, show students a tower of five cubes and ask how many cubes you have. Explain that you are going to hide some.

I have five cubes. I'm going to break my cube tower into two parts, and I'm going to hide one part behind my back.

In such a way that students cannot see what you are doing, break off two of the cubes and hide them behind your back. Place the remaining cubes so that students can see them.

Three cubes are still here. Think silently about how many cubes I am hiding behind my back. When you think you know how many I hid, you can raise your hand, but please don't say anything. We want to give everyone a chance to think about it.❶

When most students are ready, ask for volunteers to tell how many they think are hidden. Encourage students to explain how they found the answer. Model each strategy students suggest with the cubes.

Students might say:

"I counted the cubes I could see and then used my fingers to count on to 5."

"I used my cubes. I took out 5 and put 3 aside. There were 2 left."

Be sure to ask for other ideas about how many cubes are hidden, even after someone suggests the correct solution. That way, you help students think for themselves about whether they have found the correct solution.

Display the transparency of *How Many Am I Hiding?* Recording Sheet (T12) to demonstrate how to record the combinations of 5. Explain that students should first record the total number of cubes. Write 5 in the Total Number line. Then demonstrate how to record the number of cubes showing and hidden. Do this in the top row of the recording sheet.

Repeat the game until students understand the steps. Always start with all the cubes in one tower, where students can see all of them. Vary the number of cubes that you hide. Each time, record the results on the transparency of *How Many Am I Hiding?* Recording Sheet (T12). Do one example that requires using a zero to record.

Explain that pairs will play this together, taking turns hiding the cubes, but that both students will record on their own recording sheet. The game is over when all the rows of the recording sheet are filled.

ACTIVITY

2 Playing *How Many Am I Hiding?*

30 MIN PAIRS

All students start by playing with towers of 5. First one student and then the other hides some cubes. The partner figures out how many are hidden, and both record the results. The game is over when they have completely filled the recording sheet. Encourage players to vary the number of cubes they hide (including all or none), but they can hide the same number of cubes more than once. Have available copies of *How Many Am I Hiding?* (M38) as needed.

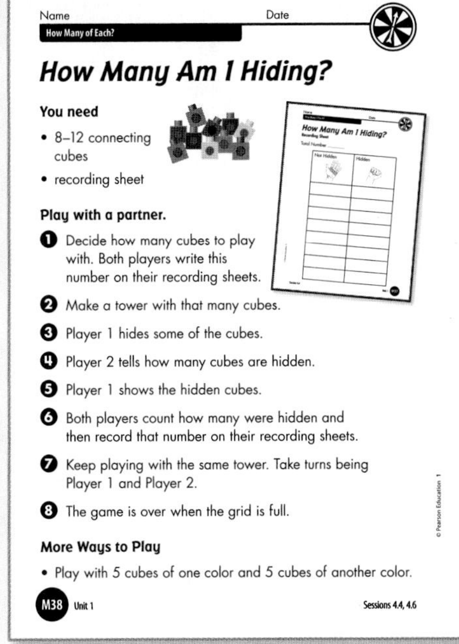

Name Date

How Many of Each?

How Many Am I Hiding?

You need

- 8–12 connecting cubes
- recording sheet

Play with a partner.

1. Decide how many cubes to play with. Both players write this number on their recording sheets.
2. Make a tower with that many cubes.
3. Player 1 hides some of the cubes.
4. Player 2 tells how many cubes are hidden.
5. Player 1 shows the hidden cubes.
6. Both players count how many were hidden and then record that number on their recording sheets.
7. Keep playing with the same tower. Take turns being Player 1 and Player 2.
8. The game is over when the grid is full.

More Ways to Play

- Play with 5 cubes of one color and 5 cubes of another color.

M38 Unit 1 Sessions 4.4, 4.6

▲ Resource Masters, M38

ONGOING ASSESSMENT: Observing Students at Work

Students are solving a problem with one part missing; they know the total number of cubes and how many cubes are in one group.

- **How do students determine the number of hidden cubes?** Do they guess? Count all the cubes they see by 1s and then continue counting on to the total number? Start with the number of cubes visible and count on? Do they use knowledge of number combinations? Do they use relationships among combinations, such as realizing that last time, there were 3 showing and 2 were hidden so if there are 2 showing, there must be 3 hidden?
- **Do students understand how to use the recording sheet?** Can they show you with cubes what one row looks like? What do students do when all the cubes are hidden (or visible)?

DIFFERENTIATION: Supporting the Range of Learners

Intervention *How Many Am I Hiding?* can be challenging for some students because it involves keeping track of and coordinating three amounts: the total number of cubes, the number visible, and the number hidden. You can help students who are having difficulty use cubes or their fingers to model the problem. Try hiding just one cube. Count the visible cubes together and remind students of the total. Then ask them to visualize what is hidden. Try the same process, this time hiding 2 cubes. Some students may need to do this activity several times with 3 or 4 cubes before they can work with a set as large as 5. Make sure that they have a chance to do the activity several times with the same total number.

Extension For students who find 5 or 6 too easy, have them work with 8 or 9. Make sure that they have a chance to do the activity several times with the same total number.

In How Many Am I Hiding?, *students know the total (whole) and one of the parts. They use that information to determine how many are in the missing part.*

3 DISCUSSION

Strategies for *How Many Am I Hiding?*

15 MIN CLASS

Math Focus Points for Discussion

- Solving a problem in which the total and one part are known

Gather the class to play several rounds of *How Many Am I Hiding?* Give each student a tower of six cubes and establish that there are six. Ask students to close their eyes while you hide some of your cubes.

Hide two cubes, and place the remaining cubes where students can see them.

Think silently about how many I hid. Everyone has six cubes. You can use them to help you solve this problem.

When most students are ready, ask for volunteers to tell how many they think are hidden, and how they figured it out. Begin, if possible, with a student who used the cubes to figure it out.

Some students will make a tower with the 6 cubes, and break it so that one part shows the cubes that are visible (4). Then, they reason, the number of cubes in their other hand (2) must be hidden. Others will count on from 4, use their fingers, or just know that 4 and 2 make 6. Model each strategy that students suggest using cubes. As you model, try to help students focus on the structure of the problem.

We know the total number of cubes. There are 6 altogether. What else do we know? We know how many cubes are showing, one part. What is it we are trying to figure out? We want to know how many cubes are hidden, the other part.

My tower had 6. [Lyle] said that I broke it into two parts, so if you put the two parts together, they have to make 6. He knew that 4 and 2 more make 6.

[Toshi] did something similar to [Lyle]. He saw my 4 showing, so he broke his tower of 6 into a 4 [count 4 and break the tower] and then saw that he had 2 left over.

As time allows, pose another combination of 6 for students to solve, and discuss their strategies.

SESSION FOLLOW-UP

Daily Practice and Homework

Daily Practice: For reinforcement of this unit's content, have students complete *Student Activity Book* page 40.

Homework: Students use coins to play *Heads and Tails* with someone at home. Each student will need a copy of the game directions, *Heads and Tails* (M36), and *Student Activity Book* pages 41–42. Suggest a total number for students to use, or give them a list of numbers to choose from (such as 6, 8, 9, 10, 11, or 12).

Student Math Handbook: Students and families may use *Student Math Handbook* page G14 for reference and review. See pages 243–252 in the back of this unit.

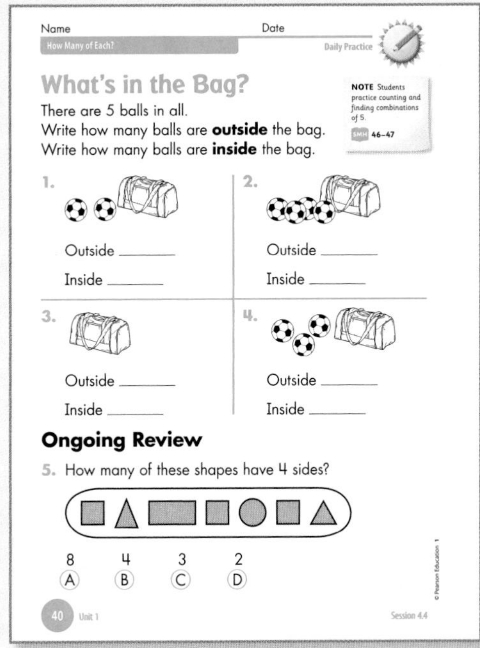

Name Date

How Many of Each? Daily Practice

What's in the Bag?

NOTE Students practice counting and finding combinations of 5. SMH 46–47

There are 5 balls in all.
Write how many balls are **outside** the bag.
Write how many balls are **inside** the bag.

1. Outside ____ Inside ____

2. Outside ____ Inside ____

3. Outside ____ Inside ____

4. Outside ____ Inside ____

Ongoing Review

5. How many of these shapes have 4 sides?

8	4	3	2
(A)	(B)	(C)	(D)

40 Unit 1 Session 4.4

▲ Student Activity Book, p. 40

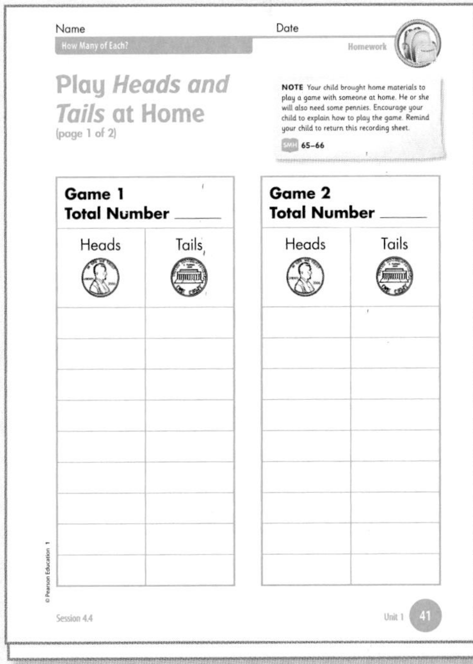

Name Date

How Many of Each? Homework

Play Heads and Tails at Home
(page 1 of 2)

NOTE Your child brought home materials to play a game with someone at home. He or she will also need some pennies. Encourage your child to explain how to play the game. Remind your child to return this recording sheet. SMH 65–66

Game 1 Total Number ____	
Heads	Tails

Game 2 Total Number ____	
Heads	Tails

Session 4.4 Unit 1 41

▲ Student Activity Book, pp. 41–42

Nine Peas and Carrots

Math Focus Points

- Finding and exploring relationships among combinations of numbers up to 10
- Solving a problem with multiple solutions
- Recording a solution to a problem
- Representing number combinations with numbers, pictures, and/or words

Today's Plan			Materials
1 ACTIVITY **Introducing Nine Peas and Carrots**	10 MIN	CLASS	• Chart: "7 in all" (from Session 4.1; optional)
2 ACTIVITY **Solving Nine Peas and Carrots**	30 MIN	INDIVIDUALS	• *Student Activity Book*, p. 43 • Cubes or counters in 2 colors; crayons or markers in same colors as cubes or counters; paper plates (optional)
3 DISCUSSION **Sharing Recording Methods**	20 MIN	CLASS	• *Student Activity Book*, p. 43 • Chart paper
4 SESSION FOLLOW-UP **Daily Practice and Homework**			• *Student Activity Book*, pp. 44–45 • *Student Math Handbook*, pp. 46–47, 48–49

Classroom Routines

Start With/Get To: Start With 1 Choose a *get to* number. Ask students to find and mark the number on the class number line. As a class, count together from 1 to the *get to* number.

ACTIVITY

Introducing Nine Peas and Carrots

10 MIN CLASS

Tell students that they will be solving another peas and carrots problem.

Do you remember the other day when we talked about peas and carrots and my special spoon that holds only seven vegetables? Today we are going to solve another peas and carrots problem, but we are going to use a different spoon. It's a little bit bigger. This time, my spoon holds nine vegetables.

Imagine that you take a spoonful from my pot of peas and carrots and put them on your plate. There are nine vegetables on your plate. Some of them are peas, and some of them are carrots. How many of each could you have? How many peas? How many carrots? Remember that you have nine things in all.

Remind students of the work they did on Seven Peas and Carrots earlier in the Investigation, perhaps pointing out the "7 in all" chart on which you recorded their work during the discussion in Session 4.1.

Today, your job is to find *more than one way* of making 9 peas and carrots, and record them on your paper.

You might also remind students of the many ways they recorded their work, using a variety of pictures, numbers, and words.

ACTIVITY

Solving Nine Peas and Carrots

30 MIN INDIVIDUALS

Students work individually to find more than one combination of peas and carrots that equals 9, but they should feel free to share their ideas with one another. They record their work on *Student Activity Book* page 43.

ONGOING ASSESSMENT: Observing Students at Work

Students find two-addend combinations of 9 and record their work.❶ ❷

- **How do students coordinate and keep track of all three pieces of information: the number of peas, the number of carrots, and the total number?**
- **How do students approach, model, and solve the problem?** Do they use manipulatives? Pictures? Numbers? Do they work mentally?

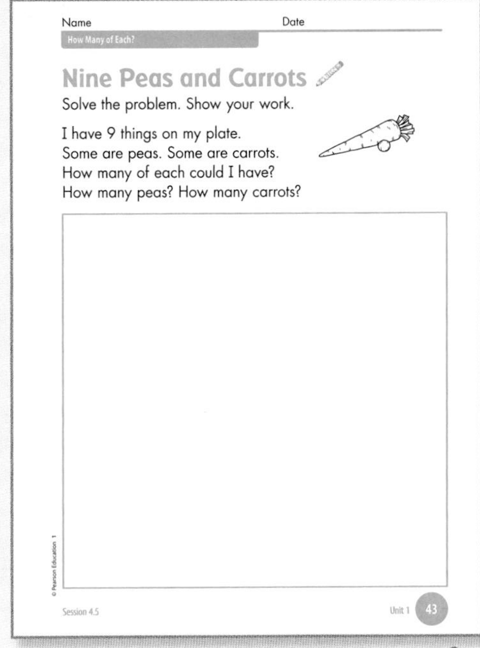
Name Date
How Many of Each?

Nine Peas and Carrots

Solve the problem. Show your work.

I have 9 things on my plate.
Some are peas. Some are carrots.
How many of each could I have?
How many peas? How many carrots?

© Pearson Education 1

Session 4.5 Unit 1 43

▲ Student Activity Book, p. 43

Professional Development

❶ **Teacher Note:** Common Issues That Typically Arise with How Many of Each?, pp. 213–214

❷ **Dialogue Box:** Observing Students at Work on Seven Peas and Carrots, pp. 239–241

Algebra Note

❸ **Number Relationships** During the course of Investigation 4, some students may begin noticing relationships among combinations of a number. For example, if 5 peas and 4 carrots is a solution, then 4 peas and 5 carrots is also a solution. Or they might notice that if 5 peas and 2 carrots is a solution, so is 6 peas and 1 carrot (turning 1 carrot into a pea). These ideas will be explored further in Solving Story Problems.

- **How do students record their work?**
- **Are students able to find more than one solution?** How does their work on nine peas and carrots compare with their work on seven peas and carrots?

As students are working, make note of students using different recording methods, including one who uses numbers and addition notation. Ask these students to share during the discussion at the end of this session.

DIFFERENTIATION: Supporting the Range of Learners

Intervention Students who struggled with seven peas and carrots might benefit from working with five or six peas and carrots.

Extension Students who quickly find a few solutions can be challenged to find more.❸

Some children use manipulatives to solve problems such as Nine Peas and Carrots.

DISCUSSION

Sharing Recording Methods

Math Focus Points for Discussion

- Representing number combinations with numbers, pictures, and/or words

Students will need their copy of *Student Activity Book* page 43 for this discussion, which focuses on different methods for recording solutions to a How Many of Each? problem.

I watched you recording your solutions to Nine Peas and Carrots in different ways. Some of you used pictures, some of you used numbers, some of you used words, and some of you used numbers *and* words or pictures *and* numbers. Who wants to share how they recorded?

Use chart paper to record samples of the different methods. As students share, they will probably want to give their solutions as well. This is fine, but keep the focus of the discussion on methods for recording. This exposure to different recording methods will give students, particularly those who are struggling to find ways to express their ideas on paper, many ideas about how they might do so in the future.

Sample Student Work

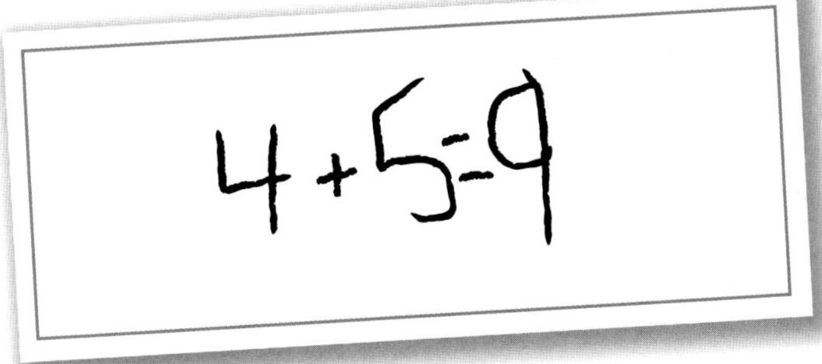

Sample Student Work

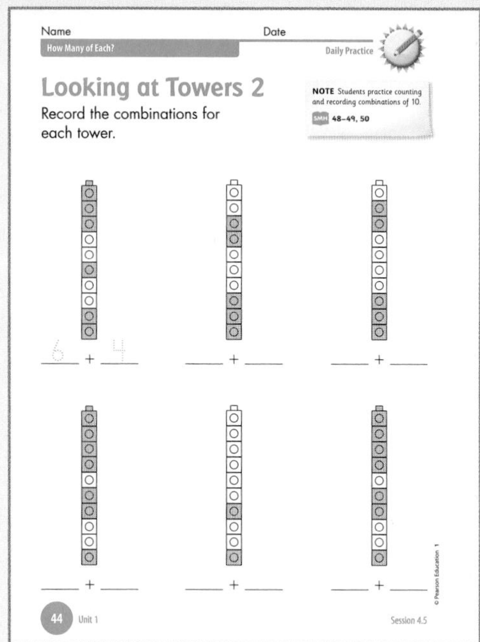
Name Date
How Many of Each?
Daily Practice

Looking at Towers 2

Record the combinations for each tower.

NOTE Students practice counting and recording combinations of 10.
SMH 48–49, 50

6 + 4

___ + ___

___ + ___

___ + ___

___ + ___

___ + ___

44 Unit 1 Session 4.5

© Pearson Education 1

▲ **Student Activity Book, p. 44**

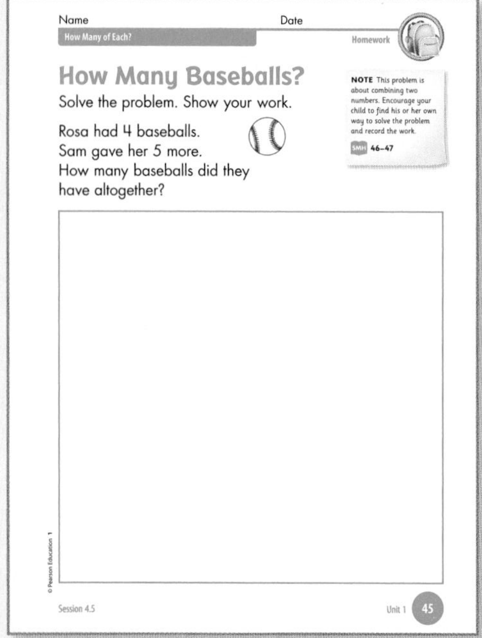
Name Date
How Many of Each?
Homework

How Many Baseballs?

Solve the problem. Show your work.

Rosa had 4 baseballs.
Sam gave her 5 more.
How many baseballs did they have altogether?

NOTE This problem is about combining two numbers. Encourage your child to find his or her own way to solve the problem and record the work.
SMH 46–47

© Pearson Education 1

Session 4.5 Unit 1 45

▲ **Student Activity Book, p. 45**

Sample Student Work

Tell students who are interested in finding more combinations of Nine Peas and Carrots that this activity will continue to be available during Math Workshop.

SESSION FOLLOW-UP

Daily Practice and Homework

Daily Practice: For reinforcement of this unit's content, have students complete *Student Activity Book* page 44.

Homework: On *Student Activity Book* page 45, students solve another addition story problem for homework. Remind them that in addition to the answer, you need to see how they figured it out. They should use numbers, but they can also use words, pictures, equations, or a combination to show their solution strategies.

Student Math Handbook: Students and families may use *Student Math Handbook* pages 46–47, 48–49 for reference and review. See pages 243–252 in the back of this unit.

SESSION 4.6

Combinations of Seven

Math Focus Points

- Finding and exploring relationships among combinations of numbers up to 10
- Solving a problem in which the total and one part are known
- Solving a problem with multiple solutions

Today's Plan		Materials
1 MATH WORKSHOP **Finding Combinations** 1A *Three Towers* 1B *Heads and Tails* 1C *How Many Am I Hiding?* 1D Nine Peas and Carrots	40 MIN	1A • Materials from Session 4.2, p. 154. Use M33* in place of *Student Activity Book* p. 35 1B • Materials from Session 4.3, p. 161. Use M35* in place of *Student Activity Book* p. 37 1C • Materials from Session 4.4, p. 167. Use M37* in place of *Student Activity Book* p. 39 1D • Materials from Session 4.5, p. 172
2 DISCUSSION **Combinations of Seven**	20 MIN CLASS	• T11 (optional) • Chart paper (optional)*; Pennies
3 SESSION FOLLOW-UP **Daily Practice**		• *Student Activity Book,* pp. 47–48 • *Student Math Handbook,* pp. 44–45, 46–47; G13, G14, G25

*See *Materials to Prepare,* p. 147.

Classroom Routines

Quick Images: Dot Cards **Show transparencies of both 6-dot cards from Dot Cards Set A (T2) and Dot Cards Set B (T7) at the same time. Follow the basic *Quick Images* activity. Ask students to determine the total number of dots. Repeat with both 5-dot cards.**

MATH WORKSHOP

Finding Combinations

40 MIN

This is the final Math Workshop in this unit. As you work with or observe students, think about how their work with composing, counting, comparing, and finding combinations of numbers has progressed. You can also use each of these activities to assess how each student's ability to write the numbers has improved over time.

The discussion at the end of today's session will focus on combinations of 7. Therefore, you might ask students to use 7 in any activity they choose today, other than Nine Peas and Carrots.

1A *Three Towers*

PAIRS

For complete details about this activity, see Session 4.2, pages 155–157. Today, have students make 3 towers of 7 (instead of 10).

1B *Heads and Tails*

PAIRS

For complete details about this activity, see Session 4.3, pages 162–164. Have students investigate the number 7 by the end of class today.

1C *How Many Am I Hiding?*

PAIRS

For complete details about this activity, see Session 4.4, pages 168–171. Suggest that students play with a total of 7 cubes today.

1D Nine Peas and Carrots

INDIVIDUALS

Some students might want to continue finding combinations of 9 peas and carrots. For complete details about this activity, see Session 4.5, pages 173–174.

2

DISCUSSION

Combinations of Seven

20 MIN CLASS

Math Focus Points for Discussion

- Finding and exploring relationships among combinations of numbers up to 10

Gather students to share the combinations of 7 they came up with when playing *Heads and Tails.* Display the transparency, or a large chart-paper display, of the *Heads and Tails* Recording Sheet (T11).

Have 7 pennies available, and ask students to bring their own copies of the recording sheet they filled in while playing *Heads and Tails* with 7 pennies.

As I was watching you play *Heads and Tails,* I noticed many different ways the pennies can land. Who would like to share one of the ways they found?

[Carol] got [6] heads and [1] tail. Did anyone else get that? Raise your hands. Did anyone get something different?

Record each combination of 7 on the class recording sheet. For two or three of the combinations, ask a student to model the number pair with the pennies. That way, you help students develop visual images of combinations of 7.①

As the list of number pairs you are recording grows, remind students that you are looking for ways that you have not already recorded. Even if you (or some students) notice that all possible ways the 7 pennies could land have been recorded, ask once more for other ways to add to the list. That way, you encourage students to look carefully at their own lists.

When no one can suggest any other ways that the pennies landed, ask students if they think they could find a way that is not recorded on the class list.

3 SESSION FOLLOW-UP

Daily Practice

Daily Practice: For reinforcement of this unit's content, have students complete *Student Activity Book* pages 47–48.

Student Math Handbook: Students and families may use *Student Math Handbook* pages 44–45, 46–47 and G13, G14, G25 for reference and review. See pages 243–252 in the back of this unit.

Professional Development

① **Dialogue Box:** Sharing Combinations of Seven, p. 242

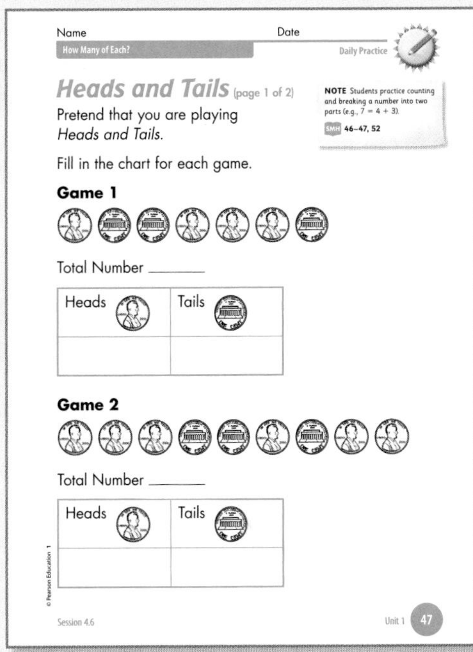

Name ______ Date ______

How Many of Each? — Daily Practice

Heads and Tails (page 1 of 2)

NOTE Students practice counting and breaking a number into two parts (e.g., 7 = 4 + 3).

SMH 46–47, 52

Pretend that you are playing *Heads and Tails.*

Fill in the chart for each game.

Game 1

Total Number ______

Heads	Tails

Game 2

Total Number ______

Heads	Tails

© Pearson Education 1

Session 4.6 — Unit 1 — 47

▲ Student Activity Book, p. 47

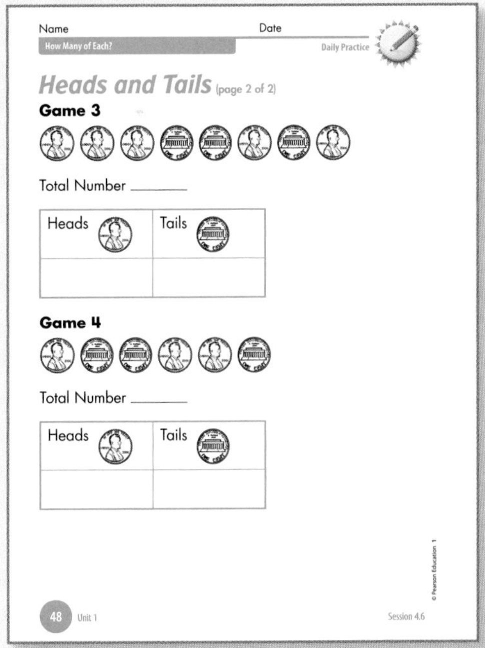

Name ______ Date ______

How Many of Each? — Daily Practice

Heads and Tails (page 2 of 2)

Game 3

Total Number ______

Heads	Tails

Game 4

Total Number ______

Heads	Tails

© Pearson Education 1

48 — Unit 1 — Session 4.6

▲ Student Activity Book, p. 48

End-of-Unit Assessment

Math Focus Points

- Finding the total of two or more quantities up to a total of 20 by counting all, counting on, or using number combinations
- Finding and exploring relationships among combinations of numbers up to 10
- Recording a solution to a problem

Today's Plan	Materials
1 ASSESSMENT ACTIVITY **End-of-Unit Assessment** 60 MIN INDIVIDUALS	• M39*; M40* • Counters
2 SESSION FOLLOW-UP **Daily Practice**	• *Student Activity Book,* p. 49 • *Student Math Handbook,* pp. 33–37, 46–47

*See *Materials to Prepare,* p. 147.

Classroom Routines

Morning Meeting: Discussing the Monthly Data **Follow your daily *Morning Meeting* Routine. During *Weather,* discuss the data that has been collected so far this month. For examples of what to focus on during this discussion, See Part 4: Classroom Routines in *Implementing Investigations in Grade 1:* Morning Meetings.**

ASSESSMENT ACTIVITY

End-of-Unit Assessment

This end-of-unit assessment focuses on three of the unit's benchmarks.

In Problem 1, students solve an addition story problem. This problem addresses Benchmark 1: Count a set of up to 20 objects and Benchmark 4: Interpret (retell the action and sequence) and solve addition story problems. In Problem 2, students find more than one combination to make 8. This problem addresses Benchmark 5: Find more than one combination of two addends for a number up to 10 (e.g., 7 is 4 and 3 and it is also 5 and 2).

Take a few minutes to explain that the class has come to the end of the first math unit of the year. Students will be exploring some new mathematical ideas tomorrow and over the next few weeks, as they begin the first geometry unit of the year.

Explain that during today's math class, students will be solving two problems. Explain to them that, because you would like to get a sense of how much students have learned and grown in their math thinking so far this year, they will work individually.

Distribute copies of End-of-Unit Assessment (M39) and begin by reading the addition story problem aloud to students.

Problem 1

Rosa made 7 cookies. Max made 8 more cookies. How many cookies did they make in all?

Have students solve the problem, record their work, and stop at Problem 2.

After students have completed Problem 1, read the second problem to them, either in small groups or individually.

Problem 2

I have 8 fruits. Some are bananas. Some are apples.

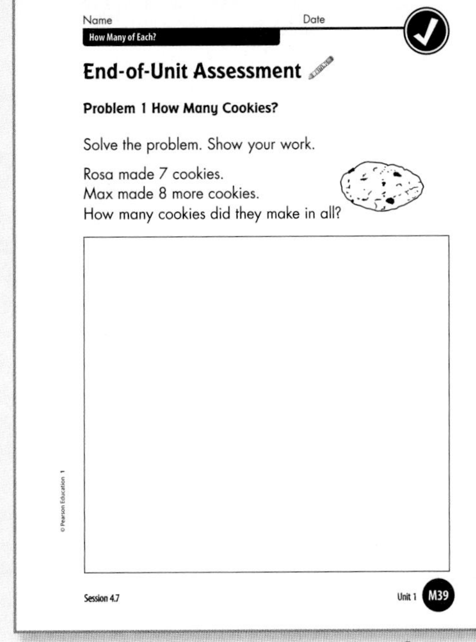
Name Date

How Many of Each?

End-of-Unit Assessment

Problem 1 How Many Cookies?

Solve the problem. Show your work.

Rosa made 7 cookies.
Max made 8 more cookies.
How many cookies did they make in all?

© Pearson Education 1

Session 4.7 Unit 1 M39

▲ Resource Masters, M39

Professional Development

❶ **Teacher Note:** End-of-Unit Assessment, pp. 216–223

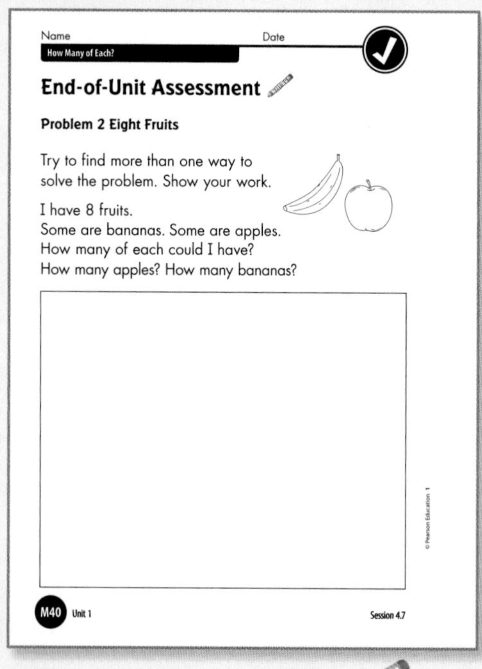
Name Date
How Many of Each?

End-of-Unit Assessment

Problem 2 Eight Fruits

Try to find more than one way to solve the problem. Show your work.

I have 8 fruits.
Some are bananas. Some are apples.
How many of each could I have?
How many apples? How many bananas?

M40 Unit 1 Session 4.7

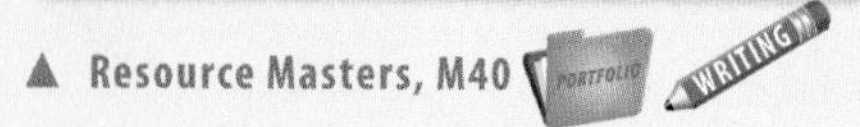

▲ Resource Masters, M40

How many of each could I have? How many apples? How many bananas?

Explain that students should try to find more than one way to solve this How Many of Each? problem.

ONGOING ASSESSMENT: Observing Students at Work

At Grade 1, it is difficult to assess students solely from their written work because there is often a gap between their thinking and what they are able to put down on paper. Therefore, make a point to observe students as they work on these problems and jot down notes about how students approach the task. A combination of your observations and students' written work can give you a much fuller sense of students' strategies.❶

As you circulate, ask clarifying questions that will later help you remember how the student was thinking. Many teachers jot down a student's verbal explanation right on the student's sheet for later reference. In particular, look for explanations that don't tell you enough about what the student did (e.g., *"I counted"*). Ask questions such as How did you count? and then write the student's response.

If you notice any mistakes, you may want to ask students to describe their strategy on the spot and note whether articulating their process aloud draws their attention to the error.

Consider the following as you evaluate students' work:

Problem 1

- **Do students get the right answer?** Can you tell what the answer is from their written work?
- **Do students count all to solve the problem?** Count on? Use a number combination they know?
- **How do students record their work?** Do they use pictures? Words? Numbers? Standard notation such as + or =? Equations? A combination of these?

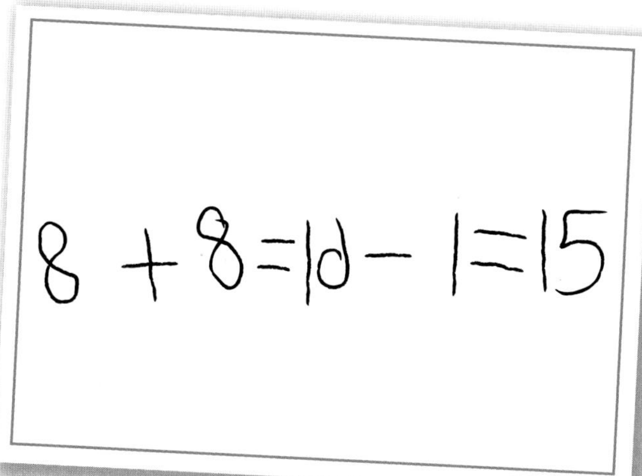

Sample Student Work

Sample Student Work

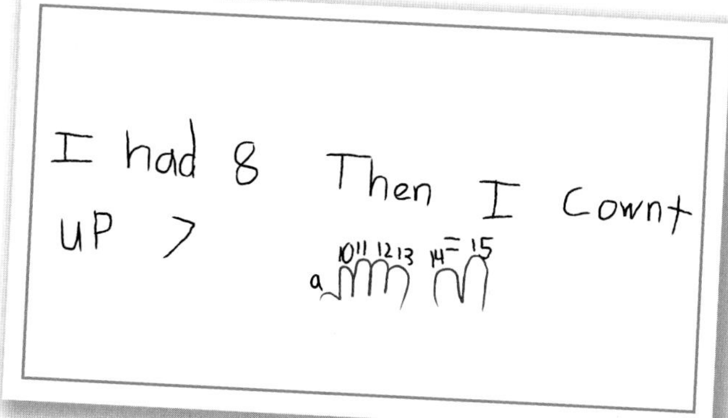

Sample Student Work

Sample Student Work

I think it is 15
Because I canteD
with the SnapCubS.
15

Sample Student Work

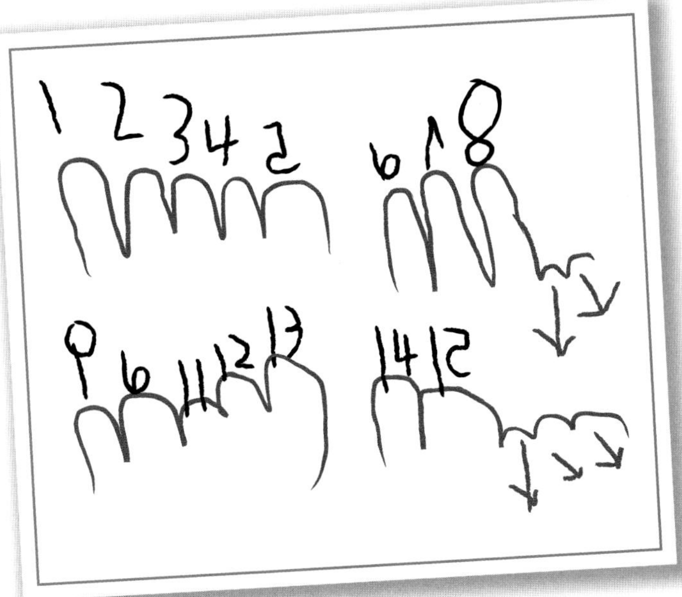

Sample Student Work

Problem 2

- **How many different combinations of 8 do students find?** Do they list repeats? Any combinations that do not equal 8? Do they specify which are bananas and which are apples?
- **How do they record their work?** Do they use pictures? Words? Numbers? Standard notation such as + or =? Equations? A combination of these?

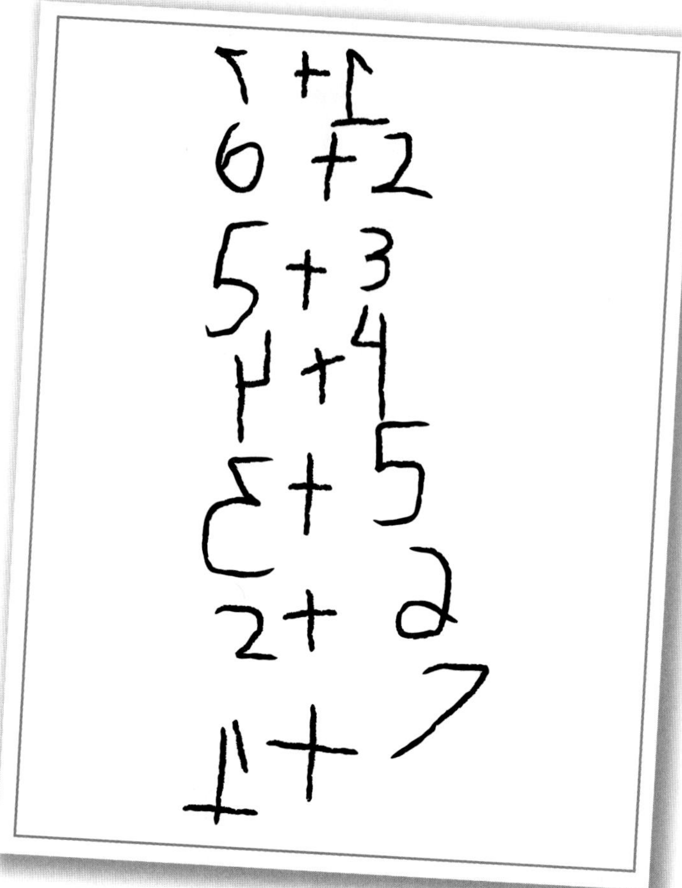

Sample Student Work

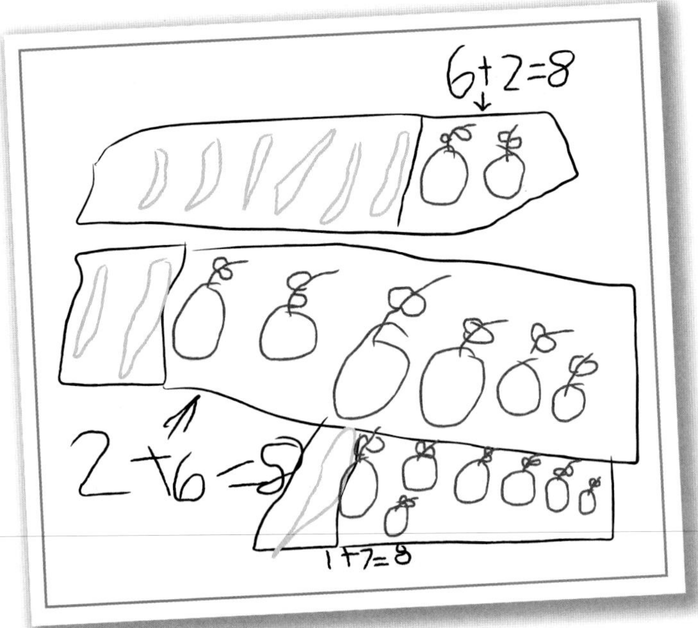

Sample Student Work

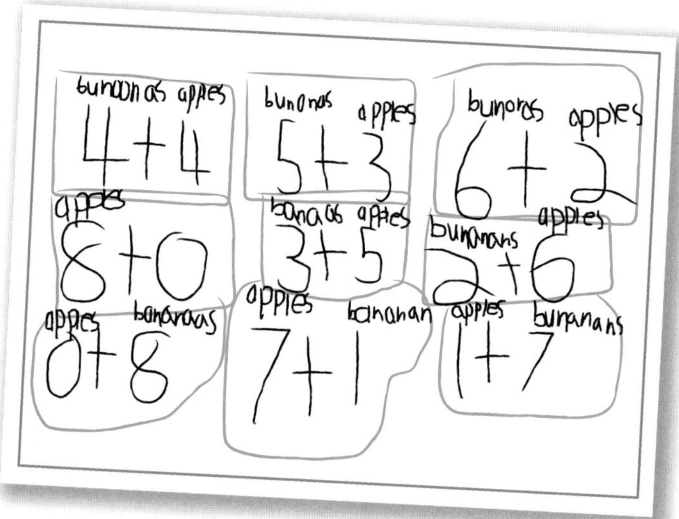

Sample Student Work

2 SESSION FOLLOW-UP
Daily Practice

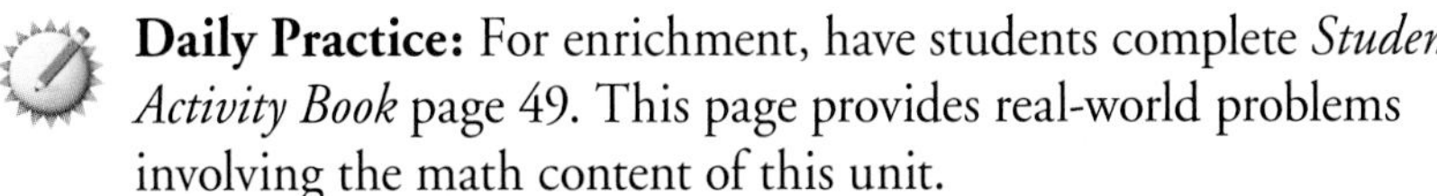

Daily Practice: For enrichment, have students complete *Student Activity Book* page 49. This page provides real-world problems involving the math content of this unit.

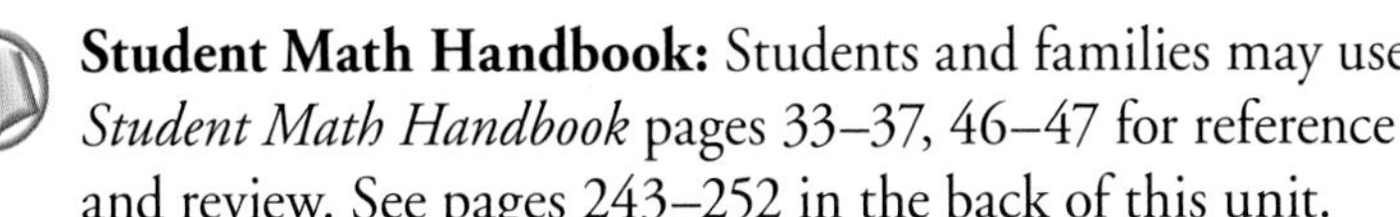

Student Math Handbook: Students and families may use *Student Math Handbook* pages 33–37, 46–47 for reference and review. See pages 243–252 in the back of this unit.

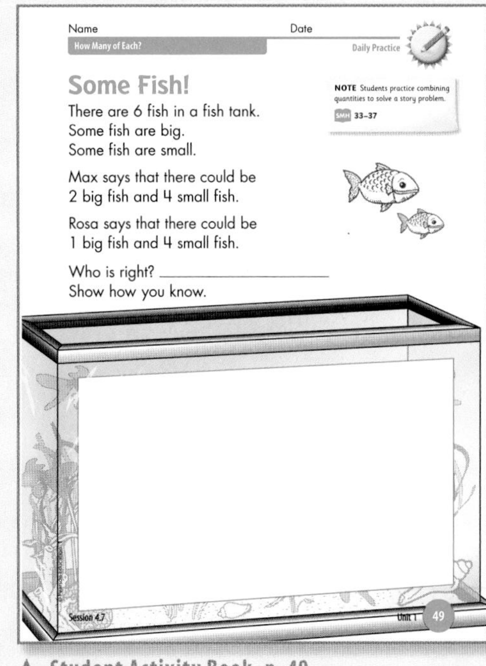

Name Date

How Many of Each? Daily Practice

Some Fish!

NOTE Students practice combining quantities to solve a story problem.

SMH 33–37

There are 6 fish in a fish tank.
Some fish are big.
Some fish are small.

Max says that there could be 2 big fish and 4 small fish.

Rosa says that there could be 1 big fish and 4 small fish.

Who is right? ____________

Show how you know.

Session 4.7 Unit 1 49

▲ Student Activity Book, p. 49

Professional Development

UNIT 1

How Many of Each?

Teacher Notes

In Part 6 of *Implementing Investigations in Grade 1,* you will find a set of Teacher Notes that addresses topics and issues applicable to the curriculum as a whole rather than to specific curriculum units. They include the following:

Computational Fluency and Place Value

Computational Algorithms and Methods

Representations and Contexts for Mathematical Work

Foundations of Algebra in the Elementary Grades

Discussing Mathematical Ideas

Racial and Linguistic Diversity in the Classroom: What Does Equity Mean in Today's Math Classroom?

Dialogue Boxes

Teacher Note

Talking About Shapes

As you observe students working with cubes, pattern blocks, Geoblocks, and Power Polygons, you can learn a great deal about what they notice about shapes: what characteristics they attend to, what relationships they recognize, and what distinctions they make. For example, you might hear students say such things as, "Hand me that little square block," "I'm using diamonds all around the edge," or "Look, three of these blue ones can fit right on top of the yellow one."

At this age, students will not use many conventional mathematical terms. For example, they will probably not know that a blue pattern block is a rhombus or parallelogram, but they may instead use the everyday term diamond. They are likely to know some geometric names, such as square, circle, and rectangle, but they may sometimes apply these incorrectly. For example, they might call a cube a square or call a triangle a rectangle.

Enter into students' conversations using the same terms they are using, but also ask them questions or make comments that challenge them to be clearer and more precise. Here is an example:

Carol: I'm using diamonds all around the edge.

Teacher: Are you going to use all blue diamonds, or are you going to use some of the tan diamonds?

You can also use interactions to introduce conventional mathematical names for two- and three-dimensional shapes, so that students hear these terms used in context.

Jacob: Look, two of these red ones can fit right on top of the yellow one.

Teacher: Jacob noticed that two of these red trapezoids can fit right on top of the hexagon. Did anyone notice any other pieces that can fit together on the hexagon?

You do not need to insist that students use the conventional terms. They will begin to learn them naturally, the same way they learn other vocabulary: by hearing the terms used correctly in context. In geometry activities in later units, the students will have many experiences in classifying, describing, and defining shapes.

For your own reference, the following shapes are included in the pattern block and Geoblock sets. Before reading these descriptions, sort the shapes in each set on your own—especially the Geoblocks, which are probably less familiar. After you have sorted the blocks into groups that you think "go together," the descriptions may make more sense to you.

Pattern Blocks

There are six shapes in the pattern block set. We treat these blocks, most of the time, as if they are two-dimensional shapes, even though they do have thickness. All the shapes are *polygons*: closed shapes with straight sides.

Yellow hexagon A hexagon is a six-sided polygon. The yellow pattern block is a *regular* hexagon because all the sides and angles are equal.

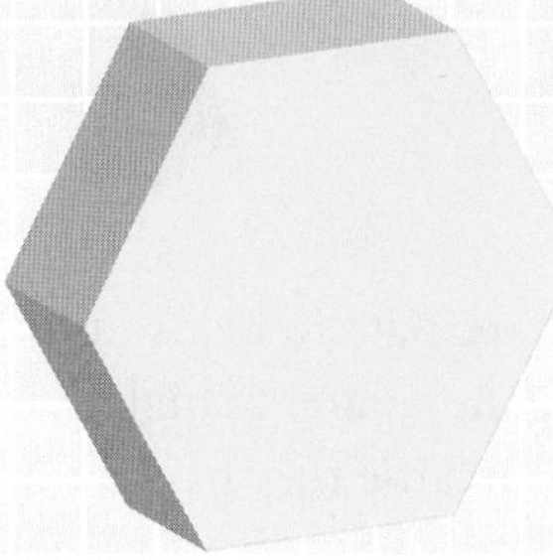

Red trapezoid A trapezoid is a four-sided polygon that has one pair of parallel sides.

Green triangle A triangle is a three-sided polygon. The green pattern block is an *equilateral* triangle because all the sides and angles are equal.

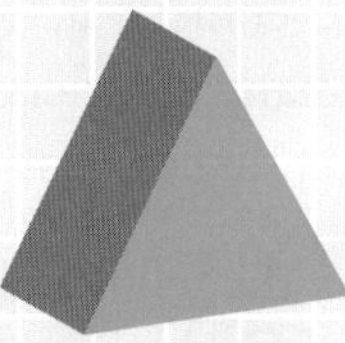

Orange square A square is a four-sided polygon with four equal sides and angles. (A square is also a rectangle.)

Blue rhombus and tan rhombus These two shapes are both parallelograms, or four-sided polygons with two pairs of parallel sides. They are each a special kind of parallelogram, called a rhombus, that has four equal sides.

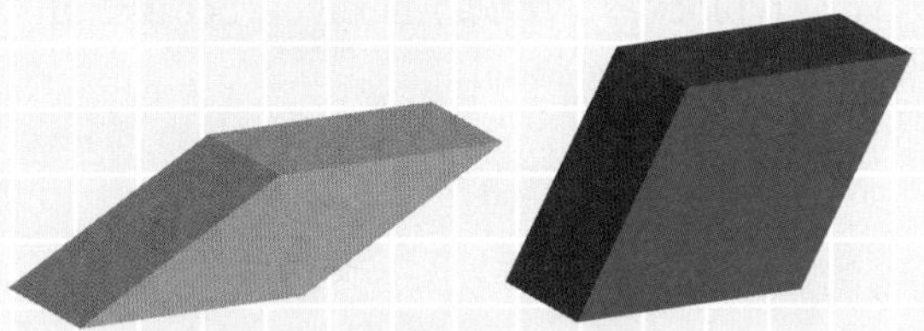

Although we name the pattern blocks as if they are two-dimensional (hexagon, square, triangle), they are technically three-dimensional, because they have a third dimension (depth). So the square is not actually a square; it is technically a rectangular solid or rectangular prism with two square faces. The convention for pattern blocks is to talk about them as if they are two-dimensional shapes, focusing on their faces. However, if any students point out their three-dimensional characteristics (for example, that the yellow hexagon also has some faces that are rectangular), certainly encourage them to talk about these ideas.

Geoblocks

There are five general kinds of shapes in the Geoblock set and 25 different blocks. All the shapes are *polyhedra:* three-dimensional solid shapes with flat faces. (See the chart on page 191 for examples.)

Rectangular prisms These prisms have two opposite faces that are the same size and shape (congruent). All other faces that connect these two opposite faces that are rectangles. In rectangular prisms, all six faces are rectangles. Most boxes are rectangular prisms. You can also call these shapes *rectangular solids.* There are 11 different rectangular prisms in the set; of these, 5 are *square prisms* and 4 are *cubes.*

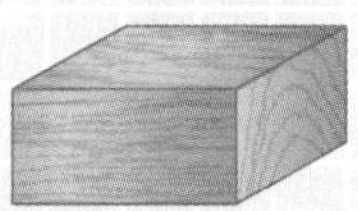

Square prisms These are a special kind of rectangular prism. They have two opposite faces that are congruent squares. The other four faces are rectangles.

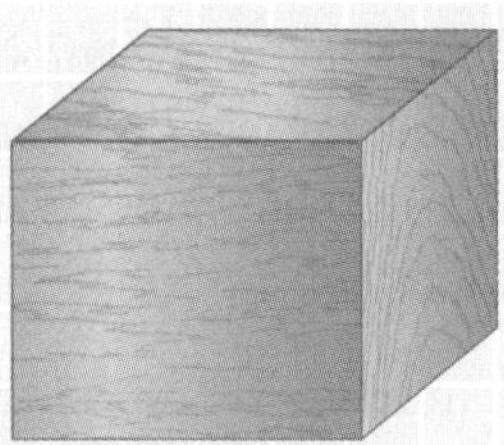

Cubes Just as the square is a special kind of rectangle, the cube is a special kind of rectangular prism in which all the faces are squares.

Triangular prisms These prisms have two opposite faces that are congruent triangles. As in any prism, the faces that connect this pair are all rectangles. There are 13 different triangular prisms.

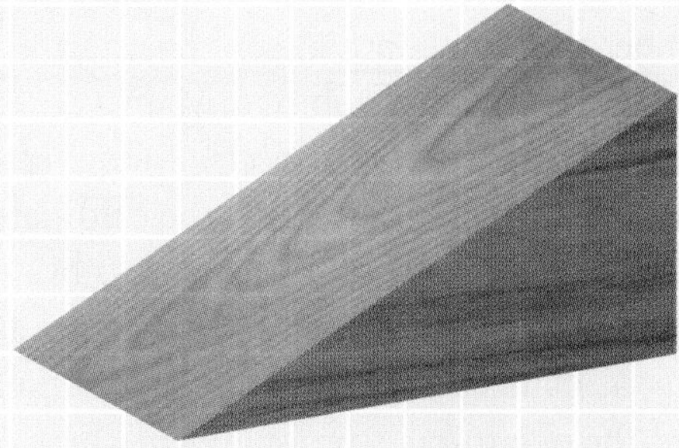

Pyramids Pyramids look different from prisms. They have one base, which can be any polygon. The rest of the faces are triangles that meet in a single point (vertex). There is just 1 pyramid in the Geoblock collection, a *square pyramid.* It has a square base and four triangular faces.

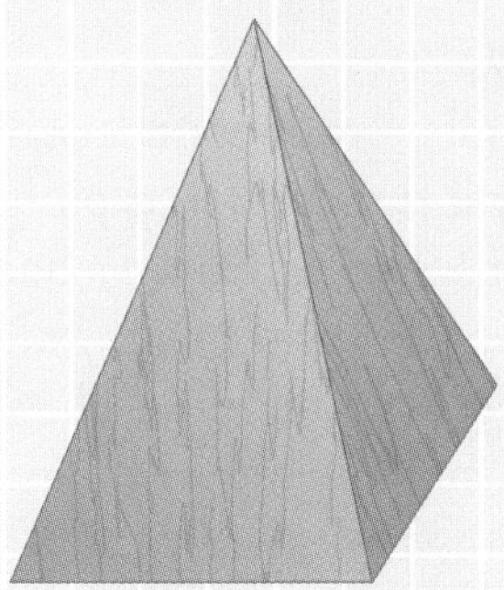

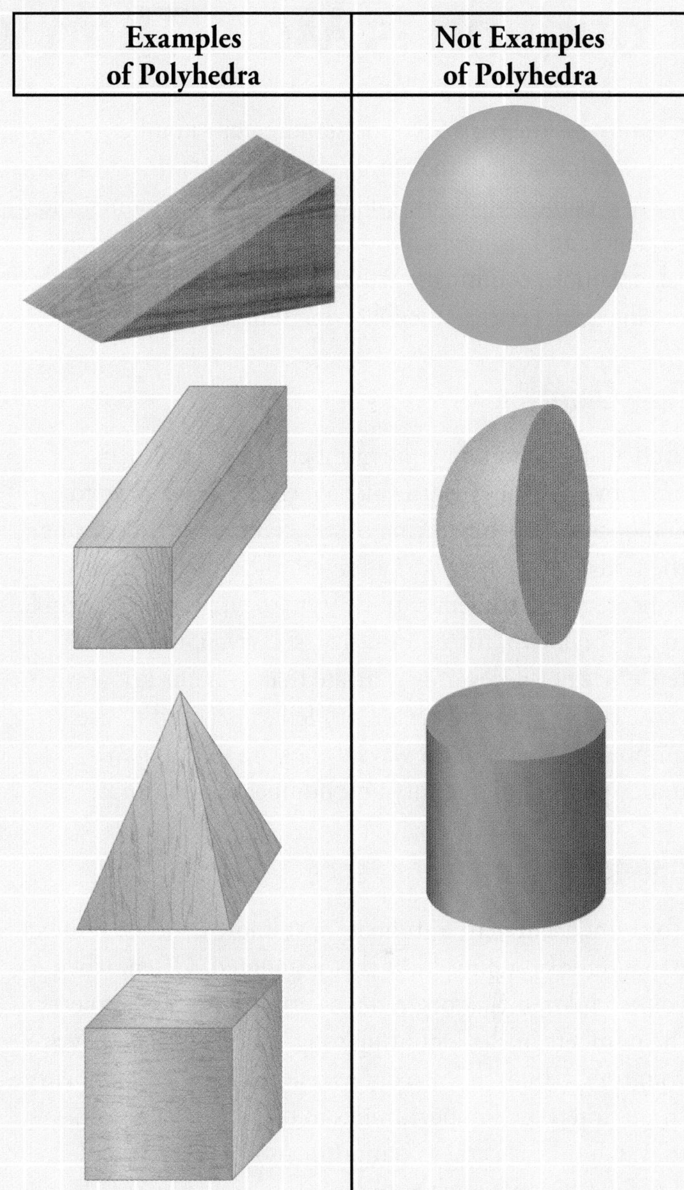

Note: Only polyhedra are included in the Geoblock set.

Teacher Note

Counting Is More Than 1, 2, 3

Counting is the basis for understanding our number system and for almost all of the number work in the primary grades. It involves more than just knowing the number names, the sequence, and the written form of each number. Although it seems simple, counting is actually quite complex and involves the interplay between the following skills and concepts:

Rote Counting

Students need to know the number names and their order by rote. They learn this sequence—both forward and backward—by hearing others count and by counting themselves. However, just as saying the alphabet does not indicate that a student can use written language, being able to say "one, two, three, four, five, six, seven, eight, nine, ten" does not necessarily indicate that students know what those counting words mean. Students also need to use numbers in meaningful ways if they are to build an understanding of quantity and number relationships.

One-to-One Correspondence

To count accurately, a student must know that one number name stands for one object that is counted. Often, when young children first begin to count, they do not connect the numbers in the "counting song" to the objects they are counting. Children learn about one-to-one correspondence through repeated opportunities to count sets of objects and to watch others as they count. One-to-one correspondence develops over time, with students first counting small groups and eventually larger groups of objects accurately.

Keeping Track

Another important part of counting accurately is being able to keep track of what has been counted and what still remains to be counted. As students first begin to count sets of objects, they often count some objects more than once and skip other objects altogether. Students develop strategies for organizing and keeping track of a count as they realize the need and as they see others use such strategies.

Connecting Numbers to Quantities

We use numbers both to count a set of objects and to describe the quantity of those objects. Many young students are still coordinating these two aspects of number—the ordinal sequence of the numbers with the cardinal meaning of those numbers. In other words, we get to 5 by counting in order—1, 2, 3, 4, 5. In this sequence, 4 comes after 3 and 5 comes after 4. Understanding this aspect of numbers is connected to the one-to-one correspondence between the numbers we say and the objects we are counting. However, being able to use this ordinal sequence to count accurately is not the same as knowing that when we have finished counting, the final number in our sequence tells the quantity of the things we have counted.

Conservation

Conservation of number involves understanding that 3 is always 3, whether it is three objects pushed or linked together, three objects spread apart in a line, or some other formation. As students learn to count, you will see many who do not yet understand this idea. They think that the larger the arrangement of objects, the more objects there are. Being able to conserve quantity is not a skill that can be taught; it is a cognitive process that develops as children grow and develop.

Counting by Groups

Counting a set of objects by equal groups, such as 2s, requires that each of the steps mentioned above happens again, at a wholly different level. First, students need to know the 2s sequence (2, 4, 6, 8 . . .) by rote. They need to realize that one number in this count represents two objects, and that each time they say a number, they are adding another group of 2 to their count. Keeping track while counting by groups becomes a more complex task as well. Students begin to explore counting by groups later in Grade 1 (Unit 8, *Twos, Fives, and Tens*) and continue to deepen their understanding in Grades 2 and 3.

Teacher Note

Observing Students as They Count

Your students will be counting many things during this unit and throughout the year. Counting involves more than knowing the number names, their sequence, and the way to write them. It is the basis for understanding our number system and for almost all of the number work primary-grade students do.

In Grade 1, expect a great deal of diversity among your students. By the end of the year, many students will have learned the oral counting sequence up to 100, and will begin to recognize patterns in the sequence of numbers from 1 to 100. However, many first graders will not end the year with a grasp of quantities greater than 40 or 50 or so. Students develop their understanding of quantity through repeated experiences with organizing and counting sets of objects. In Grade 1, many of the activities that focus on quantity can be adjusted so that students can work at a level of challenge that is appropriate for them. Early in Grade 1, some students will need repeated experiences with quantities up to 10, and others will be able to work with larger collections. Some students may be inconsistent—being successful one time and having difficulty the next.

Your students will have many opportunities to count and use numbers in this unit and throughout the year. You can learn a great deal about what your students understand about counting by observing them as they work. Listen to students as they talk with one another. Observe them as they count objects and as they count orally and in writing. Ask them about their thinking as they work. You may observe some of the following:

- **Counting orally** Generally, students can count orally further than they can count objects or correctly write numbers. For some students, the oral counting sequence is just a song; they do not necessarily know that when they count one more, they are referring to a quantity that has one more. Students need many experiences counting and adding small quantities as they learn about the relationship between the counting words and the quantities they represent. Counting backward is not as familiar to students as the forward counting sequence. They frequently know "10, 9, 8 . . . 3, 2, 1, Blast off!" but will need plenty of practice counting back from other numbers.

- **Counting quantities** Some students may correctly count quantities above 20; others may not consistently count quantities smaller than 10. Some students may count the number of objects correctly when they are spread out in a line, but may have difficulty with organizing objects for counting. They may need to develop techniques for keeping track of what they are counting.

- **Counting by writing numbers** Many beginning first-grade students are just gaining some competency in writing numbers. Young students frequently reverse numbers or digits. Often this is not a mathematical problem but simply a matter of experience. Throughout the year, students need many opportunities to see and practice the sequence of written numbers.

Teacher Note

Assessment: Counting 20

Problem: Counting 20

Benchmark addressed:

Benchmark 1: Count a set of up to 20 objects

In order to meet the benchmark, students' work should show that they can:

- Show 20 circles.

Some students draw 20 circles as they count them, with no particular system for keeping track. Others organize their circles into rows or groups. Some use no labels, and others label each circle, each group, and/or the total number of circles.

Name Date

How Many of Each?

Assessment: Counting 20

Draw 20 circles.
Show how you know that there are 20.

▲ Resource Masters, M23

Meeting the Benchmark

The following examples of student work provide a range of typical responses. All of these students met the benchmark—they drew exactly 20 circles. Note that students who label their work, or organize their circles in some way, are working more efficiently.

Just circles Some students draw exactly 20 circles. When asked how they know they have 20, they recount but do not add any numbers to their drawing. Some of these students, like Jacob, show little evidence of organization; they scatter circles across the page, counting aloud as they draw.

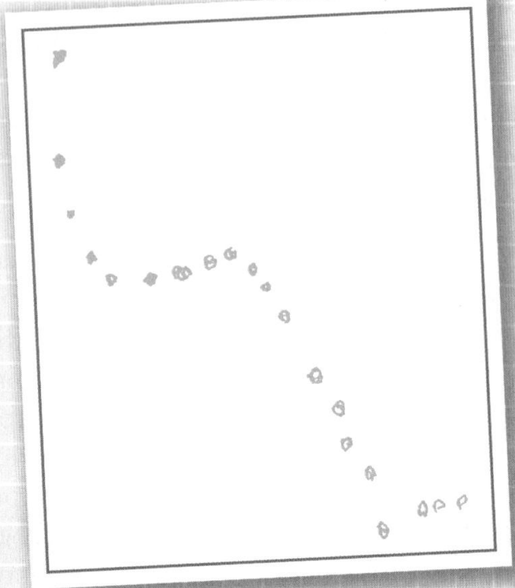

Jacob's Work

Others organize their work in some way, drawing their circles in rows or in groups of 2, 4, 5, or 10. Because there are no labels, it can be unclear how purposeful the use of such groups is. For example, when asked how they knew they had 20, Allie counted each circle by 1s while Deshawn said, "I know 5 and 5 is 10, and 10 and 10 is 20."

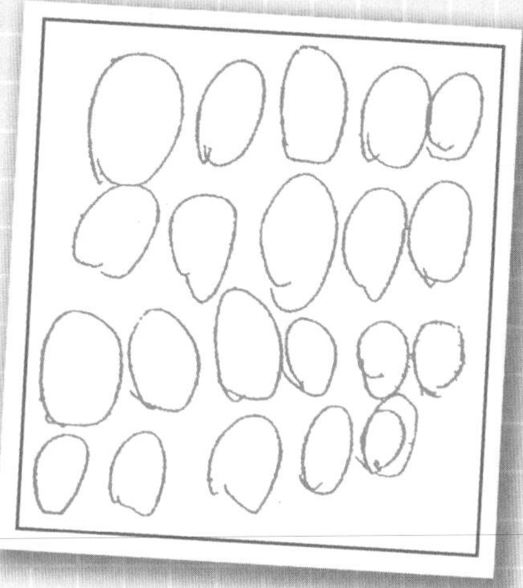

Allie's Work

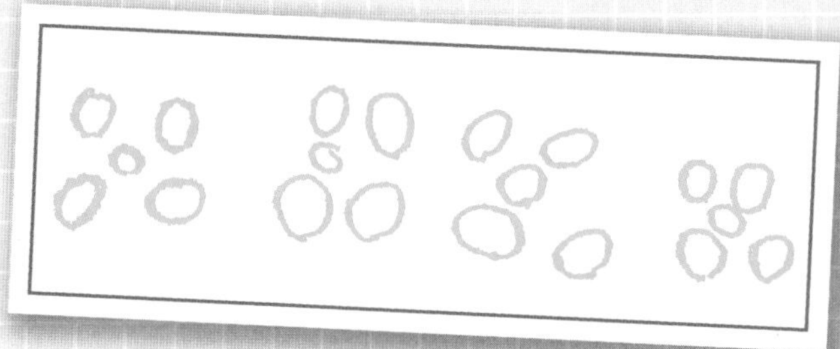

Deshawn's Work

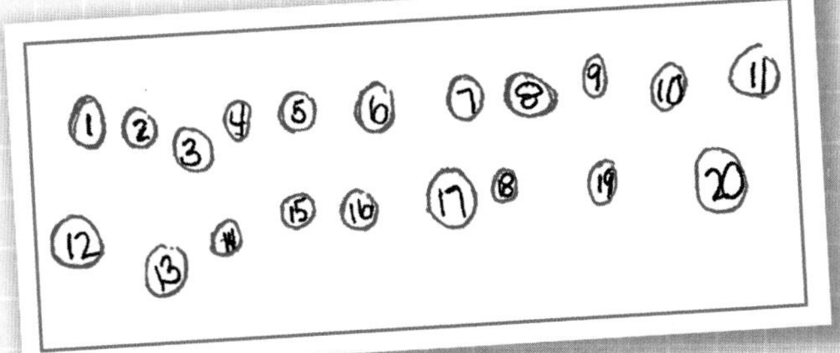

Edgar's Work

Circles and numbers Some students draw exactly 20 circles and also label their work to show that there are 20. As above, students' work ranges from unorganized (Sacha) to somewhat organized (Edgar), to quite organized. Some students use number combinations they know, as did Teo, who said, "I did 10 plus 10 and then I put numbers over them." Others count by groups (Keena).

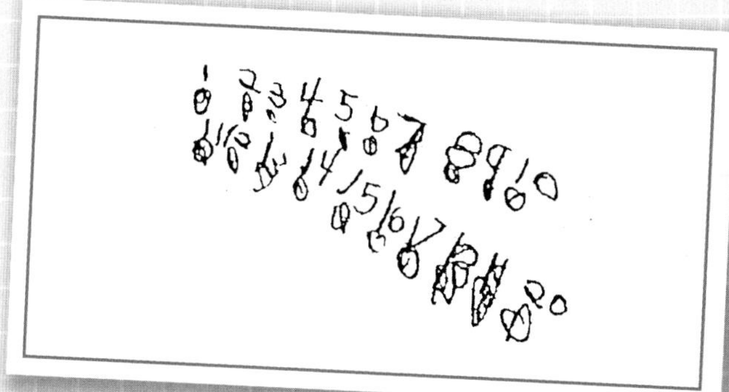

Teo's Work

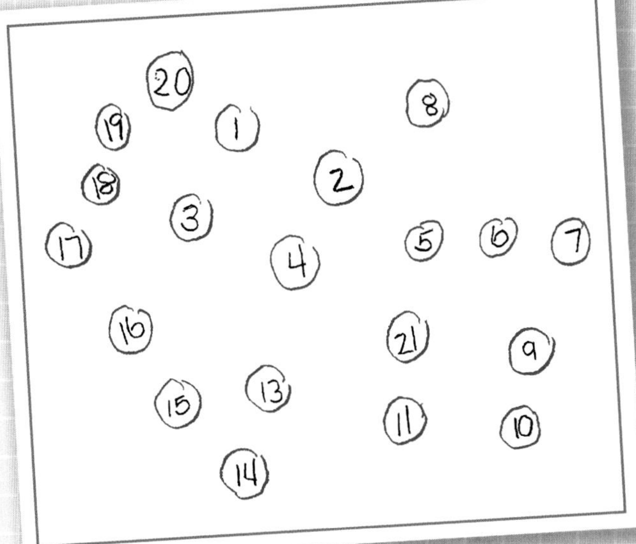

Sacha's Work

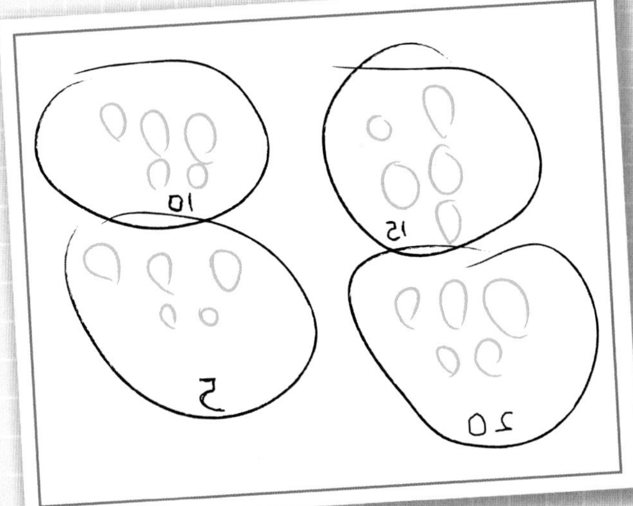

Keena's Work

Connecting numbers and quantities Like Diego and Isabel, some students draw 20 circles and write the numbers 1–20, but do not connect these in any way.

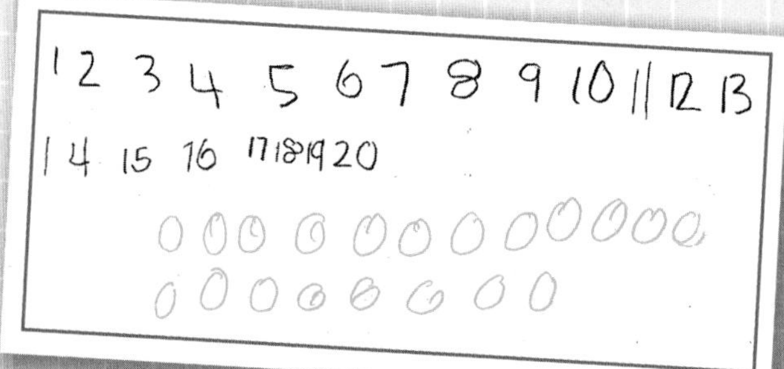

Diego's Work

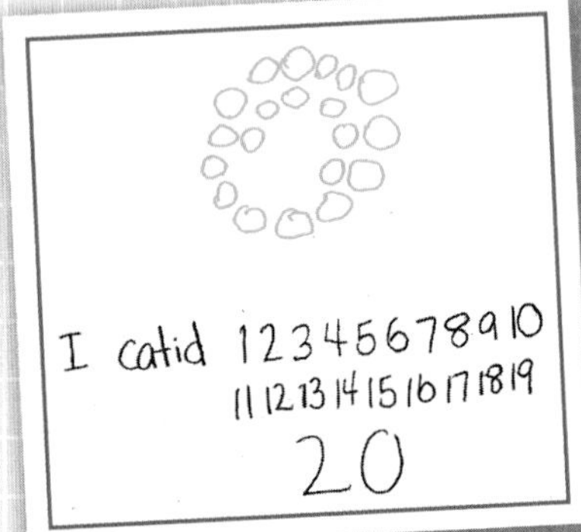

Isabel's Work

In contrast, Stacy drew 20 circles, labels each with a counting number, and then represents the quantity in the circle (as long as there is room to do so).

Stacy's Work

Partially Meeting the Benchmark

Some students, like Lyle, understand the structure of the problem—that it is about drawing exactly 20 circles—but make mistakes as they count or recount. For many, this is a keeping-track issue, and their work will show about 20 circles (e.g., 18, 21, and so on).

Lyle's Work

Other students make similar types of errors as they attempt to label their circles. Some students omit a counting number (Vic), and others have difficulty writing one number for each circle (Paula).

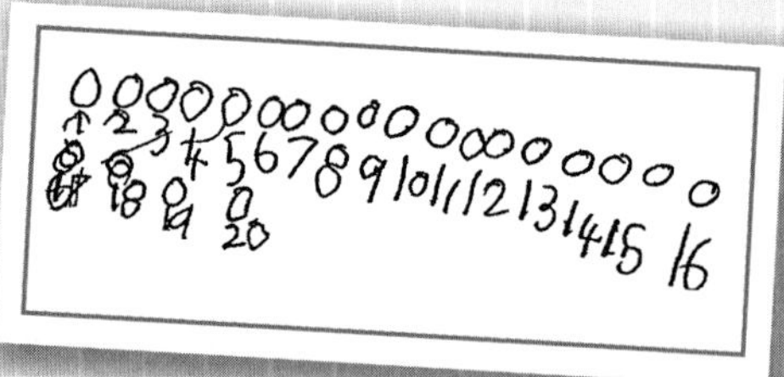

Paula's Work

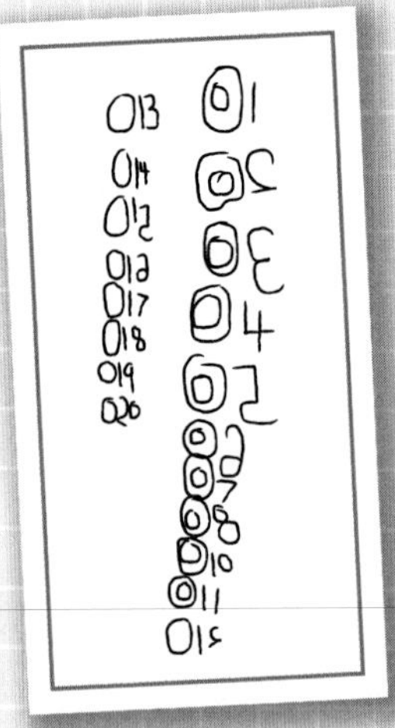

Vic's Work

After you review their assessment, ask these students to double-check their work (e.g., "Can you show me how you know you have 20 circles?"). See whether they can find and correct such errors on their own. Encourage these students to take time and work carefully to avoid such errors in the future. In addition, note whether these kinds of errors are consistent across problems or more of a one-time occurrence.

Not Meeting the Benchmark

Some students cannot accurately count objects that are static, or unmovable, on a page. Ask these students to count 20 objects, such as cubes or buttons. If they are successful, ask them to record their work on paper. For example, Paul was struggling to draw 20 but could count out 20 buttons and then draw them.

Paul's Work

Other students cannot answer the problem correctly because they may not yet understand the different aspects of counting. For example, Bruce understood that the problem was about drawing circles. However, he could not count his circles as he drew them. Instead he would periodically count his circles, sometimes missing a number or two in the sequence, and other times skipping circles as he counted haphazardly around his drawing. Bruce, and students like him, need many opportunities to practice counting sets of objects.

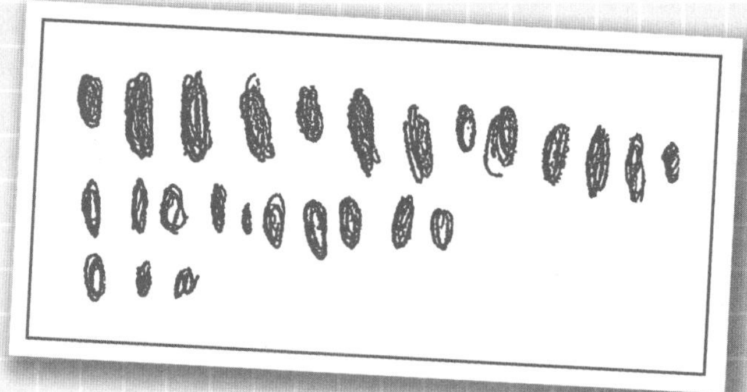

Bruce's Work

Teacher Note

Introducing Notation, Part 1

Some students enter first grade with many ideas about standard notation. Consider this vignette from a first grade teacher:

In the beginning of first grade, when students are expected to record their work, I always encourage them to use numbers, pictures, counters, their fingers, and so on, to record. What is interesting to me is their immediate desire and need to write equations and number sentences. So many of them think this is how you write in math. Regardless of how many representations students come up with and share, there are almost always several students who try to use equations. The symbols are often meaningless to most of them.

Lyle always records his addition equations like this: $3 = 3 \times 6$ *or* $4 = 2 \times 6$*. When I asked him to tell me about the sentence he pointed to each number and symbol from left to right and said:*

Lyle: 3 plus 3 is 6. See, I wrote it here.

Teacher: Show me the plus please.

Lyle: This right here [pointing to the x]. Haven't you seen one before?

Libby always records her equations like this: 3 + 3 ll 6 or 33 ll 6.

Teacher: Libby, tell me about this.

Libby: 3 and 3 and 6.

Teacher: 3 and 3 and 6? What's this? [I pointed to the parallel lines.]

Libby: I don't know.

Jacob is totally freed from the need for symbols and records all of his number information like this: 7 3 10 or 6 2 8 or 4 4 8.

Teacher: Tell me about this.

Jacob: Oh, well that's 7 plus 3 equals 10.

I'm always left wondering, where do children get these ideas about mathematical notation? (In my case, I had these children in kindergarten, so I know it didn't come from the K program!) How do I help them develop an understanding of what these symbols mean and how they are used? And how do I help them see that other methods of recording—drawing pictures, making tables, using words—are also good ways to share one's mathematical thinking?

Clearly, introducing standard notation to young children is not as simple as showing them the way to write an equation. The equation format may seem very straightforward to us as adults, but it actually assumes some complex ideas about number relationships. In first grade, many students are grappling with problem situations and deciding what actions are required to solve them. They are moving from counting by 1s in all situations to sometimes thinking of numbers in larger chunks. They are just becoming familiar with some number combinations. The emphasis for students must remain firmly on making sense of the problem situation and finding a way to solve it and record their work.

For the above reasons, many activities in Grade 1 introduce equations naturally, as one way to record student strategies. For example, suppose that one of your students describes this approach to combining 4 and 8: "I knew that 2 and 2 is 4, so I said 8 and 2 is 10, and then I added the 2 more, and 10 and 2 is 12." This strategy can be nicely recorded with equations:

$$2 + 2 = 4$$
$$8 + 2 = 10$$
$$10 + 2 = 12$$

Often such numerical strategies are best shown with standard notation, and other strategies are modeled better in other ways. For example, if a student says, "I counted up from 8, so that was 9, 10, 11, 12," this strategy does not suggest equation format. It would be better recorded like this:

8 • • • •
9 10 11 12

Try your best to match your way of recording to what the students say. In this way, different modes of thinking about and recording the problem are valued and shared. As you model the use of such notation, students can see equations used correctly, and many will incorporate them in their own recording. However, even students who are familiar with addition notation may find it more natural to represent their strategies for solving the combining problem in other ways, particularly early in the year.

The real focus of modeling standard notation in Grade 1 is helping students develop language and form images of the actions these symbols represent. Students' understanding and use of such notation will develop over time through plenty of experience seeing, talking about, and using such symbols and language throughout first and second grade.

A Note About the Equal Sign: When you do use equations to record, be sure to model them correctly. For instance, if a child adds 8 + 2 + 2 and writes

$$8 + 2 = 10 + 2 = 12,$$

use separate equations

$$8 + 2 = 10$$
$$10 + 2 = 12$$

to model consecutive steps for the class. Of course, what a first grader means by the string of expressions is clear: she added 8 and 2 first and then added 2 to get 12. The child who writes this way simply understands the notation as a sequence of events, rather than as an equation. (8 + 2 is *not* equivalent to 10 + 2.) Likewise, some first graders will not recognize that "order matters" when using subtraction notation. They might record 2 − 9 to show that they took 2 away from 9. Encourage students to think about whether 2 − 9 means the same thing as 9 − 2.

Teacher Note

Adapting Story Problems

The story problems in Unit 1 focused exclusively on finding the total of two numbers. Story problems in this unit and in later units present additional problem types, such as subtraction, and problems in which students are finding a missing part. Many teachers like to adapt the story problems that are provided. This allows them to use story contexts that reflect the interests, knowledge, and environment of their own students or to use students' names. We expect and encourage this; however, it is important to think carefully when changing a problem in order to avoid altering its underlying structure.

Related Problems

Periodically, students are given two related story problems to solve. That is, the numbers in the problems are related in such a way that some students might use their solution to the first problem to help them solve the second. For example, the relationship between the story problems in Session 3.3 of Unit 1 involves the idea that if 1 is added to one addend, the total increases by 1.

Leah and Diego were working together at the art table. Diego had 3 crayons, and Leah had 3 crayons. (How many crayons did they have altogether?)

Leah and Diego are still working together at the art table. Diego still has 3 crayons. But now Leah has 4 crayons. (How many crayons do they have altogether?)

Some students will explain that because 4 is one more than 3, the answer to the second problem is one more than the answer to the first. In later units, students are given related story problems that involve different relationships. For example, the two problems might be $3 + 5$ and $5 + 3$, or $6 + 3$ and $7 + 2$. If you adapt related story problems by changing the context or changing the numbers, make sure that you preserve the numerical relationship between the problems that the students are to explore.

Adjusting Numbers in the Problem

You will probably have some students who are comfortable working with numbers in the teens and higher, and other students who need to work with smaller numbers. A good rule of thumb is first to ask students to solve the problem provided. After you see how students solve it, you will be better able to provide an appropriate next problem. When adapting the size of numbers, be sure to consider what strategy, or piece of mathematics, the numbers provided are pushing students toward.

Isabel has 5 pennies. She earned 6 cents. How many pennies does she have now?

If a student quickly solves the following problem by using $5 + 5$ (and then adding 1) and clearly shows the work, it would be interesting to see if the student uses doubles facts to solve a related problem.

Isabel has 10 pennies. She earned 11 cents. How many pennies does she have now?

Understanding addition (and, later, subtraction) at this level involves making sense of story problems, having strategies for solving them, and being able to communicate strategies orally and in writing. Although you may want to challenge students by giving them larger numbers, you can also challenge them by asking them to find answers in more than one way and to find clearer ways to explain their work.

Teacher Note

Double Compare: Strategies for Combining and Comparing

Through the game of *Double Compare,* students develop their strategies for combining two numbers and for reasoning about quantity. The following scenes from a classroom illustrate situations that commonly arise and show how to adjust the game for students at different levels.

Counting Objects

As Bruce turns up 3 and 0 and Sacha turns up two 8 cards, Bruce begins by reminding himself, "Count those little things [the pictures on the cards]." Then, as Sacha watches, he counts each picture on the 3 card, touching them as he says the numbers. He announces that he has 3.

Sacha places her cards side by side, overlapping the edges. She counts slowly, touching all the pictures as she says the numbers, but she skips a few pictures, counts a few twice, and comes up with a total of 13. Bruce says that he thinks 8 and 8 is 18. Although they are aware that at least one of these totals is inaccurate, they realize that regardless, Sacha's total is greater than Bruce's total of 3, and they are ready to move on.

At this point the teacher steps in and asks them to recount Sacha's total, slowly. After a couple of trials, Sacha and Bruce both come up with a total of 16. The teacher suggests that they use connecting cubes to help them find the totals on their cards. Because cubes—unlike the pictures on the card—can be moved around, they can make it easier for students to keep track of what they have counted and what they have left to count.

Sacha and Bruce both need to count by ones to be sure of their totals, and counting totals greater than 10 is challenging for them. The teacher plans to return in a few minutes to see whether the cubes are helpful. If Sacha and Bruce are still having difficulty working with larger numbers, she will suggest that they play with only the 1–6 cards. Later in the session, she will call together students having difficulty and will work with them as they play *Double Compare.*

Sacha and Bruce benefit from using connecting cubes to find the totals on their cards.

Counting and Counting On

Vic's cards, Diego's cards

Vic and Diego get right to work finding their totals. Diego counts quietly to himself. He begins at 9, and then counts "10, 11, 12, 13, 14." With each number he says, Diego uses his right index finger to bend back one of the fingers on his left hand. When he has bent back all the fingers on his left hand, he stops counting and announces that he has 14.

Meanwhile, Vic is still counting. He begins by looking first at the 7 card and counting from 1 to 7. Then, he turns to the 4 card and begins counting "8, 9 . . ." When Diego announces his total of 14, Vic loses his place and begins counting again. He counts to 7, and then he counts the pictures on the 4 card, saying "8" as he points to the first picture, "9" as he points to the second, and so on, until he reaches 11. The boys agree that Diego has the greater total.

Like Sacha, Vic puts the two quantities together and counts them all, starting at 1. Diego can begin with one quantity and count on. In order to do this, Diego treats 9 as a unit; that is, he can think of it as 9 without breaking it down into 1s again. Then he counts on—"10, 11, 12, 13, 14"—while keeping track with his fingers of how many he needs to add (1, 2, 3, 4, 5). The teacher believes that the game is at an appropriate level of challenge for Diego and Vic. In future sessions, she will observe them to see how their strategies for counting and combining are developing. For example, she will note whether Vic continues counting from 1 each time, and whether they have begun developing strategies for determining particular combinations without counting.

"Just Knowing" Number Combinations

Nicky's cards, Isabel's cards

As Nicky and Isabel turn over their cards, Nicky immediately announces that she has 15 and then looks over at Isabel's cards. The teacher reminds Nicky to let Isabel find her own total. Meanwhile, Isabel counts almost inaudibly to herself "10, 11, 12," and then says that her total is 12. Nicky says, "Me! I won."

Teacher: How did you get your totals?

Nicky: Because I know 8 and 7 makes 15. Because it's easy.

Isabel: I counted in my mind.

Nicky's cards, Isabel's cards

On the next round, Nicky again immediately announces her total, and then waits impatiently while Isabel slowly counts on from 9.

When the teacher again asks how the girls found their solutions, Nicky is still unable to explain. She seems either to have memorized some number combinations, or to have developed strategies for finding solutions to number combinations quickly. As Nicky is eager to play at a faster pace than she can with Isabel, the teacher decides to ask her to play with Paul, who is also finding number combinations quickly. To provide further challenge, she may ask Nicky and Paul to turn over three cards on a round.

Reasoning About Number Combinations

Jacob's cards, Paula's cards

Jacob: 1 and 5 is 6. I have 6.

Paula: 8, 9. [Short pause] Me! Because you have 6 and I have more. Let's do it again.

Jacob: Me! 9 is bigger than 0. You know because it's just your eyes that tell you.

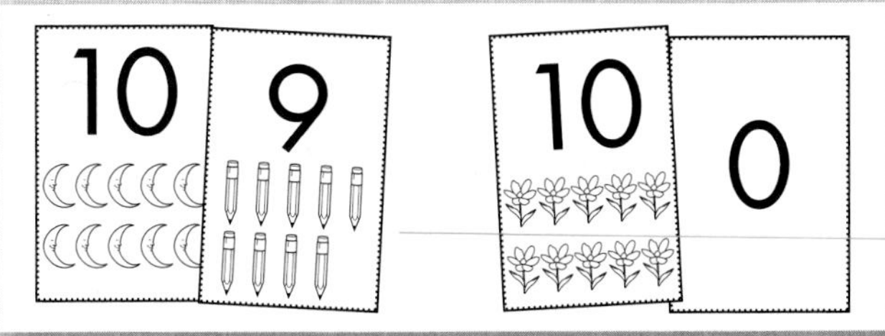

Jacob's cards, Paula's cards

Paula and Jacob are reasoning about the number pairs without necessarily needing to add them up. The teacher has observed in previous sessions that Jacob and Paula are skilled at counting, comparing, and combining numbers. However, she believes that this game is deepening their understanding of numbers and number relationships as they explore ways to reason about numbers.

Evidence of Early Algebraic Thinking?

When students are able to determine who wins without actually finding the two totals, they probably have a rule in mind—a generalization about how the numbers work. For example, when Jacob had 1 and 5, and Paula had 7 and 4, they knew that Paula's total would have to be larger because 7 is *already* larger than 1 and 5. (The rule underlying their strategy could be written using algebraic notation: If $a + b < c$ and $d > 0$, then $a + b < c + d$.) When Jacob's cards were 10 and 9, and Paula's were 10 and 0, they knew that Jacob's total was higher by comparing 9 and 0. (If $x > y$, then $z + x > z + y$.) Clearly, such notation is not appropriate for first graders. What *is* appropriate is helping them learn to verbalize their ideas as they work in small groups or have whole-class discussions.

Libby: Sometimes you can tell who gets to say "me" without counting.

Teacher: Can you explain how you can tell?

Libby: If one person has two really big numbers, and the other person has two tiny numbers, then you know.

Teacher: Felipe, how did you know so quickly that Tamika's cards showed more?

Felipe: We had one round where I got 2 and 5 and Tamika got 2 and 6, and we didn't have to count. You only have to look at 5 and 6 because the 2s don't matter.

Tamika: Yeah, we both had a 2, so we just did 5 and 6 and 6 is bigger!

Edgar and Stacy played a round. Edgar's cards were 2 and 3, and Stacy's were 5 and 5. Edgar "just knew" that 5 and 5 was bigger than 2 and 3. Although getting him to verbalize his thinking was difficult, he eventually explained it.

Edgar: I have one 5 (2 + 3). She's got two 5s. 2 is more than 1.

In this struggle to verbalize the thinking behind one's strategy lies the important algebra work of the elementary grades.

Teacher Note

Recording Strategies for a Combining Problem

Students are working on the following problem.

> How Many Pencils?
>
> I was cleaning the classroom.
>
> I found 5 pencils on the floor.
>
> I found 6 pencils under the window.
>
> How many pencils did I find?

The teacher circulates to help them describe their strategies clearly and to help them find ways to record their work. The three interactions included here illustrate common difficulties students had in approaching the task of recording and ways that the teacher helped students.

Drawing Pictures

After writing 5 + 6, Sacha is looking at her paper and seems unsure of what to do next.

Teacher: Can you tell me what you have on your paper?

Sacha: It stands for 5 plus 6. Um, you do 5 plus 6 to get the answer.

Teacher: Tell me what we're trying to find. What's the problem about?

Sacha: 5 pencils. And 6 pencils.

Teacher: And what happens to the pencils?

Sacha: You find them. Um, you want to know how many you have.

Teacher: So, how could you show that? How could you show what the problem is about?

Sacha: You could draw pencils.

Teacher: How many pencils would you draw?

Sacha: 5. And 6.

Sacha draws a group of five pencils and a group of six pencils. She thinks for a moment and then says quietly to herself, "Count the pencils." As she counts the pencils out loud, she writes a number below each one. Then she records = 11 after 5 + 6.

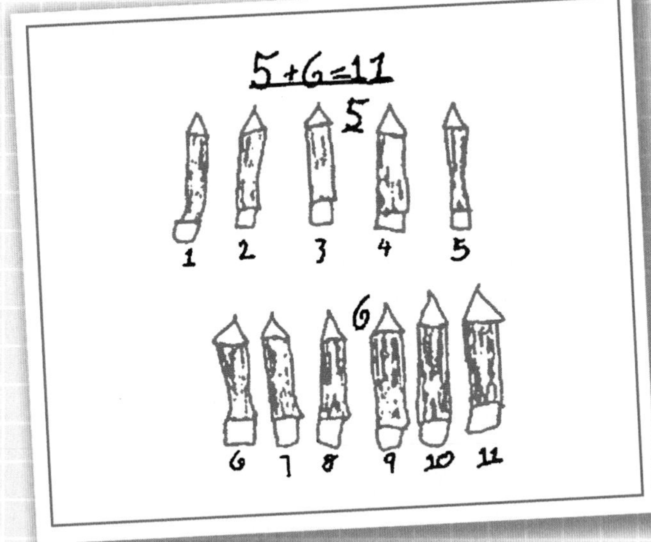

Sacha's Work

Although Sacha was able to quickly "translate" the story problem into an arithmetic expression, she did not have a way of solving the problem readily. The teacher encouraged her to find a way to model the problem and to use the model to find a solution. For Sacha, the process of recording served both to give her an image of the problem and to give her a strategy for solving it.

How to Record Counting

When the teacher visits Stacy, she has written 11 on her paper. She tells the teacher that she found her answer by counting.

Teacher: Tell me what you counted.

Stacy: I went 6 and then I, like, counted up.

Teacher: How did you know how much to count up?

Stacy: 5 numbers, because 6 and 5. Take the biggest number to start with, and then count up the rest.

Teacher: That's a great strategy. Is there a way you could put that down on paper?

[Stacy glances around at the papers of the students sitting nearby, and sees that they are drawing pictures of pencils or of cubes that they used to model the problem.]

Stacy: But how can I draw a picture of counting?

Teacher: What if you just wrote down what you told me you did to solve the problem?

Stacy: 6 and then count up 5?

Teacher: Yes, you could just write that down.

Stacy sets to work describing her strategy.

5+6
\/
11
I Start at 6
and count up 5
and I got 11

Stacy's Work

If You "Just Know" The Answer

Chris has recorded 11. He tells the teacher that the problem was easy because he knew by heart that 6 plus 5 is 11.

Teacher: So you just knew it in your mind. How could someone who doesn't know it in his or her mind figure it out?

Chris: They could just memorize it. Or know it by heart.

Teacher: Let's say they didn't know it by heart. How could you teach them?

Chris: Umm. Count on your hands?

Teacher: That's an excellent way. Tell me what you'd show them.

Chris: Count 5 [with the fingers on his left hand], then count 6 more [counts to 10 on the right hand] and land on 11 [left thumb]. Oh, I have another way, too. They could know 5 plus 5 is 10.

Teacher: How would knowing 5 plus 5 is 10 help them?

Chris: 6 is 1 more than 5, and 1 more is 11.

Teacher: Great! So you have two different ways to solve the problem. Try to write down what you did for both of them.

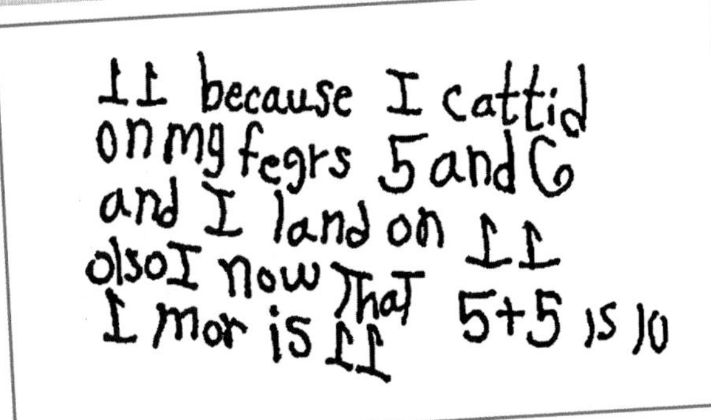

Chris's Work

Teacher Note

Discussing Story Problems

Discussions about story problems (such as the one in Session 3.3, page 116) will be more productive if you are purposeful about choosing the strategies that get shared and the ways you model those strategies as you record them for the class. While students are working on story problems, circulate to observe the strategies they are using to solve the problem and to record their work.

What Strategies Do I Want Shared?

As you observe students at work, think about which strategies are the most common, as well as the range of strategies students are using. At this point in the year, most of your students will be counting all to solve addition problems. Therefore, you will want several students who have counted all to share their strategy for solving the problem (i.e., a student who drew 11 pencils, a student who counted all with cubes, and a student who counted all on fingers). Some students, however, will be counting on, or using numerical strategies to solve this problem. Ask these students to share their strategy as well, because others may be ready to think about, try, or even adopt such a strategy.

How Should I Record Students' Strategies?

The ways you record will give students models for how they can record their own work. For example, here are the ways one teacher recorded four different approaches:

Deshawn: I counted out 5, counted out 6, and then counted them all.

Allie: I started at 5 and counted 6 more.

Vic: I counted 5 on my fingers, and then I counted 6 more on my fingers.

Paula: I knew 5 + 5 is 10, so 5 + 6 is one more.

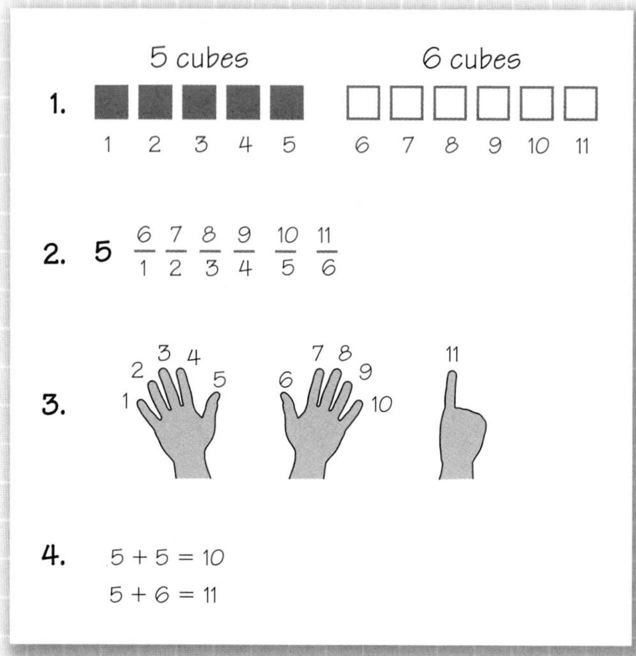

Whenever possible, base your recording on the way the student recorded. If the student drew pictures of pencils, draw pictures of pencils. If a student used tallies, use them yourself. Sometimes, a student will explain a strategy but will not know how to put it in writing. You may need to develop your own way to show what a student did. For example, Vic counted on his fingers but recorded only the numbers he counted. To record this strategy, you could show a picture of numbered fingers. (See the third example.) Use addition notation if students themselves have used it or if you find it a natural way to record a particular strategy. For example, Paula's strategy would be an appropriate place to introduce equations as one way of recording. (See the last example.)

How Do I Help Students to Listen To One Another?

Particularly early in the year, it is important to help students listen to and make sense of one another's strategies. Seeing other students' methods of recording might help them find a way to show their own work. Similarly, listening to others' solution strategies can help students find more efficient and flexible ways to solve problems. Therefore, encourage students to look at and compare the various strategies that are shared and to consider how their own is similar or different. This can also keep more students engaged during a discussion. See **Dialogue Box:** Discussing Addition Strategies, pages 232–233.

Another way to encourage students to compare and contrast strategies is by using a different number, letter, or color for each approach. These labels enable students to refer easily to the various posted strategies with statements such as, "I did it just like way 3," or "Mine is like the pink way," or "Mine is almost the same as D, but . . ." Avoid using students' names to label strategies (e.g., Toshi's way, Sacha's way) because other students are likely to have approached the problem in similar ways, and all students enjoy feeling ownership of their own approaches.

These strategies can also help with a common beginning of the year challenge—every single student wanting to share during the whole class discussion. Although you want to value each individual's hard work, having every child share his or her strategy is not a useful way to spend class time. Many children "check out" of a discussion after several students have shared, and many children will use the same strategy. You can validate all students' work by asking, at the end of a discussion, for a show of hands for each strategy posted (e.g., "Who solved it this first way? The second way?"). Reassure students that there will be many such conversations during math this year and that everyone will have many chances to share his or her work with the class. If you have students who are eager to present their methods, you might let them share with one another for a few minutes after the whole group has dispersed or in a time just before or after lunch or recess.

Assessment: *Double Compare*

Problem: *Double Compare*

Benchmarks addressed:

Benchmark 2: Compare and order quantities to 20

Benchmark 3: Combine two small quantities

Depending on how students solve it, this problem can also provide information about

Benchmark 1: Count a set of up to 20 objects

In order to meet the benchmarks, students' work should show that they can:

- Show that 4 and 9 is more than 6 and 5.

Most students add both pairs of numbers and compare the totals. Most count all to add the pairs of numbers, but some count on, and a few may use combinations they know. Others reason about the numbers, comparing individual cards rather than the totals (e.g., comparing 4 and 5 and 9 and 6).

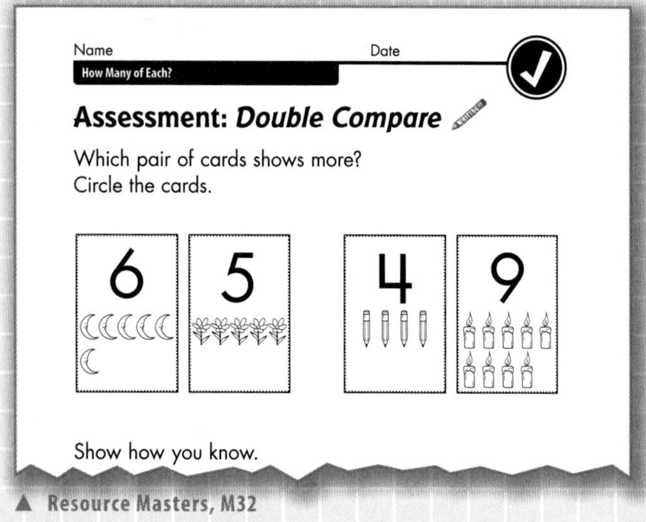

Name Date

How Many of Each?

Assessment: *Double Compare*

Which pair of cards shows more?
Circle the cards.

Show how you know.

▲ Resource Masters, M32

Meeting the Benchmarks

The following examples of student work provide a range of typical responses. All of these students met the benchmark—they showed that 4 + 9 is larger than 6 + 5. Note that students who count on, or those who reason about how to add the pairs of numbers, are working more efficiently than those who count all.

Count all Most first graders count all to add the pairs of numbers. How they show that on paper varies. Some cross out the pictures on the cards (Marta) or label each picture (Jacob) as they count them. Others make tallies or draw pictures of their fingers or the number line. Others describe their process in words: "I counted the pictures on the cards."

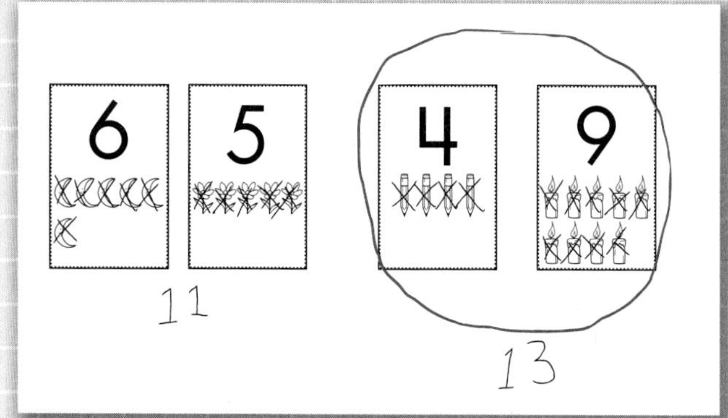

Marta's Work

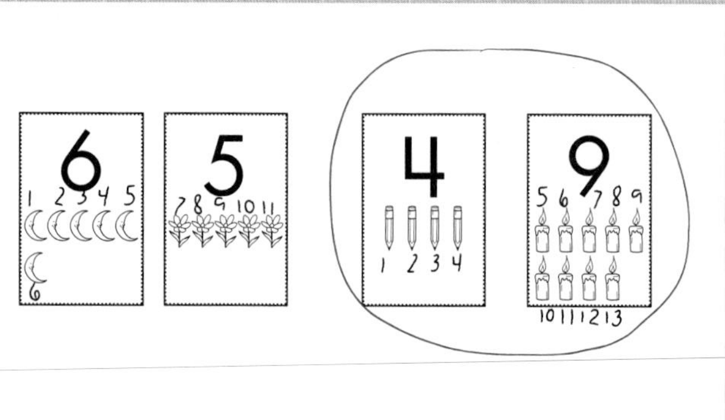

Jacob's Work

Count on Some students use their fingers (Felipe), the pictures on the cards (Nicky), or the number line (Emilia) to count on. Many count on from the 4 because it is listed first, although counting on from the 9 is more efficient.

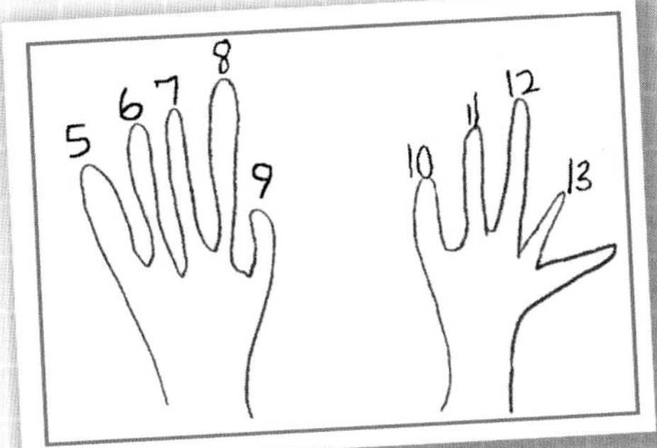

Felipe's Work

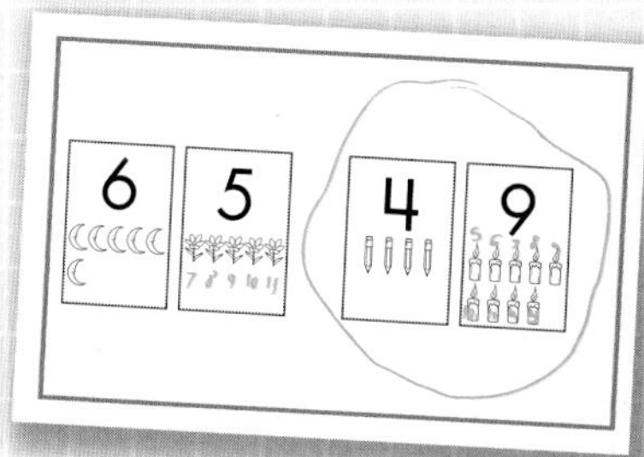

Nicky's Work

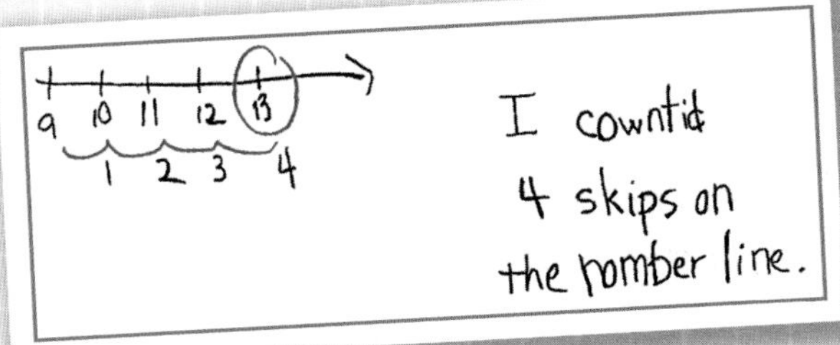

Emilia's Work

Numerical reasoning You may have one or two students (Toshi and Tamika) who use addition combinations they know to add. For example, some students use what they know about 5 + 5 to solve 5 + 6, and the fact that 9 is close to 10 to solve 4 + 9.

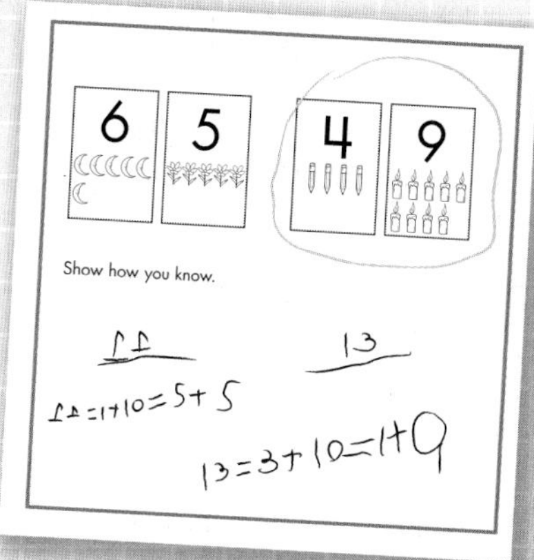

Toshi's Work

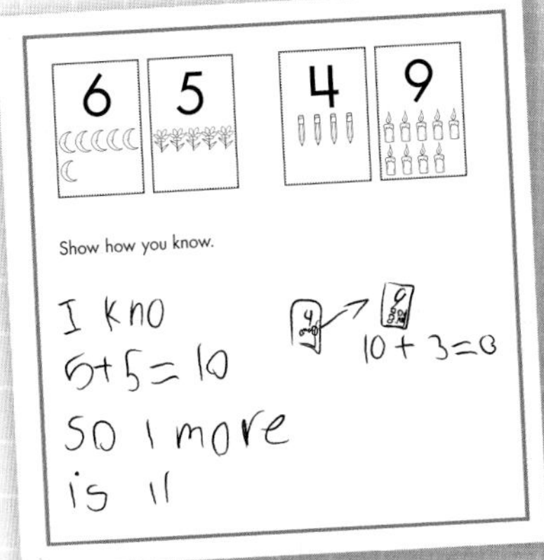

Tamika's Work

Others use strategies that do not rely on adding the numbers at all. Although Diego's work is difficult to understand, when you read the teacher's notes, you realize that the thinking behind his solution is quite sophisticated.

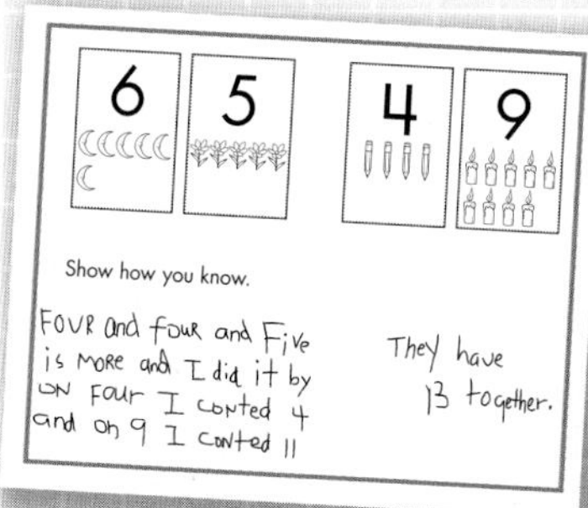

Diego's Work

Teacher Notes: Diego looked at the 5 and the 4 and said that 5 is 1 more. Then he looked at the 6 and the 9 and said that 9 is 3 more. He said that 9 and 4 is more "because 3 more is more than 1 more." Then he counted to double-check.

Partially Meeting the Benchmarks

Like Seth, some students understand the structure of the problem—adding the two pairs of numbers and comparing the totals to see which is larger—but make mistakes as they count or recount.

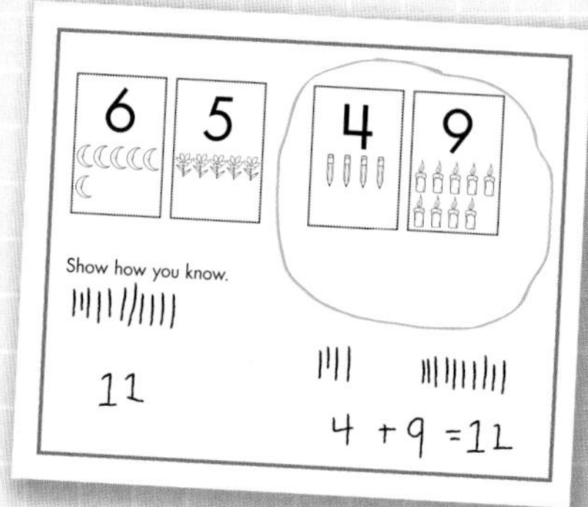

Seth's Work

After you review their assessment, ask these students to double-check their work (e.g., "Can you show me how you know that 4 and 9 is 11?"). See whether they can find and correct such errors on their own. Encourage these students to take their time and work carefully to avoid such errors in the future. In addition, note whether these kinds of errors are consistent across problems or more of a one-time occurrence.

As some students (Carol) attempt to count on, particularly on their fingers or the number line, they lose the connection between the numbers and the situation. They also struggle with where to start and stop counting and with how many numbers to count. Model counting on with these students, using the cards. If the first card shows 4 pictures, it makes sense that the first picture on the second card should be 5 because 4 plus 1 more is 5.

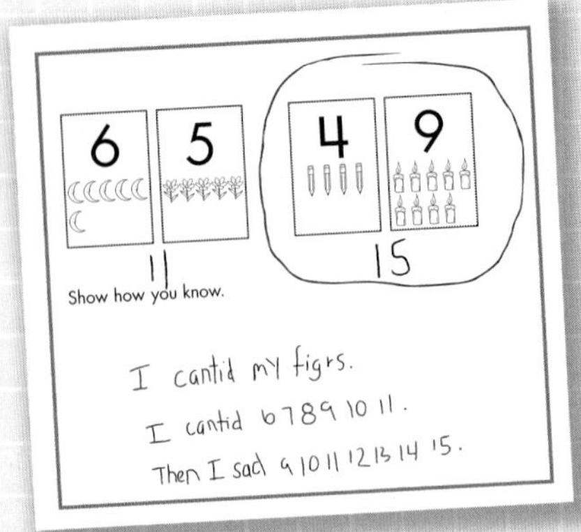

Carol's Work

Not Meeting the Benchmarks

Some students, like Talisa, do not understand the structure of the problem or do not have an idea about how to go about solving it. Talk with these students to find out what part of the task they are struggling with. Some of these students need additional practice counting sets of objects by 1s. They may also benefit from directly modeling such problems with cubes. For example, count out 6 cubes and then 5 cubes, and then combine them into a tower of 11 cubes. Do the same for 4 + 9, and then compare the two towers to see which has more cubes. Additional practice with this type of problem is provided by *Student Activity Book* pages 9, 31, and 36.

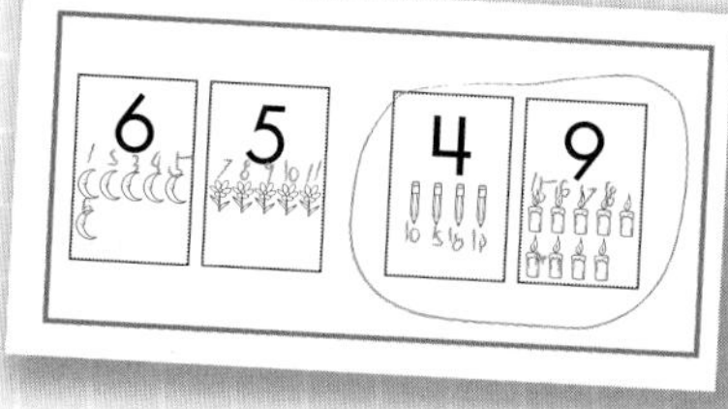

Talisa's Work

About How Many of Each? Problems

How Many of Each? problems such as Seven Peas and Carrots in the *Student Activity Book* page 33 are complex problems that require coordinating and keeping track of three pieces of information—in this case, the total number of peas and carrots, the number of peas, and the number of carrots. In order to solve the problem, students must count and keep track of a set of objects while comparing the number accumulated so far with the required total.

- Do I have 7?
- Do I need more? Fewer?

At the same time, they need to keep in mind how the two parts combine to reach that total.

- If I take away 2 things so that I only have 7, now how many peas will I have? How many carrots?
- How can I change what I have to get a different combination?

Another feature of How Many of Each? problems is that they present a problem that has many solutions. Working on problems with multiple solutions opens up possibilities for clarifying one's thinking and for exploring a variety of mathematical relationships.

- Have I found all the solutions?
- Is there another way of thinking about the problems that would yield more solutions?
- Are there any relationships among the solutions I found?

Exploring questions such as these can be very exciting for some students, but initially quite challenging for others. Many of us—at all levels of mathematical knowledge—are more familiar and comfortable with problems that have a single correct answer (e.g., how much is $4 + 3$?).

One of the major benefits of a How Many of Each? problem is that all students can engage with it at levels that are appropriate and challenging for them. There is no single best way of approaching the problem or recording solutions. In fact, you are likely to see many strategies and ways of recording work in your class.

Strategies for Solving the Problem

Although adults can see that the solutions to this problem are all the combinations of 7 with two addends, your students are unlikely to think of the problem in this way. Early in first grade, some students may find just one solution. Students who find several solutions are likely to work almost randomly, not noticing relationships among solutions and not using one solution to find another. Although they keep a record of their work, they may not notice when they arrive at the same solution more than once. Some of these students may even tell you that they have found all possible solutions—not because they have ways to check, but because they have so many solutions that they think there could not possibly be more. A few students may notice and use relationships among solutions and even challenge themselves to find all the possible solutions. All students will be challenged to find as many combinations as they can in Unit 3: *Solving Story Problems.* Over the course of the year, more students will begin to develop ways of working strategically.

The strategies you are likely to see are often based on counting, number combinations, and relationships among combinations. For more on the range of strategies, see **Dialogue Box,** Observing Students at Work on Seven Peas and Carrots, page 239.

Counting Some students will solve the problem by collecting and counting a set of objects and adjusting the number until they have 7. For example, they count out 7 counters, alternating one of each color and then counting the number of each. Or, they randomly take counters of two different colors, count them, and then add to or take away from the collection so that they have 7 in all—perhaps recounting the set each time they make an adjustment.

Number combinations Some students will use strategies that involve combinations of 7, such as beginning with a number of counters less than 7 and then counting up to 7 to find how many more they need. Others might start with 7 counters of one color and then replace some with counters of a different color, or they might even use number combinations that they know.

Relationships among combinations Some students will realize that the solution(s) they have found can help them find others. For example, if they have 4 carrots and 3 peas then take away a pea and make it a carrot, they have another way: 5 carrots and 2 peas. Alternately, students may find and use "opposites" or "reversibles" such as 6 peas and 1 carrot and 1 pea and 6 carrots.

Strategies for Recording

Some students will draw pictures of peas and carrots to show their work. Others will draw squares (e.g., cubes), circles (e.g., buttons), or other symbols to represent the counters they used to model the problem. Others will use numbers, words, and even equations. Many will use a combination of these methods.

All of these are important ways of showing mathematical thinking. You should insist that students record their work in some way, but *not* that they use one particular method. Students need many opportunities to discover what is important to record about a solution and to find different ways to show their work. For example, some students will record just the number in each group, without distinguishing which are peas and which are carrots. You can challenge these students to find a way to show what each number represents, perhaps by asking: "How can we tell whether that means 4 peas and 3 carrots or 3 peas and 4 carrots?" Modeling the solution with counters of different colors may help these students.

Keep in mind that for many students at the start of first grade, finding any way of recording their work is challenging. Over time, as students share methods for recording, they will develop more efficient ways of doing so.

Connections Between Solution and Recording Strategies

It is significant to note that the way students solve the problem will not necessarily relate to how they organize and record their work. One student might find his solutions by using combinations of 7 that he knows, but choose to record his work with pictures of peas and carrots as a way of connecting the numbers and the things they represent. Another might use concrete materials to arrive at her solutions, but record with numbers or equations. Another might use trial and error to find several solutions, notice some relationships among those solutions, and then use those relationships to find other solutions mentally. Yet another student might have a systematic strategy for using combinations of counters of two different colors to find all the possible solutions.

Teacher Note

Common Issues That Typically Arise with How Many of Each?

This section presents issues that came up in field test classrooms as they tackled How Many of Each? problems over the course of the year. There are also some strategies for handling these issues.

Difficulty Getting Started

Because this is a complex problem involving the coordination of several pieces of information, some students have difficulty getting started. Encourage those students to use materials to model the problem; but do not do it for them. Students need the chance to find their own approaches.

- You might suggest that they begin by taking a few counters of one color and then ask, "Suppose that those are the peas. How could we find out how many carrots there are?"
- You might put out a combination of 8 or 9 counters in two colors and ask students whether they can adjust the number of counters so that there are 7 in all.

If there are students who still seem not to know how to begin, give them 7 orange and green cubes and ask them to count the cubes. Assess whether they can

- Count 7 objects accurately
- Tell you how many are peas and how many are carrots

Some of these students may benefit from working with a smaller number of peas and carrots, such as 5. See page 240 for more on making these kinds of decisions.

Interpreting the Problem as 7 + 7

Some students will interpret this problem as 7 peas *plus* 7 carrots, or struggle with the idea that 7 is the *total.* Encourage these students to remember the situation as it was posed, to imagine it in their minds, to retell it to you, and to model it with counters.

- Do you remember how many vegetables there were altogether?
- How many vegetables fit in my spoon?

Here are two strategies that might benefit students who continue to struggle with this idea. Provide them with 7 two-sided counters (e.g., green-and-orange beans). Work with them on the problem using *only* 7 counters until they seem to grasp the structure of the problem.

Another strategy is not to limit the number of cubes but to provide a plate showing only 7 spots for vegetables.

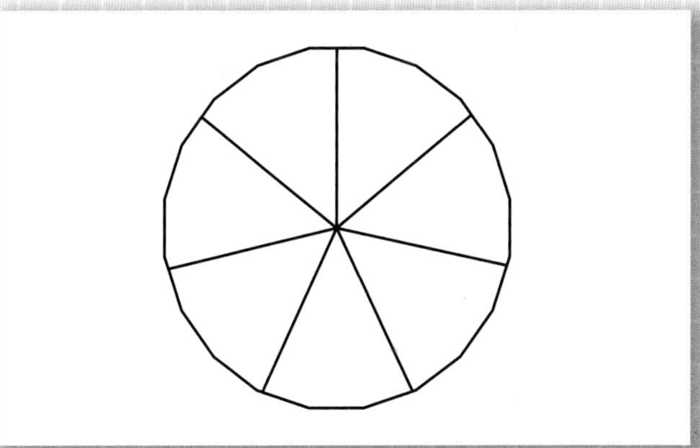

Cubes as Counters

In field test classes that used connecting cubes for modeling this problem, there were children who

- Linked the cubes together to make an object that looked like a carrot (e.g., 5 orange cubes with 2 green on top)
- Made pattern trains and could not find ways other than 4 and 3 (o-g-o-g-o-g-o) and 3 and 4 (g-o-g-o-g-o-g)
- Snapped the cubes together and drew a rectangle to record their work, but struggled to figure out how to break it into 7 squares

Be on the lookout for students who are struggling with these problems. For example, children in the second and third groups might benefit from working with loose cubes, either when solving or recording.

Debating Same and Different

In discussions about solutions teachers often ask for a *new* solution, one that has not been shared yet. This can trigger debates about what is the same and what is different. For example: Is 1 pea and 6 carrots *the same as* 6 peas and 1 carrot? What about 1 pea and 6 carrots and 6 carrots and 1 pea? Of course, *same* or *different* depends on what you pay attention to. In the first example, you get the same total amount, but the number of peas and carrots is different. In the second example, the total number *and* the number of peas and carrots are the same. However, when represented by two cube towers facing opposite directions, they *look* different. Encourage students to consider such similarities and differences, but do not expect all students to reach agreement on what qualifies as a *different* solution.

Stacy: You could put 1 dog and 5 cats.

Sacha: We have it already. [Points to 5 cats and 1 dog.]

Lyle: No, it is not the same. [Lyle shows 2 cubes towers: cccccd and dccccc.]

Sacha: Just flip it (the second tower). Then it matches the first.

Teacher: Let's think about the story. Close your eyes and imagine 5 cats and 1 dog. Try to picture that in your mind. Got it? Now, picture 1 dog and 5 cats. Do you have the same thing or not?

Nicky: Yes, the animals move around but you have the same thing.

Debating Zero

In some classrooms, students wonder whether 0 peas and 7 carrots (or vice versa) is an acceptable answer because the question is phrased "some are carrots and some are peas." This problem can be a useful context for encountering the idea of zero, but we encourage teachers and students to decide together about this issue for their class.

Sacha: I did 9 marbles and 0 blocks.

Teacher: Let's write that up here.

Vic: That doesn't work because you're supposed to have at least one block or a little bit more in each one. You should use at least one block in each one.

Teacher: Let me read the problem, and you tell me when it says that you have to have at least one. "There are 9 toys altogether. Some are blocks and some are marbles."

Vic: Right there. It says *some* are blocks and *some* are marbles.

Libby: Yeah, but the whole point is to get 9.

Teacher: I agree with both of you, so let's put it up—but we'll put a star next to it because we don't all agree with that one.

Using Subtraction

Some students may show ways to make 7 with subtraction (e.g., 10 – 3). Acknowledge that 10 – 3 *is* 7, but also encourage them to think about whether subtraction yields a solution to the problem at hand.

You might say, "Your goal is to find a number of peas and a number of carrots that make up 7 in all. You wrote down '2p 5c.' Does that solve the problem? What does it show? You also wrote down 10 – 3. Does that show the number of peas and the number of carrots you need to make 7 in all? What does it show?"

Finishing Quickly

Some students will find and record a solution before most of the others are finished. Those who are ready can be encouraged to look for additional solutions to the problem or even challenged to try to find all the solutions to the problem.

Teacher Note

When the Teacher Records Students' Solutions

When you are recording a solution for the class to consider, use one of the recording methods you saw students using: pictures, schematic representations (such as lines or dots), numbers, words. Varying the method will expose students to a range of representations and give them practice interpreting each.

For some discussions, you will want to focus the class sharing on all the different ways students recorded their work. However, when you want to highlight the solutions, it is better to use just one method.

Students must understand that even though you are recording in a particular way today, they need not always record their solutions in this manner. Emphasize that you are using just one of the many valid recording strategies you saw them using in class.

You might say, "All of you found good ways to record your work: with pictures of peas and carrots, with orange and green squares, with circles, with words, and with numbers. Today I'm using one of those ways to record your solutions on the board. Next time I'll use a different way to show your solutions so that we can see all the different ways you've found."

Plan to include numbers as you record, whether the students do or not. Recording three different solutions with pictures, your chart would look something like this:

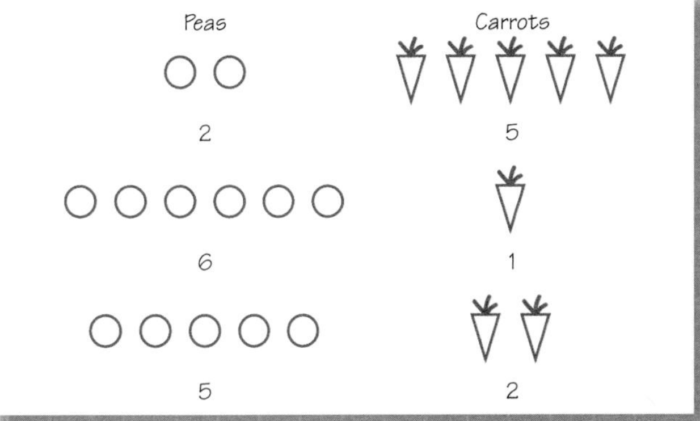

On another day, you might record similar solutions in one of the following ways:

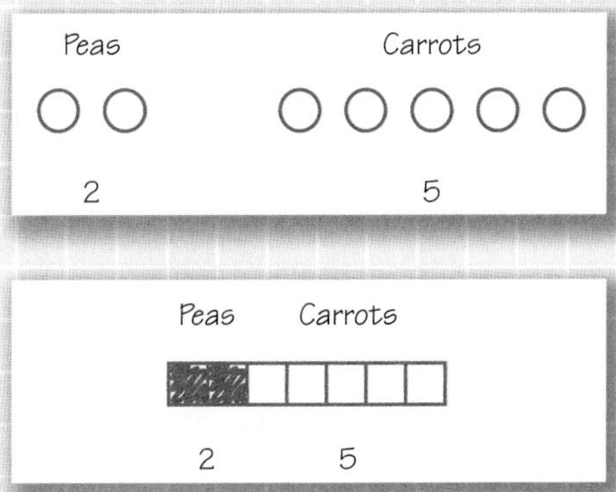

Record solutions in the order students give them, instead of organizing them in any specific way (e.g., in order from smallest to largest number of peas, or linking "opposite" pairs, such as 5 peas 2 carrots and 2 peas 5 carrots). This can change later in the year. You will occasionally want to model a particular way of organizing solutions or a particular way of recording work (especially with numbers or with equations). However, in this first unit, avoid suggesting a particular way of recording. As students find their own ways of recording their work, they begin to think about what is important to communicate about a solution and what the different representations show. As they find their own ways to organize their work, they begin to seek out relationships among different solutions on their own.

Teacher Note

End-of-Unit Assessment

Problem 1: How Many Cookies?

Benchmarks addressed, depending on how students solve the problem:

Benchmark 1: Count accurately a set of up to 20 objects

Benchmark 3: Combine two small quantities accurately

Benchmark 4: Interpret (retell the action and sequence) and solve addition story problems

In order to meet the benchmarks, students' work should show that they can:

- Interpret a combining situation;
- Accurately find the total;
- Show how they solved the problem.

Some students count all to combine the two numbers. Others count on or use number combinations they know to solve the problem.

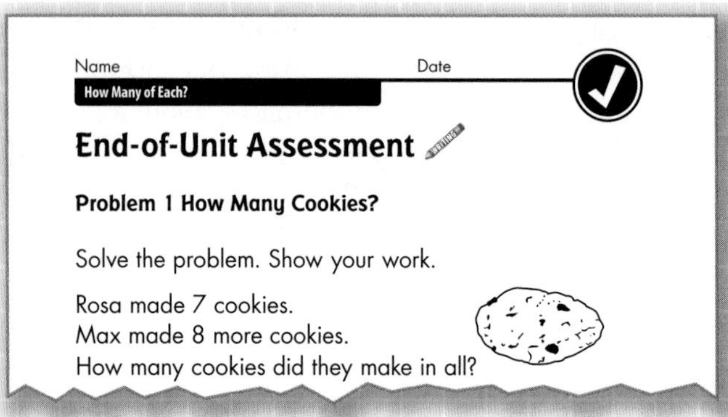

Name Date

How Many of Each?

End-of-Unit Assessment

Problem 1 How Many Cookies?

Solve the problem. Show your work.

Rosa made 7 cookies.
Max made 8 more cookies.
How many cookies did they make in all?

▲ Resource Masters, M39

Meeting the Benchmarks

The following examples of student work provide a range of typical responses. All of these students met the benchmark—they were able to interpret the problem and solve it accurately. Note that students who are counting on or are reasoning about the quantities in the problem are working more efficiently than those who are counting all.

Count all Most first graders count all to solve this problem. They draw or count out a group of 7 and a group of 8 and then recount the combined group of 15. They use a variety of methods to show their work. Some use words (e.g., "First I took 7 and then I took 8 and I got 15"). Others use slash or tally marks, or draw pictures of cookies.

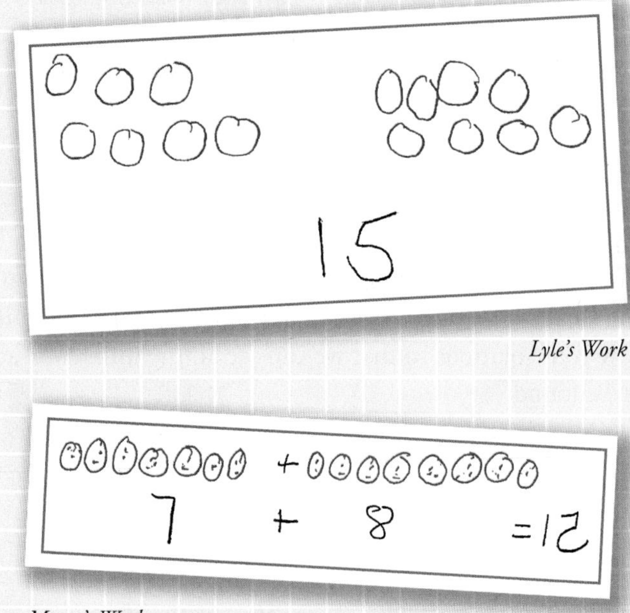

Lyle's Work

Marta's Work

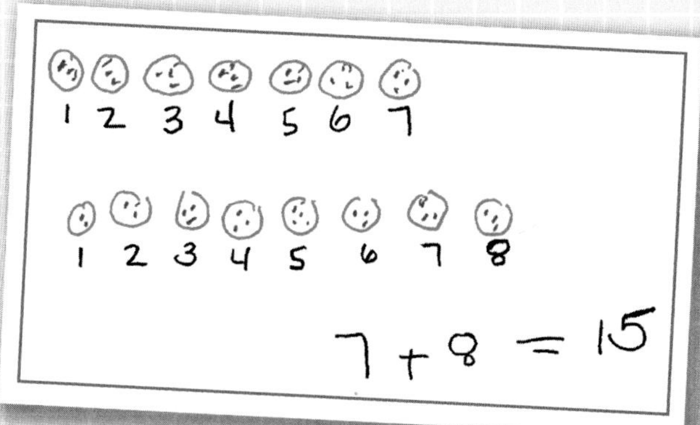

Richard's Work

Still others draw pictures of the tools they used to solve the problem. For example, Talisa counted on her fingers and William used cubes.

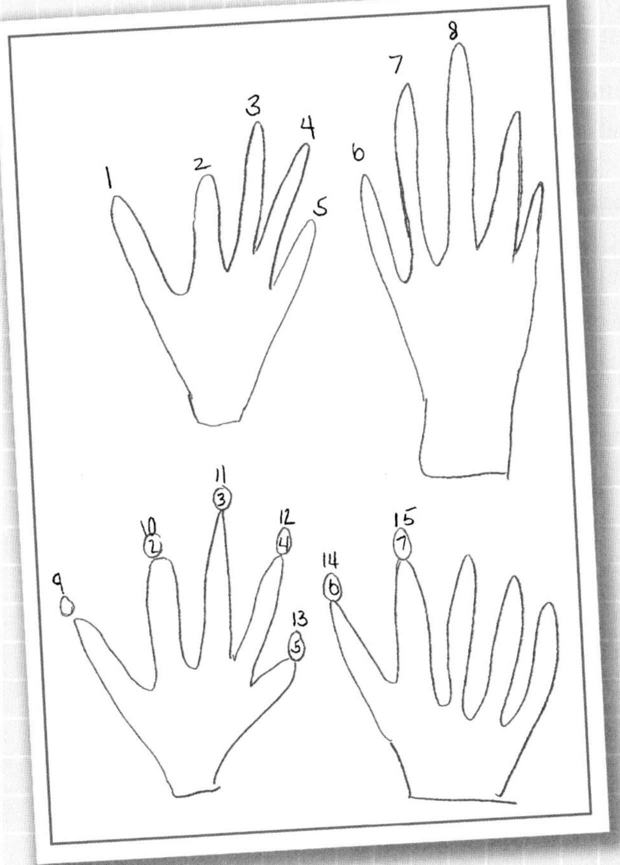

Talisa's Work

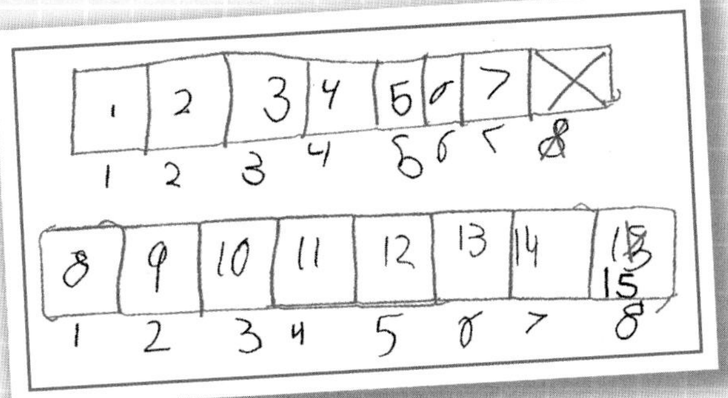

William's Work

Note the variety of tools that students reference, and consider the range of detail that they choose to show. Some students show only a group of 15, with no clear groups of 7 and 8, others show distinct groups of 7 and 8. Some of these students do not label the groups in any way (Lyle); others label the totals of each group (Marta), each item in each group (Richard), each item in the whole group (Talisa), or the number in each group *and* the number in the entire group (William).

Count on Some students may count on to solve this problem. They use pictures of cookies (Bruce), their fingers (Leah), or the number line (Tamika) to show how they counted on. Again, note the range of labels that children choose to include. Note that most beginning first graders count on from the first number in the problem, even if it is more efficient to start with the latter.

Bruce's Work

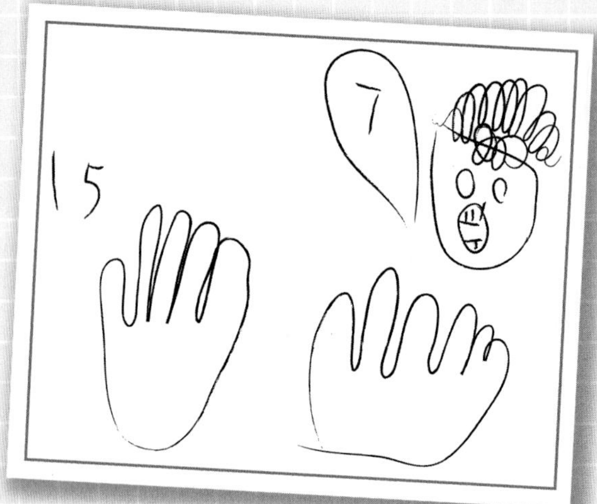

Leah's Work

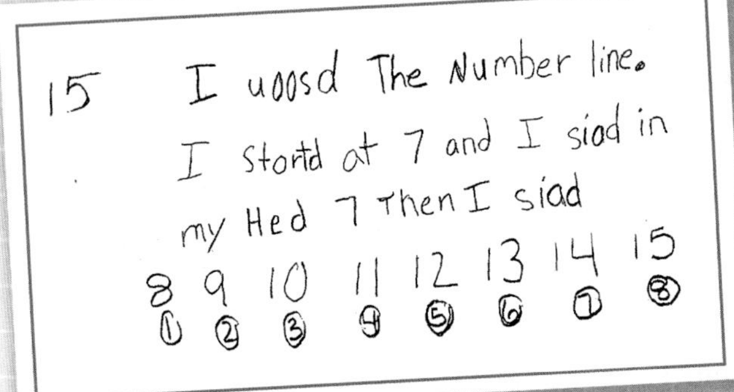

Tamika's Work

Numerical strategies Typically, there are not many first graders in this category this early in the year. However, you may have one or a few students who use a number combination they know, such as 7 + 7 (Toshi) or 8 + 8, to solve the problem. Others may add one number to the other in two parts: first adding to 10 and then adding the remainder (7 + 8 = 7 + 3 + 5 = 10 + 5 or 8 + 7 = 8 + 2 + 5 = 10 + 5).

Toshi's Work

Partially Meeting the Benchmarks

Some students understand the structure of the problem—that it is about combining two quantities and finding the total number—but make mistakes as they count the quantities in the problem. For example, some students accurately draw a group of 7 and a group of 8 but get a total that is 1 or 2 off when they recount the whole group.

Danielle's Work

Chris's Work

Others, Vic for example, miscount as they draw or count out the groups.

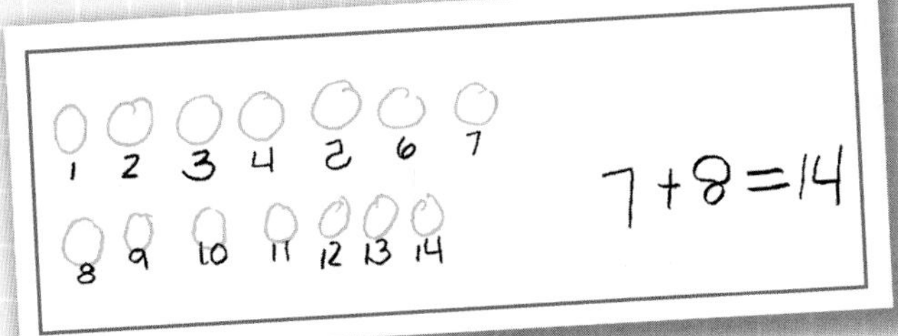

Vic's Work

After you review their assessment, ask these students to double-check their work. (For example, "Your paper says that 7 plus 8 is 14. How could you double-check that?") See whether they can find and correct such errors on their own. Encourage these students to take their time and work carefully to avoid such errors in the future. In addition, note whether these kinds of errors are consistent across problems or more of a one-time occurrence.

Other students understand the structure of the problem but struggle with knowing where to start and stop when counting on. These students may be losing the connection between the numbers and the situation, and may benefit from conversations that model counting on with cubes. For example, if there are already 7 cubes in one pile, then it makes sense to start counting on with 8, because 7 plus one more would be 8. (Plus 2 more would be 9, etc.) Once they can model counting on clearly with cubes, they can compare and connect it to the process of counting on with their fingers or the number line.

I hold 8 in my had and countid on, 8 9 10 11 12 13 14

Libby's Work

Not Meeting the Benchmarks

Some students may still be constructing an understanding of the structure of the problem. Although Felipe and Paula's drawings match their answers (suggesting accurate counting), they seem unable to hold onto the information in the problem about a group of 7 and a group of 8. Neil seems to grasp this aspect of the problem, but is unable to show those quantities accurately and find the total.

Felipe's Work

Paula's Work

Neil's Work

It is likely that these students need more experience counting quantities by 1s. They will also benefit from directly modeling the action of such problems with cubes. *Student Activity Book* pages 22 and 34 (and others modeled after them) provide more practice with addition story problems. Keep in mind, though, that students will have many opportunities to solve addition problems over the course of first grade, both in class and in homework assignments.

Problem 2: Eight Fruits

Benchmark addressed:

Benchmark 5: Find more than one combination of two addends for a number up to 10 (e.g., 7 is 4 and 3 and it is also 5 and 2)

In order to meet the benchmark, students' work should show that they can:

- Find and record at least two combinations of 8.

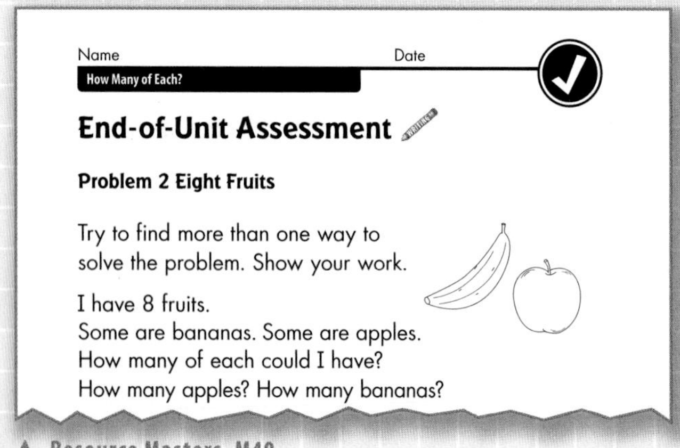

Name Date

How Many of Each?

End-of-Unit Assessment

Problem 2 Eight Fruits

Try to find more than one way to solve the problem. Show your work.

I have 8 fruits.
Some are bananas. Some are apples.
How many of each could I have?
How many apples? How many bananas?

▲ Resource Masters, M40

Some students find and record two combinations of 8; others find several, many, or even all of the possible combinations. Some draw pictures of apples and bananas. Some use numbers to label pictures of apples and bananas. Others use a combination of pictures, words, numbers, and equations to represent their work.

Meeting the Benchmark

The following examples of student work provide a range of typical responses. All of these students met the benchmark—they were able to find at least two combinations of 2-addends that make 8 and to record their work.

There are different ways to organize the responses. Consider sorting this set of student work twice. First tally the total number of solutions found. Then, tally the total number of *accurate* solutions. For example, although Deshawn found 6 combinations, 1 + 9 does not equal 8, and 3 + 5 is listed twice, so he found 4 *accurate* solutions: 3 + 5, 4 + 4, 5 + 3, and 2 + 6.

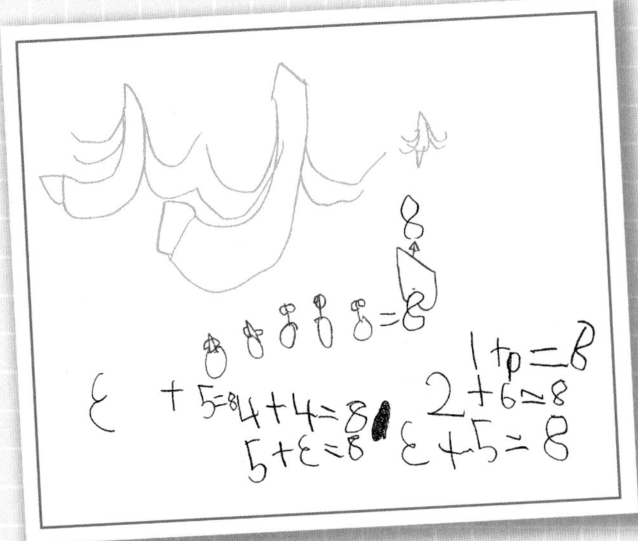

Deshawn's Work

Two combinations Some students find only two combinations that make eight.

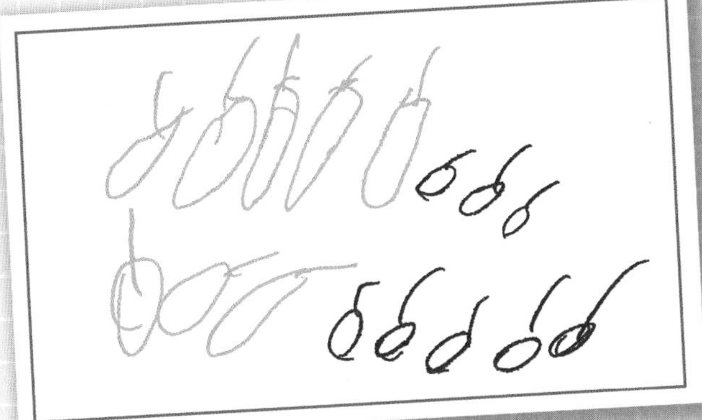

Neil's Work

Three to five combinations After their experience with How Many of Each? problems in this unit, most students find 3 to 5 different combinations.

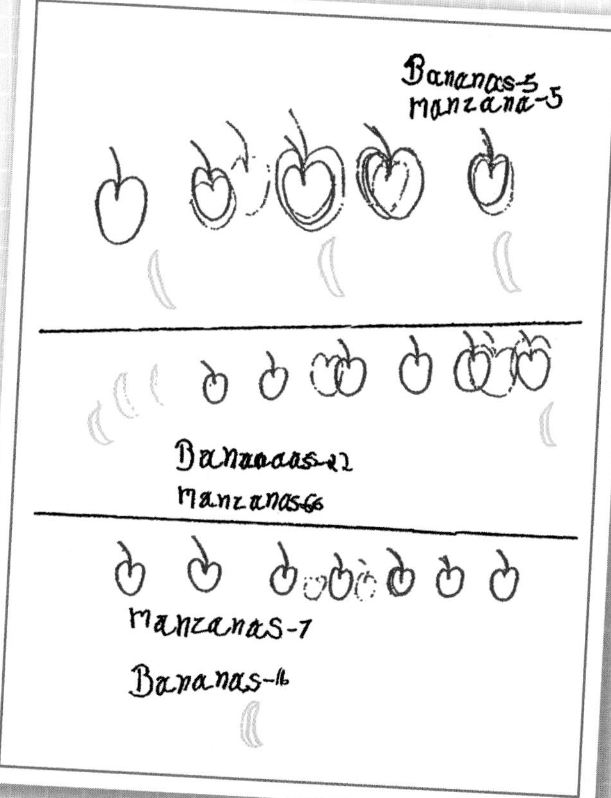

Jacinta's Work

More than five combinations A few students may find more than five combinations of 8. Like Stacy, some students may even find more than 7 (or 9) combinations, which is the maximum number of possible combinations (depending on whether your class includes 8 + 0 and 0 + 8 or not). This gives you information about the inclination or ability of these students to organize and keep track of their work.

7+1=8 1+7=8
6+2=8 2+6=8
5+3=8 3+5=8
4+4=8 4+4=8
3+5=8 5+3=8
2+6=8 6+2=8

Stacy's Work

One or several students may find all the combinations, as well as a system for keeping track, such as working with "opposites" (Seth) or using an ordered list (Sacha).

Seth's Work

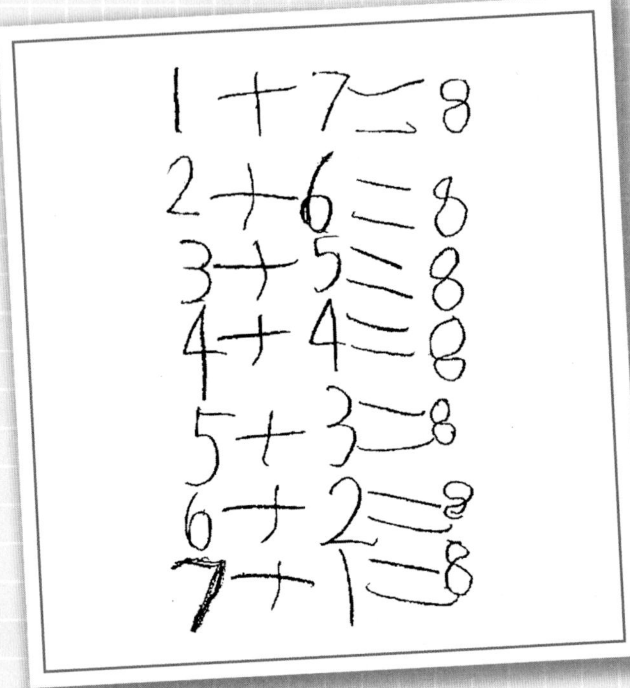

Sacha's Work

Partially Meeting the Benchmark

Some students understand the structure of the problem—that it is about finding two addend combinations of 8—but finding one combination and recording their work is as much as they can manage.

Leah's Work

Not Meeting the Benchmark

Some students do not understand the structure of the problem. Often these students will add 8 + 8 instead of finding a combination that makes 8.

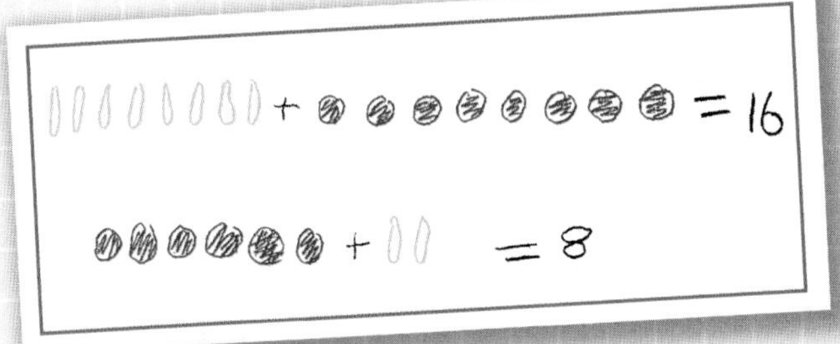

Toshi's Work

After seeing Toshi's work, his teacher reread the problem to him. She stressed the fact that there were 8 fruits in all and asked whether his solution showed a total of 8 apples and bananas. After this interaction he was able to find one 2-addend combination of 8. Students like Toshi need more practice with problems of this type, which the curriculum will provide throughout first grade.

Other Ways to Look at Student Work

Looking at the number of different solutions that students found is only one way to sort this set of student work. Consider making additional tables to look at how students are recording their work, how they use standard notation, or which combinations seem most familiar.

Recording Method	# of Students
Pictures only	
Numbers only	
Words only	
Pictures and numbers	
Pictures and words	
Numbers and words/letters	
Pictures, numbers, and words	

Use of Standard Notation	# of Students
Uses only the + symbol	
Uses only the = symbol	
**** + oooo = 8	
Uses an equation	

Combination*	# of Occurrences
0 + 8/8 + 0	
1 + 7/7 + 1	
2 + 6/6 + 2	
3 + 5/5 + 3	
4 + 4	

*Some teachers make this table with 1 row per combination. (Rather than grouping 1 + 7 and 7 + 1 together, each would get its own row.) If you prefer that organization, you will need to decide how to handle solutions in which you cannot tell which number represents bananas and which represents apples.

Dialogue Box

Mine Is a Sailboat

Students vary widely in the amount of structure and direction they need as they freely explore materials. Guiding students' exploration with questions can be an effective way of structuring a free exploration experience. This can extend students' thinking about a particular material and lead them into new ways of using it. When students work with a partner or small group, they benefit from observing how others use materials. Inviting students to share their constructions and designs is a natural way for students to exchange ideas.

The following dialogue occurred early in the year during free exploration. The teacher joins a small group of students working with pattern blocks and asks them to tell her about their constructions.

Deshawn: Mine is a sailboat. Here's the boat part, and then I made the mast with the skinny diamonds, and the sail is made with green triangles.

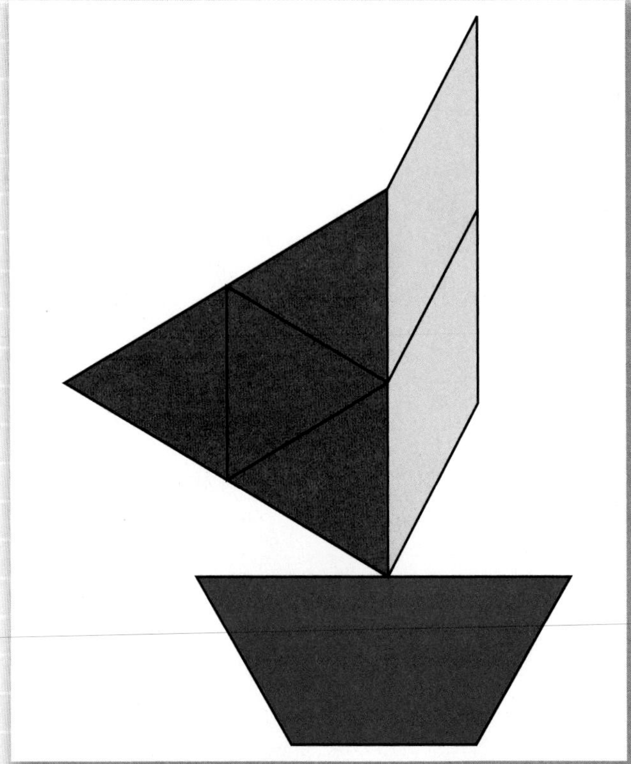

Isabel: Mine is just a design. I started with this hexagon in the middle and then I built out and around. And now it looks like a pinwheel.

Teacher: Your design is similar to Stacy's design, but she started with two red trapezoids in the center.

Isabel: It's the same thing, because she just used two of these [trapezoids] instead of this [hexagon].

Paul: Stop shaking the table! I don't want my wall to fall down.

Teacher: I can see that some of you have decided to use the pattern blocks flat on the table and some of you have used them to build up, sort of like blocks. It is harder to keep them in place when they're on their edges, the way Paul has them. Paul, it looks like your wall has a pattern. Tell me about it.

The conversation is interrupted by some commotion at a table of students using connecting cubes. Three students are building elaborate constructions and two are just sliding cubes back and forth across the table. The teacher addresses these two students.

Teacher: Vic and Emilia, I noticed that yesterday when you were working with the Geoblocks, you were trying to build a very tall skyscraper. Do you suppose there's a way to use these cubes to build a tall skinny building?

Vic: You could put them together in a long line, like this. [He snaps together a row of 7 cubes.]

Emilia: You could make it fatter by adding more on the bottom. [She builds a 2-by-2 square and then begins to attach more cubes on top of her base.]

Teacher: I wonder how many floors your building could have? I live in an apartment building that has 6 floors.

Vic: My building has 11 floors. I'm going to make a building with 11 floors.

Dialogue Box

Start With/Get To

It is the second week of school, and students are seated in a circle on the rug. The teacher explains that they are about to learn a new routine called *Start With/Get To.*

Teacher: The first few times we do *Start With/Get To,* we will start with 1. In this basket are the numbers we can get to. [She closes her eyes, reaches in, and picks 21—the total number of children in the class. She holds it up.] Raise your hand if you can tell me what number this is.

Allie: A 1 and a 2.

Teacher: Do you know what that's called?

Allie: 12?

Teacher: Let me write 12. [She writes 12 on the board.] Does that match? Does someone think this number is something different?

A few students say, "21."

Teacher: Let me write 21. [She writes 21 on the board beneath 12 and holds the chosen number next to 12.] Are these two numbers the same? Do they start the same way?

Teacher: And what number will we get to?

Class: 21.

Teacher: Start with 1 and get to 21. OK, here we go. Let's count.

The class counts more or less in unison from 1 to 21. When they get to 21, the teacher and the majority of the class stop. Several students keep on going: 22, 23, 24, 25, 26.

Teacher: Some of you kept going right past 21. Maybe we should look at something that can help us know when to stop. Is there a tool in the classroom that could help us?

Talisa: This can. [Points to the calendar.]

Teacher: Yes, the calendar might help us. Anything else?

Deshawn: That line with all the numbers.

Teacher: Yes, the number line could help us too. I even have something special to help us know when to stop. [She marks 21 with a red clothespin.] I'm going to use this pointer to help us all stay together. Remember: start with 1; get to 21.

The class counts together from 1 to 21 while the teacher points to each number on the number line.

Teacher: Marking the end number helped us all to stop. Let's try one more number. Talisa, why don't you choose? [Talisa picks a number out of the basket. At first the number is upside-down. She seems uncertain about its name.] Do you want to show it to a friend who can help? [Talisa chooses Richard.]

Richard: 15.

Talisa: You can put it [the green clothespin] on 15.

Teacher: Is this 15 [pointing to 51]?

Class: No.

Teacher: Is this 15 [pointing to 5]?

Class: No.

Teacher: Is this 15 [pointing to 15]?

Class: Yes! Yes!

The class counts from 1 to 15 while the teacher points to the numbers on the number line.

Notice how the teacher reinforces the work done earlier by asking students to find 15 on the number line, and by asking about similar numbers that students would likely confuse with it (5 and 51). She knows that students will need lots of experience with counting activities to become familiar and comfortable with the number sequence and the way numbers are written.

Dialogue Box

Discussing Staircases

This class has spent several sessions with the Staircases activity as a part of Math Workshop. This teacher begins a discussion of the Staircases work by setting up the following towers from left to right: 1, 2, 3, 4, 6, 5, 7, 10, 9, 8, 11, 12. Notice how she encourages students to listen to one another by asking them to compare and contrast the thoughts they share aloud.

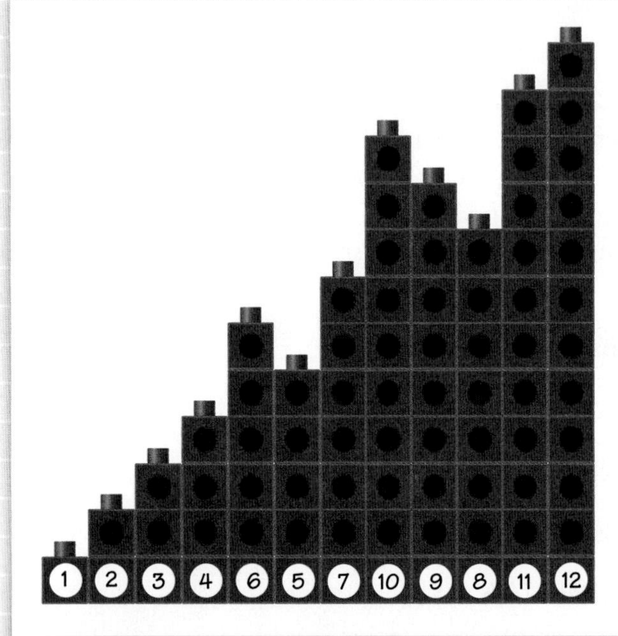

Teacher: What do you notice about this staircase?

Carol: That's not in order.

Isabel: Yeah, each of these goes 1 more than the other and then it goes down and up. [Isabel points to the 6 and 5 towers and to the 10, 9, and 8 towers.]

Teacher: Is that what you meant, Carol?

Carol: Yeah, it goes [points to the number labels] 1, 2, 3, 4, 6. The 5 isn't there.

Teacher: So raise your hand if you agree with Isabel that it shouldn't go up and then down. Raise your hand if you agree that this happens in two places. Raise your hand if you agree with Carol that the numbers are out of order. [All students raise their hands each time.] If we put these in the right order, what would it look like?

Jacob: 1, 2, 3, 4, 5, 6, 7, 8, 9, 10, 11, 12. It would start down here and then go up [moves his finger diagonally through the air, up and to the right].

Danielle: When you look at it now it goes up and down.

Teacher: How should it go? [She holds up a tower for 4 and 6, pushing students to articulate their ideas more fully.] Is this right?

Stacy: No, because that's 2 taller.

Teacher: Why can't it be 2 taller?

Bruce: Because if a person, if it was 2 taller, they wouldn't be able to get up it. Or they might fall.

Teacher: So you're thinking about stairs.

Tamika: Because that's not how the numbers go. You don't count 3, 4, 6. You say 3, 4, 5.

Teacher: Tamika is thinking about the numbers. Who can say more about the numbers?

She gently directs the conversation toward one of the big ideas of the lesson: each counting number represents a quantity with 1 more [or less] than the previous.

Lyle: They should be 1 taller. Each number is 1 taller, so each tower should have 1 more cube.

Teacher: So Lyle is saying that each tower should be 1 taller. Let's look at 2 towers. [She shows a 6 and 7, using both cubes and words to demonstrate the important math idea.] Both have 6 cubes, but 7 has 1 more.

Teacher: I have one last thing to show you. [Teacher arranges cube towers from 1 to 12 and down to 1.] What do you notice now?

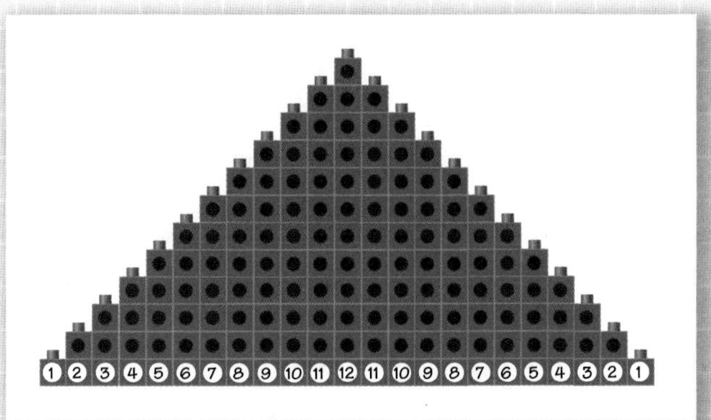

William: It looks like a triangle.

Deshawn: Or a pyramid!

Paula: There is only one in the middle and 2 on each side.

Teacher: Is this the one you notice [points to the 12 tower]?

Paula: Yeah. Only 1 has 12, then 11 and 11, 10 and 10, 9 and 9 . . .

Sacha: I noticed that you go up this way [starting at the 1 tower on the left] and count 1 to 12 and then you count 12 to 1.

Teacher: What do you think about what Sacha said? What do the numbers do when I say 1, 2, 3, 4, 5, 6, 7, 8, 9, 10, 11, 12, 11, 10, 9, 8, 7, 6, 5, 4, 3, 2, 1?

William: They go up that way when you count to 12 and then they went back to 11 and then down.

Teacher: When they go down, how am I counting?

Class: Backward!

Teacher: So when I'm going up the staircase, I count forward, and when I'm going down the staircase, I count backward. Count with me.

This discussion focused on the number sequence and how the quantities in that sequence are related to one another. Notice how the teacher pushed students to articulate their thoughts and to think about the numbers and quantities involved.

Dialogue Box

Counting What's in a Mystery Box

This teacher has posted five completed Mystery Boxes pages for Box C (*Student Activity Book* page 7), which has 23 magnetic letters in it. Three students counted 23, one counted 22, and one counted 21.

Teacher: Let's see what we notice. Edgar counted 22 and Paul counted 21. Emilia counted 23, and so did Libby and Tamika. How can this be possible? Can this box sometimes have 21, sometimes 22, and sometimes 23? How can this be?

Teo: Maybe kids counted the same letter twice.

Teacher: Which kids do you think did this, the kids who have more or fewer letters?

Teo: People who have higher letters.

Teacher: So kids who have more, maybe they counted twice. Does anyone else have an idea? Libby, should there be the same number or not?

Libby: The same. Unless someone put in more or took some out.

Teacher: Then why are the numbers not the same?

Libby: Because maybe some people miss them and other people don't miss them.

Seth: I think kids are skipping numbers.

Paul: I think some kids . . . maybe some fell out on the floor and some don't.

Danielle: What you should have is the whole alphabet in that bag. It would be easier for kids if they know they have all the letters.

Teacher: You have lots of ideas about how someone could make a mistake when they are counting. You might skip a number, or count one of the letters twice. Or maybe some letters fell on the floor. Who has a good system for counting so that there are no mistakes? What did you and your partner do to make sure that you counted accurately?

Leah: At first Danielle and I got different numbers. Then we decided we better try again. We counted slower and that helped.

Teacher: Double-checking is always a good idea. Can you show us how you counted?

Leah counts the contents of Box C by emptying it and counting each letter as she puts it back into the box. She counts 23.

Teacher: Your system is to take all of the letters out and then put each one back in as you count it. Who has a different system?

Jacinta: Count as you take them out.

Jacinta counts each letter aloud as she takes it out of the box. Her friend points out, "You said 14 twice." Jacinta starts again, this time counting in Spanish. She also gets 23.

Teacher: Jacinta did sort of the opposite of Leah—she counted them as she took them out of the box. Who noticed what Jacinta did when she got confused with what number came next? That's right, she started again. That's a great strategy. Does anyone have another way to count and keep track?

Felipe pours out the letters and moves each from one pile to another as he counts aloud in English. He skips 15.

Paula: He got mixed up.

Leah: He missed a number.

Felipe: Yeah, I missed 15. [He counts again, agreeing with the other counters that there are 23.]

This class seems to understand that Box C should always have the same number of items in it (unless some were added or lost). Students have many ideas about why different people found different numbers, which serves as a good opportunity to discuss and demonstrate strategies for counting accurately together as a class.

Dialogue Box

Seeing Dot Images

These students have been doing *Quick Images* with the 5-dot card from Dot Cards, Set A. They have finished their two attempts at making the image, and now the teacher is showing it so that students can compare their work with the actual image. Here, students are sharing the different ways they thought of the image; some broke the image into smaller parts, some "translated" the image into numbers, and some saw the image as a whole shape.

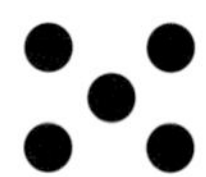

Teacher: How many dots did you see altogether?

Vic: 5.

Teacher: Did anyone else see a different number? [Pause.] What helped you remember what the image looked like?

Danielle: 2 dots on each side, and one in the middle is 5.

Vic: 2 [indicates the top row] plus 2 [the bottom row] is 4, and then 1 more is 5.

Libby: 1 diagonal, 2 diagonals.

Teacher: And how many in each diagonal?

Libby: There's 3 in each. They cross in the middle, so it's 5.

Deshawn: It's an X.

Later, students discuss the 10-dot card.

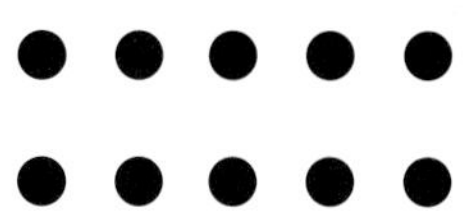

Teacher: How did you see this one? What helped you to make your own copy?

Chris: I counted 5 on the top. And then I looked at both of them (both rows) and they were both the same, so I counted 5 and did 5 again.

Teacher: What does it equal if you have 5 and 5 again?

Chris: 10.

Nicky: Up at the top, I saw 3 and 2. Then I knew the bottom was the same so I did the same thing. 3 plus 2 for both makes 10.

Teacher: Chris and Nicky saw that the top and bottom rows were the same, and that really helped them.

Allie: It has flowers in it. A lot of the pictures did.

Teacher: Can you show us what you mean?

Allie comes to the overhead, arranges 4 counters in a 2 by 2 array, and explains that this "flower" contains 4 dots.

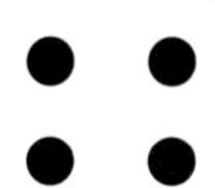

Teacher: How many flowers in this one [10-dot image]?

Allie: 2.

Teacher: How many left over?

Allie: 2. So it's 10.

As students work with images containing more dots, they develop ways to break the image into manageable parts like repeating sections or component "objects." They also develop strategies for keeping track of and combining all the parts to find the total number of dots.

An Addition Story Problem Aloud

In the previous session, this class was introduced to the routine for solving story problems aloud as a group. Today, the class solves another problem together, and, for the first time, the teacher models some ways to record the students' strategies for solving the problem.

Teacher: I have a story that I am going to share with you. Listen carefully. Then I am going to call on some students to retell the story. Here we go. *Kylie and Koni were on a rock hunt. Kylie found 4 smooth rocks. Koni found 5 bumpy rocks.* [She reads this story aloud to the class, twice.] Raise your hand if you can tell that story to the class.

Stacy: Kylie and Koni went to find rocks. Kylie found 4 smooth rocks and Koni found 5 bumpy rocks.

Felipe: Kylie and Koni went on rock hunt. Kylie found 4 smooth rocks, Koni found 5 bumpy rocks.

Teacher: OK, I'm going to read it again and I want you to close your eyes while I'm reading it and make a movie of it in your head. [She rereads the story.] OK, now open your eyes and I have a question for you. How many rocks did they find? I don't want you to tell me the answer; tell me how you figured out the answer.

Keena: I put 4 on my fingers [holds up 4 fingers] then I added 5, 6, 7, 8, 9 [holds up one finger for each additional number].

The teacher models Keena's strategy with her hands and then draws a face with an open mouth and hands that are holding up 9 fingers.

Teacher: OK, so here's Keena and she has an open mouth because she talks to solve this and her answer is 9 rocks.

Teacher: Raise your hand if that was your strategy. [Six students raise their hands and the teacher writes their initials under the drawing.] Who can share a different strategy that they used?

Paula: I put up 4 fingers, then I put up 5 fingers and I counted them all together.

Teacher: OK, so that's a little bit different. [She holds up 4 fingers, then 5 fingers and has Paula count them.] So you have 9 what?

Paula: Rocks.

The teacher draws a girl with an open mouth, and 4 fingers and then 5 fingers, and then numbers the fingers 1–9.

Teacher: How is Paula's strategy different from Keena's?

Keena: Because she put them up and then counted them all together. But I didn't. I went 4; 5, 6, 7, 8, 9.

Teacher: If you did it Paula's way, raise your hand. [Four students raise their hands.] Does anybody have a totally different way?

Vic: I didn't use my hands at all. I thought and I saw 5 smooth rocks and 4 bumpy rocks at the top and I counted the 4 bumpy rocks and the 5 smooth rocks and I put them altogether and I counted them up and it equaled 9.

The teacher draws a boy with his mouth closed and a thought bubble with 9 rocks in it, which are numbered 1 to 9.

Teacher: Who did it Vic's way? [Two students raise their hands.] Vic's way reminds me of Paula's way. See? They both showed 4, showed 5, and *counted them all.* I even wrote all of the same numbers! But Paula used her fingers and Vic used rocks. Anybody have another way?

Libby: I did 5 plus 4. I did 5; 6, 7, 8, 9.

Teacher: Did you use your fingers like Keena? [She points to the drawing of Keena's strategy.]

Libby: Yeah.

Teacher: Which way is most like Libby's?

Nicky: Keena's because she did 4 and she did 5.

Teacher: Right, they both used the same idea, but they started with different numbers. Keena counted on from 4—and Libby counted on from 5. These are all awesome ways to solve the problem. Tomorrow we are going to do some more work with this.

Notice how, even this early in first grade, this teacher encourages students to compare their own strategies with those of their classmates ("How is Paula's strategy different from Keena's?" and "Which way is most like Libby's?") and helps them do so ("Vic's way reminds me of Paula's" and "Keena counted on from 4, and Libby counted on from 5"). Discussions like this one help take different strategies for (in this case) adding two numbers and make them public and explicit for all to think about and possibly try. They encourage students to listen to and learn from one another and set the stage for discussions about strategies and efficiency that will unfold over the year.

Dialogue Box

Discussing Addition Strategies

The challenge for any teacher is to figure out what strategies students are using currently and how successful they are in using them. With a sense of this, the question becomes how to move students toward more efficient strategies without pushing them into using a strategy by rote that they are not yet ready to understand and therefore cannot yet use meaningfully.

One thing that helps students try, and eventually adopt, new strategies for adding, is having many opportunities to hear a variety of strategies named, described, and modeled. There are many ways that you can build these opportunities into your math class, as you talk with students at work, and during whole class discussions. Consider the following examples:

This teacher is introducing Roll and Record *to the class by playing a game with a partner. Notice how she very briefly and naturally models a strategy that she has seen at least one student in the class using. She is not teaching students how to count on. She is sharing counting on as one possible way to add two numbers, expecting only those who are able to make sense of it to use it.*

Teacher: I rolled 5 and 3. So now I need to add those numbers together. I'd like to show you something that Emilia does when she adds. She starts with the higher number, 5, and then she counts, 6, 7, 8 [points to the 3 dots on the other dot cube]. So I am going to write an 8 in the box above the 8 on my paper. William, your turn.

This teacher is discussing a Math Workshop in which Double Compare *and games that involved adding two dot cubes were available. Notice how she helps students name and record the strategies they are using.*

Teacher: When you were playing *Double Compare, Roll and Record,* or *Five-in-a-Row,* how did you figure out how many you had?

Bruce: When we played, Chris thought he had a taller number than I did. He said "Me" but I said, wait, maybe you don't. So we counted and he had 14 and I had 19.

Teacher: Double-checking is always a good idea. Who has another idea?

Lyle: If you memorize it then you don't have to count. Like 3, you can say 3 and don't have to count it and if the other card is 4, you could just say 3. 4, 5, 6, 7.

The teacher sketches two cards showing 3 and 4. She labels the pictures on the 4 card: 4, 5, 6, and 7.

Teacher: So you did something called *counting on.* What are some other ways we could add 3 and 4? [She displays cards and dot cubes, each showing 3 and 4.]

Isabel: First count 3, then count 4. 1, 2, 3, 4, 5, 6, 7. [She counts each dot on the dot cube].

The teacher draws dot pictures of 4 and 3, and labels each dot with a number.

Teacher: Who else *counted all* of the dots or pictures? Who used a different way?

Nicky: I did it sort of the same as Isabel, but I used my fingers. [The teacher has Nicky come up to chart paper. She traces three fingers of one hand and four of the other. She puts a number inside each finger.]

Diego: I saw 3 and 3. I knew 3 and 3 is 6, so 3 and 4 is 1 more. That's 7.

Teacher: All right, Diego used a *doubles combination* that he knows: 3 and 3 are 6. He used that to help him with $3 + 4$.

She models Diego's thinking on the chart paper with 2 equations:

$$3 + 3 = 6$$
$$3 + 4 = 7$$

Chris: I just know that 3 and 4, that makes 7.

Felipe: You could do 4, 5, 6, 7.

Teacher: What Felipe did, that's called *counting on,* just like Lyle's. [She records Felipe's way underneath Lyle's.] There are many different ways to add, so I am making this chart to remind us all of the different ways we came up with.

This class is discussing Double Compare. *They have turned over a 9 and a 6 and now are sharing ways to add those numbers. Notice how the teacher helps students name and describe the strategies and how she decides to delay the discussion of a strategy that she knows all but a few students are not ready to grapple with.*

Teacher: What are some ways I can add these two numbers?

Edgar: [points to the 9 card] 9. [Then he points to each object on the 6 card as he counts on.] 10, 11, 12, 13, 14, 15.

Tamika: You can start with 6 and then count the same way. [She demonstrates.] 7, 8, 9, 10, 11, 12, 13, 14, 15.

Leah: You can also count each thing by 1. [Leah demonstrates.]

Teacher: So far we've gotten 15 all three times. Edgar started at 9 and *counted up* 6, Tamika started at 6 and *counted up* 9, and Leah *counted everything* and they all got 15.

Tuan: I think it's supposed to be 16.

Neil: No, it's not 16 because, well, you use 1 up from 10 and that takes away from the teens. So subtracting 1 equals it to be 15.

Teacher: If that's confusing to other first graders, you might not want to use that way, but it is something to think more about.

Stacy: I think it's 15 because let's say this is a 10 and this is a 6. It would be 16 but 9 is 1 less than 10, so the answer is 1 less than 16 and that's 15.

Teacher: So you were thinking kind of what Neil was thinking. Let's flip over Shaquana's cards [0 and 5]. What do you do with a zero?

Leah: Just don't count it. So Shaquana has 5.

Is It *Always* 11?

This class has had repeated practice adding two numbers in various games and activities, as well as through story problems, during their work in Investigations 3 and 4. The teacher wants to make sure that the whole group has a chance to see and discuss the various strategies she has been seeing students use to add two numbers. But she is also interested in exploring a question raised by her observations of students: do students know that 5 + 6 is always 11, whether it comes on number cubes, with counters, in a story, or with the Primary Number Cards? She begins by asking for strategies to add two numbers, in the context of one of the games they have been playing.

Teacher: So let's say we were playing *Double Compare.*

She flips over two cards—5 and 6. Around the circle, many students begin counting on their fingers, in the air, or using cubes from the center of the rug. There are calls of both 10 and 11.

Teacher: How could we figure out how much 5 and 6 is?

Teo: Count the pictures on the cards. [He demonstrates, counting carefully, and getting 11.]

Paula: The way I do it, you don't have to count one of the cards. I already know this card is 6, right? So, 6 [gestures over that card], 7, 8, 9, 10, 11 [points to each object on the 5 card].

Teacher: Some people call that way of solving the problem *counting on* or *counting up.* Paula knows there are 6 on this card, and then she adds 5 more. [She demonstrates as Paula did.] I saw some students use Paula's strategy with their fingers too. [She demonstrates counting on her fingers.] That's a little different than what Tuan did. He *counted all* the pictures. Would anyone solve it a different way?

Stacy: I know that 5 and 5 is 10, but this problem is 5 and 6, not 5 and 5. 6 is 1 more than 5, so I need to add 1 more.

Teacher: Stacy said that sometimes she "just knows" something that helps her find the answer. Sometimes people call that knowing something *by heart.* Stacy knows a lot of her doubles combinations, the ones where you add two of the same number like 5 + 5, by heart. So she used what she knew about 5 + 5 to solve 5 + 6.

After students shared their ways for solving 5 + 6 if it came up in *Double Compare,* the teacher posed a "new" problem. She was interested to see whether students saw it as a new problem.

Teacher: What if we were playing *Five-in-a-Row,* and I rolled the number cube and this [5 and 6] is what I rolled. How would you figure out that problem?

Again, many students prepare to solve the problem with their fingers or with counters. A few, however, immediately respond, "11" and "it's the same" and "we just did that." The teacher asks students to wait until everyone has had a chance to solve it.

Teacher: Keena says it's 11. Keena, how did you solve it so fast? I didn't see you count or use your fingers or anything.

Keena: Well we just *did* 5 plus 6 [pointing to the cards, still on display].

Teacher: But we did 5 pictures and 6 pictures. This is 5 dots plus 6 dots.

Allie: But that doesn't matter. It's still 5 and 6.

Teacher: So it doesn't matter if it's 5 pictures and 6 pictures, or 5 dots and 6 more dots? Let's double-check. Who will share how they solved 5 dots plus 6 dots?

A student who solved the problem shares his counting on strategy and agrees that the total is 11. The teacher decides to try one more example.

Teacher: What if we were playing *Roll and Record* and we rolled a 5 and a 6? How would you figure out that problem?

This time more students seem to realize that the numbers in the problem are the same, although some proceed with solution strategies. Many call out "it's the same!" and "we don't have to figure it out!"

Teacher: Many of you knew this one really fast. How come you could answer so fast? How come the answer to this problem is 11 *too?*

Paula: Because it's 5 and 6 *again.*

Teacher: But these are pennies. Before it was dots.

Keena: Yeah, but the numbers don't change. It's what you count that changes. And that doesn't matter, there's still 11 of whatever you count.

Stacy: *And* it would be the same if it was 6 plus 5, too. That's still 11.

During this discussion, the teacher notices that some students solve the problem each time they see it; they are not yet secure with the fact that 5 + 6 is always 11. Others seemed to be coming to an understanding during the discussion, and still others seem quite sure. She plans to observe students as they continue to play addition games and solve story problems, to determine whether students seem to be using these ideas—she knows that they will need many opportunities to wrestle with these ideas to truly make sense of them.

Dialogue Box

How Many in All?

These students heard the story *Rooster's Off to See the World* by Eric Carle and then worked to find out how many animals in all set off on the trip together. Here they are sharing their work in a follow-up discussion;

Teacher: Let's talk about how you solved this problem. Listen closely to your classmates. Think about what they tell you. How did they find the answer? See whether you did it the same way they did or a different way. When you share, hold up your paper so that everyone can see.

Felipe: I did it with Jacob. We used cubes.

Felipe's Work

Teacher: Can you tell us more? Or show us what you did?

Felipe: [He arranges cubes in a staircase.] 1, then 2, then 3, then 4, then 5. Because 1 rooster, 2 cats, 3 frogs, 4 turtles, 5 fish.

Jacob: I drew what we did a different way.

Jacob's Work

Teacher: So how did you figure out how many went altogether?

Felipe: Um . . . Jacob, I need your help.

Jacob: I counted until I was at 15. We counted the cubes.

Teacher: So they showed all the groups of animals with cubes, and then counted them up. Look and see whether what you did was like what Felipe and Jacob did. Did anyone do something similar? [Several students raise their hands.]

Teacher: Let's hear from one person who did something similar. How was your way like their way?

Talisa: It was like theirs but I didn't use cubes. I got 15 too because I counted, all the way to 15.

Talisa's Work

Teacher: What did you use to help you keep track?

Talisa: I drew a picture for each animal.

Libby: I did that too, but I did it like in the book.

Libby's Work

Teacher: Did anyone else draw pictures of animals, and then count them all? [Many hands.] Lots of you did! Let's hear from someone else.

Isabel: I drew pictures too. Then I drew lines and counted them.

Isabel's Work

Teacher: Some of you drew pictures to show the groups of animals, some of you showed them with cubes, and some of you showed them with lines. Then you counted them up. Did anyone do something different?

Diego: I did numbers [shows his work].

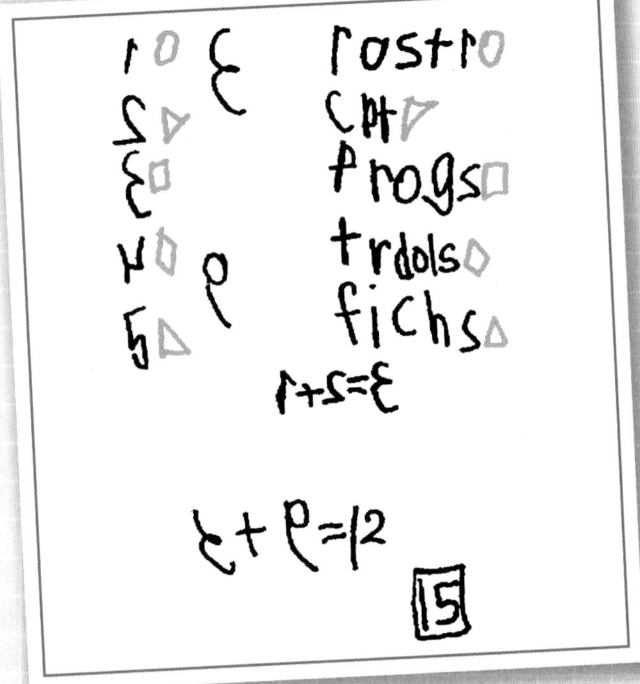

Diego's Work

Teacher: Can you show us how you put those numbers together?

Diego: [Pointing to the 1 and 2 at the top left of his page] One plus two is three. [Next he points to the 4 and 5 at the middle left.] Four and five is nine. [Finally, he indicates the 3 + 9 at the bottom of the page.] Then I put those numbers together and got . . . 20? Three and nine is . . . 20? (Diego speaks English as a second language and cannot readily recall the name of the number.)

Teacher: Remember the name of that number? Anyone want to help?

Diego: Um, 12?

Teacher: Good for you. I know sometimes it's hard to remember the names of all these numbers. So, Diego found out that the 1 and the 2 together made 3, and he wrote that down here. Then he took this 4 and 5, put them together, and made 9. Then he put the 9 and the 3 together, and he wrote that at the bottom: 3 + 9 = 12. Then, Diego, how did you get to 15? Where did you get that?

Diego: I had to add in the 3, so I just counted, 13, 14, 15.

Teacher: All of you came up with a lot of ways to show how you thought about this problem! They're all good ways to show how many in each group, and good ways to help you find how many in all. You will have many more chances to keep finding ways to show your work this year.

Dialogue Box

Observing Students at Work on Seven Peas and Carrots

As you observe students at work on Seven Peas and Carrots, you can learn a great deal about how they are thinking about number combinations, how they solve complex problems, and how they keep track of and record their work. The examples below illustrate the range of approaches observed in one class and the ways that the teacher supported students in working at an appropriate level and pace.

Thinking About Relationships Among Combinations

Soon after students begin working, the teacher visits Jacinta. She is counting silently on her fingers, working with intense concentration. After a moment, she relaxes and records:

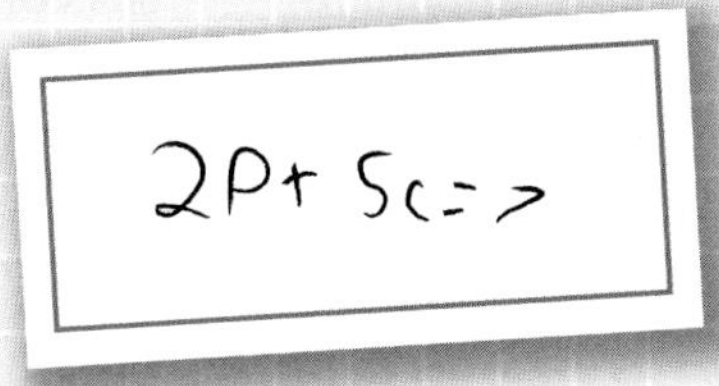

Jacinta's Work

She thinks for an instant, and then writes:

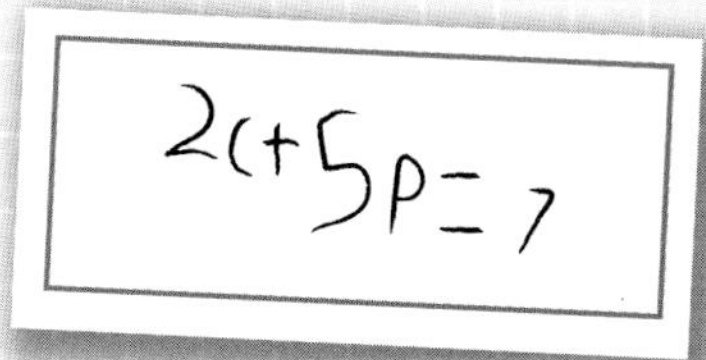

Jacinta's Work

Only then does she look up at the teacher.

Teacher: Can you tell me what you did to get your answers?

Jacinta: I figured out that 2 and 5 is 7. Then, I knew this one [2c + 5p] from this one [2p + 5c]. I was doing it backward.

The teacher moves on and returns to Jacinta about 10 minutes later. She has recorded the following:

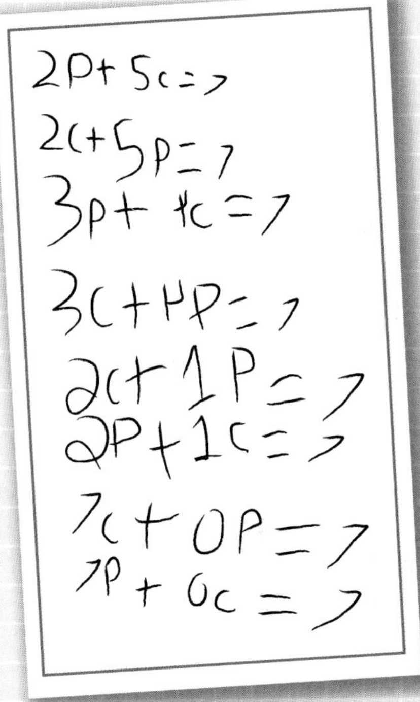

Jacinta's Work

Jacinta explains that she found ways to make 7 and then "made opposites." The teacher asks if she has found all the solutions, and Jacinta says that she thinks so but is not sure.

The teacher suggests that Jacinta compare her solutions with Libby, who has also found many solutions. She hopes that as they compare their work they will determine with more certainty whether they have a complete list, and will perhaps begin thinking about how they know they have a complete list. They will also have an opportunity to share their different ways of organizing their solutions.

Difficulty Coordinating the Parts of the Problem

Seth has just begun counting a set of green and orange cubes when the teacher arrives. He tells her that he thinks there are 7. He counts out loud quickly, touching the cubes as he counts. He skips 2 cubes, and comes up with a total of 9. The teacher asks him to count again, slowly. He does this and gets 11, the actual number of cubes. Again, she asks him to count slowly, and once more, he gets 11.

Teacher: How can we fix that to make it 7?

Seth: Take a little bit of this [green cubes]. A little bit of this too [orange cubes].

He takes off some of both colors, without apparently counting the number he is removing. He seems to be focusing only on the fact that he has too many cubes and that he needs to remove some. When he says he is finished, he has 3 orange and 3 green. He counts them and gets 6.

Teacher: How many do we want?

Seth: 7.

Teacher: We have 6 here. What can we do to make it 7?

He adds 1 green cube and 1 orange cube, so there are now 8 on his paper. The teacher asks him to count; he does, and gets 8. Again, she asks how many are needed in all, and he replies, "7."

Teacher: So, what could you do to get 7?

Seth: I could take 1 out.

Seth removes a cube and, on the teacher's prompting, recounts and gets 7. He is pleased, as he recognizes that he has found a solution. But he seems to think his solution consists of getting a total of 7 things, rather than using a particular combination of peas and carrots to make up 7 things.

Teacher: How could we show how you solved the problem?

Seth: We could make a 7. We did 7 things.

Teacher: That's right, we made 7 things. How many carrots did we use?

Seth: [counting] 1, 2, 3.

Teacher: How many peas?

Seth: [counting] 1, 2, 3, 4.

Teacher: So, we need to show how many peas and how many carrots you used to make 7 in all.

Seth decides to draw 7 squares to show his solution. When he has finished, the teacher reminds him once again to think about how many of the 7 represent carrots and how many represent peas. Seth recounts the cubes of each color on his paper and then colors in the circles accordingly.

Although Seth was able to count up to 7 objects accurately, he had difficulty coordinating the various components of the problem: counting and keeping track of a set of objects, keeping in mind the total number of objects needed, remembering to compare the number accumulated with the desired total, and keeping in mind the two parts he combined to reach that total.

The teacher decides that when students work on another How Many of Each? problem, she will ask Seth to work with a total of 4 peas and carrots. With a smaller total, he may be better able to focus on the goal of the task and on relationships between the total and the two parts that make up the total. When Seth seems comfortable finding, explaining, and recording one or more solutions with a total of 4, the teacher will ask him to work with a larger total, such as 6.

The Beginnings of a Strategic Approach

Near the end of the session, the teacher visits Danielle. She has recorded the following:

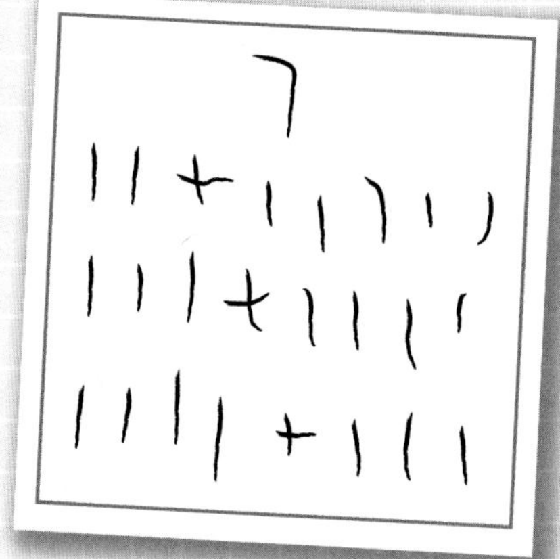

Danielle's Work

Danielle explains that she is recording the combinations she is making with green and orange buttons. The lines on the left part show peas, and those on the right show carrots.

Teacher: Are there more ways you can make 7 peas and carrots?

Danielle: There might be. I could try 5 peas.

Teacher: How did you think of 5?

Danielle: Because it goes 2, 3, 4, 5.

She counts out 5 green buttons on her blank paper.

Danielle: I need to have 7, so I'll add 2 carrots. [She picks up 2 orange buttons to place on her paper.] 1, that's 6, and another 1, that's 7.

She records her new solution:

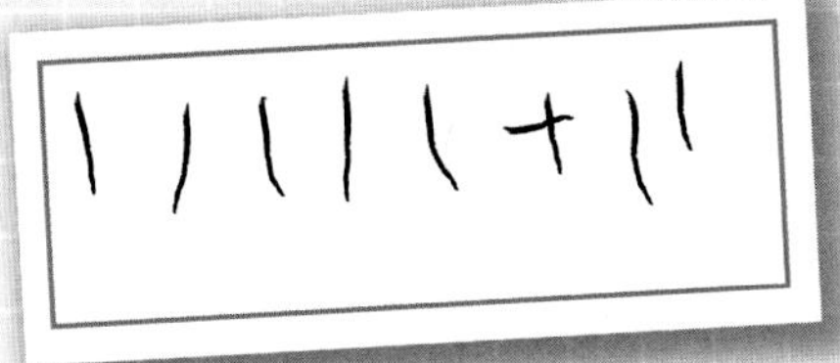

Danielle's Work

Although Danielle appears to be working strategically and to have some sense of combinations of 7, she needs to work with concrete materials in order to find and verify her solutions. She is not comfortable recording solutions without first building them, as Jacinta did. It is not clear whether she is using relationships among the combinations that she has found, to find new solutions. She may not notice these relationships, or she may simply not yet be able to articulate the relationships she does see. For example, she does not show that she recognizes that as the number of peas increases by 1, the number of carrots decreases by 1, or that she can use one solution to find "opposite" solutions.

The teacher encourages Danielle to continue trying to find all the solutions she can. She believes that as the girl continues her work on this problem and then solves other How Many of Each? problems, she will begin recognizing and articulating relationships among combinations and using these relationships to find new solutions.

Dialogue Box

Sharing Combinations of Seven

Students have gathered to share the combinations of 7 they made when playing *Heads and Tails.* The teacher records each combination on a large copy of the game grid.

Jacinta: I have a 4 and 3.

Teacher: 4 heads or tails?

Jacinta: 4 heads and 3 tails.

Teacher: Who else got 4 heads and 3 tails? Raise your hands. Many of you did! Who has another one?

Diego: 2 heads and 5 tails.

Teacher: Who else had 2 heads, 5 tails? What else?

Bruce: 4 heads and 3 tails.

Stacy: That's already on the list.

Teacher: Do you have one we haven't listed yet?

Bruce: 7 heads.

Teacher: 7 heads and how many tails?

Bruce: 0.

Teacher: Hands for 7 heads and 0 tails? Another?

Emilia: 2 heads and 6 tails.

Teacher: Interesting. Up here we have 2 heads and 5 tails, and you're saying 2 heads and 6 tails. Can we have both?

Emilia: Oh, that's 8.

Teacher: Which?

Emilia: 2 and 5. No, 6.

Teacher: Everyone figure it out. What's 2 and 6?

Some students check by counting on their fingers, others use counters, and others work mentally. Although students are eager to call out the answer, the teacher insists that they wait until most of the class has arrived at a solution. Students confirm that 2 and 6 is 8.

Teacher: OK, Emilia, do you have another one?

Emilia: 3 heads and 4 tails.

Teo: We have that. At the top.

Teacher: 3 heads and 4 tails. Do we have that?

Teo: Oh, we have it with 4 first.

Teacher: Is that the same or different?

Emilia: It's like it, but I have 3 and 4, not 4 and 3.

Students suggest two more combinations. Then, no one can come up with another way the counters landed.

Teacher: Are there other ways the pennies could land, even if they're not on your sheets?

Tamika: 8 minus 1.

Teacher: We're talking about ways to break 7 into two parts. Some pennies land heads up and some land tails up. How could we show that with 8 minus 1?

Tamika: Um, 8 heads and 1 tail?

Teacher: Let's try it. Who would like to show us?

Diego volunteers. He models 8 heads and 1 tail with counters, and notes with surprise that there are 9 counters in all, not 7. Tamika says that it would be 7 if you take away 1 from 8, but that you need to find a way to do it with 7 in all. Although a few students seem to recognize why 8 minus 1 is not a solution, they are beginning to see that this game is not a subtraction situation. The teacher is not sure that everyone is following. She decides that for now she will not pursue this any further but will leave the chart up for students to think about.

Student Math Handbook

The *Student Math Handbook* pages related to this unit are pictured on the following pages. This book is designed to be used flexibly: as a resource for students doing classwork, as a book students can take home for reference while doing homework and playing math games with their families, and as a reference for families to better understand the work their children are doing in class.

When students take the *Student Math Handbook* home, they and their families can discuss these pages together to reinforce or enhance students' understanding of the mathematical concepts and games in this unit.

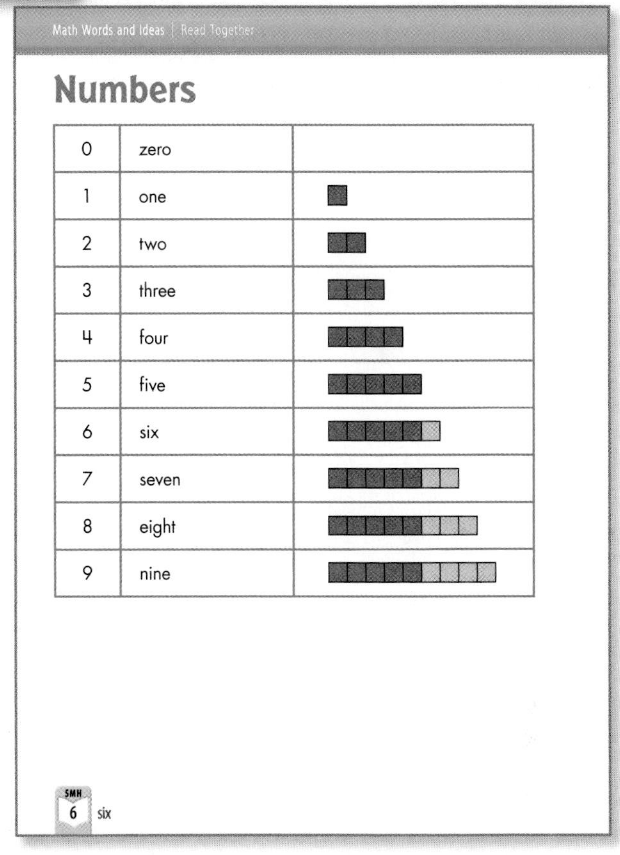

Math Words and Ideas | Read Together

Numbers

0	zero	
1	one	
2	two	
3	three	
4	four	
5	five	
6	six	
7	seven	
8	eight	
9	nine	

SMH 6 six

◄ Math Words and Ideas, p. 6

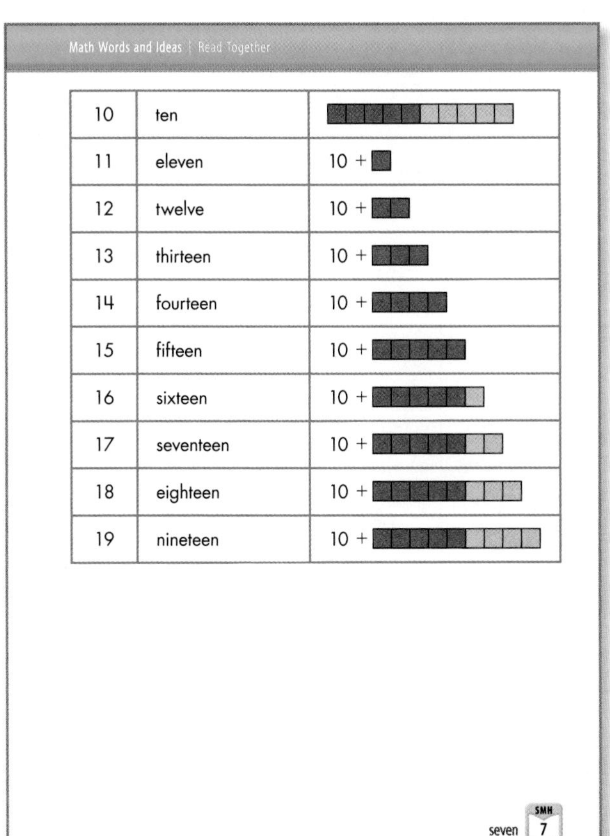

Math Words and Ideas | Read Together

10	ten	
11	eleven	10 +
12	twelve	10 +
13	thirteen	10 +
14	fourteen	10 +
15	fifteen	10 +
16	sixteen	10 +
17	seventeen	10 +
18	eighteen	10 +
19	nineteen	10 +

seven SMH 7

◄ Math Words and Ideas, p. 7

Math Words and Ideas | Read Together

20	twenty	
21	twenty-one	20 +
22	twenty-two	20 +
23	twenty-three	20 +
24	twenty-four	20 +
25	twenty-five	20 +
26	twenty-six	20 +
27	twenty-seven	20 +
28	twenty-eight	20 +
29	twenty-nine	20 +

SMH 8 eight

◄ Math Words and Ideas, p. 8

Calendar

Math Words
- **calendar**

A calendar is a tool. It shows days and months in a year. A calendar can also show important days and events.

month

days of the week

year

September 2009

Sunday	Monday	Tuesday	Wednesday	Thursday	Friday	Saturday
		1	2 First Day of School	3	4	5
6	7	8 Family Breakfast	9	10	11	12
13	14	15	16	17 Trip to the Park	18	19
20	21	22 First Day of Fall	23	24	25	26
27	28	29	30			

What happens on Tuesday, September 8?
What day of the week is the first day of school?
When does fall begin?

Math Words and Ideas, p. 17

Calendar: Days of the Week

Math Words
- **days**
- **week**
- **hours**

There are 7 days in a week.

Sunday	Monday	Tuesday	Wednesday	Thursday	Friday	Saturday

What day comes before Wednesday?
What day comes after Friday?

There are 24 hours in a day.

A day is the time between bedtime tonight and bedtime tomorrow.

One day lasts from sunrise to sunrise.

What day is today? What day is tomorrow?
What day was yesterday?

Math Words and Ideas, p. 18

Calendar: Months of the Year

Math Words
- **month**
- **year**

There are 12 months in a year.
This calendar shows all 12 months in 2009.

January

S	M	T	W	T	F	S
				1	2	3
4	5	6	7	8	9	10
11	12	13	14	15	16	17
18	19	20	21	22	23	24
25	26	27	28	29	30	31

February

S	M	T	W	T	F	S
1	2	3	4	5	6	7
8	9	10	11	12	13	14
15	16	17	18	19	20	21
22	23	24	25	26	27	28

March

S	M	T	W	T	F	S
1	2	3	4	5	6	7
8	9	10	11	12	13	14
15	16	17	18	19	20	21
20	23	24	25	26	27	28
29	30	31				

April

S	M	T	W	T	F	S
			1	2	3	4
5	6	7	8	9	10	11
12	13	14	15	16	17	18
19	20	21	22	23	24	25
26	27	28	29	30		

May

S	M	T	W	T	F	S
					1	2
3	4	5	6	7	8	9
10	11	12	13	14	15	16
17	18	19	20	21	22	23
24	25	26	27	28	29	30
31						

June

S	M	T	W	T	F	S
	1	2	3	4	5	6
7	8	9	10	11	12	13
14	15	16	17	18	19	20
21	22	23	24	25	26	27
28	29	30				

July

S	M	T	W	T	F	S
			1	2	3	4
5	6	7	8	9	10	11
12	13	14	15	16	17	18
19	20	21	22	23	24	25
26	27	28	29	30	31	

August

S	M	T	W	T	F	S
						1
2	3	4	5	6	7	8
9	10	11	12	13	14	15
16	17	18	19	20	21	22
23	24	25	26	27	28	29
30	31					

September

S	M	T	W	T	F	S
		1	2	3	4	5
6	7	8	9	10	11	12
13	14	15	16	17	18	19
20	21	22	23	24	25	26
27	28	29	30			

October

S	M	T	W	T	F	S
				1	2	3
4	5	6	7	8	9	10
11	12	13	14	15	16	17
18	19	20	21	22	23	24
25	26	27	28	29	30	31

November

S	M	T	W	T	F	S
1	2	3	4	5	6	7
8	9	10	11	12	13	14
15	16	17	18	19	20	21
22	23	24	25	26	27	28
29	30					

December

S	M	T	W	T	F	S
		1	2	3	4	5
6	7	8	9	10	11	12
13	14	15	16	17	18	19
20	21	22	23	24	25	26
27	28	29	30	31		

Some months have 30 days. Some months have 31 days. February has 28 days. Every 4 years, February has 29 days. This is called a *leap year.*

What month comes after April?
What month comes before October?
Find a month with 30 days.

Math Words and Ideas, p. 19

Coins

These coins are used in the United States.
Each coin has a name and a value.

Coin	Name	Value
	penny	1¢ 1 cent
	nickel	5¢ 5 cents
	dime	10¢ 10 cents
	quarter	25¢ 25 cents
	half dollar	50¢ 50 cents

Is a bigger coin always worth more?

Math Words and Ideas, p. 20

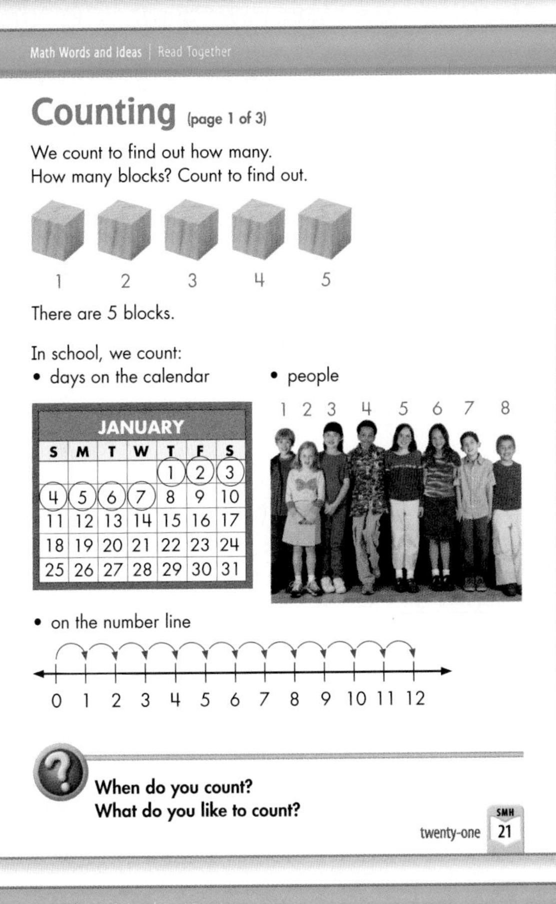
Math Words and Ideas | Read Together

Counting (page 1 of 3)

We count to find out how many.
How many blocks? Count to find out.

1 2 3 4 5

There are 5 blocks.

In school, we count:

- days on the calendar
- people

JANUARY						
S	M	T	W	T	F	S
				1	2	3
4	5	6	7	8	9	10
11	12	13	14	15	16	17
18	19	20	21	22	23	24
25	26	27	28	29	30	31

1 2 3 4 5 6 7 8

- on the number line

0 1 2 3 4 5 6 7 8 9 10 11 12

When do you count?
What do you like to count?

twenty-one SMH 21

Math Words and Ideas | Read Together

Counting (page 2 of 3)

Math Words
- **total**

When you count, you say one number for each object. You need to keep track of what you are counting. The last number you say is the total. The total tells you how many are in the group.

Look at how some children count.

Sam touches each button as he counts it.

Rosa puts each button in the cup as she counts it.

Kim arranges the buttons in a row to count.

Max puts them in groups of 2 to double-check.

What do you do when you count?

SMH 22 twenty-two

Math Words and Ideas, p. 22

Math Words and Ideas | Read Together

Counting (page 3 of 3)

Look at these pennies.
They are mixed up.
They are hard to count.

Here are some different ways to organize the pennies so that they are easier to count.

Which group of pennies is easiest for you to count?

twenty-three SMH 23

Math Words and Ideas | Read Together

Counting by Groups (page 1 of 2)

You can count more quickly if you count by groups. Each time you say a number, you add another group. Every group must have the same number of objects in it.

Each hand has 5 fingers. You can count by 5s to find the total number of fingers. You say every fifth number when you count by 5s.

Counting fingers by 5s

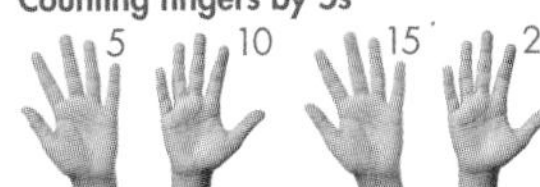

Counting shoes by 2s

Counting toes by 10s

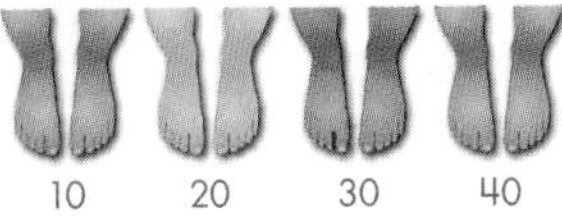

How many eyes would 10 people have in all?

SMH 24 twenty-four

Math Words and Ideas, p. 24

Math Words and Ideas | Read Together

Counting by Groups (page 2 of 2)

Here are 23 pennies.

You can count the pennies in different ways.

Counting by 2s

2 4 6 8 10 12 14 16 18 20 22 23

Counting by 5s

5 10 15 20 23

Counting by 10s

10 20 23

How many different ways can you count 18 pennies?

▲ Math Words and Ideas, p. 25

Math Words and Ideas | Read Together

Number Line

A number line is a tool. It shows numbers in order.

0 1 2 3 4 5 6 7 8 9 10 11 12 13 14 15

You can use it to count forward or back.

When we count forward, the numbers go up.

1, 2, 3, 4, 5, 6.

0 1 2 3 4 5 6 7 8 9 10 11 12 13 14 15

When we count back, the numbers go down.

5, 4, 3, 2, 1, 0.

0 1 2 3 4 5 6 7 8 9 10 11 12 13 14 15

Start with 0 and count to 15.
Start with 12 and count to 0.

0 1 2 3 4 5 6 7 8 9 10 11 12 13 14 15

▲ Math Words and Ideas, p. 26

Math Words and Ideas | Read Together

100 Chart (page 1 of 3)

The 100 chart is a tool that shows numbers from 1 to 100, in order. It can help you count, add, and subtract.

row → column ↓

1	2	3	4	5	6	7	8	9	10
11	12	13	14	15	16	17	18	19	20
21	22	23	24	25	26	27	28	29	30
31	32	33	34	35	36	37	38	39	40
41	42	43	44	45	46	47	48	49	50
51	52	53	54	55	56	57	58	59	60
61	62	63	64	65	66	67	68	69	70
71	72	73	74	75	76	77	78	79	80
81	82	83	84	85	86	87	88	89	90
91	92	93	94	95	96	97	98	99	100

How many rows are in the 100 chart?
How many numbers are in each row?
How many columns are in the 100 chart?
How many numbers are in each column?

▲ Math Words and Ideas, p. 27

Math Words and Ideas | Read Together

100 Chart (page 2 of 3)

1	2	3	4	5	6	7	8	9	10
11	12	13	14	15	16	17	18	19	20
21	22	23	24	25	26	27	28	29	30
31	32	33	34	35	36	37	38	39	40
41	42	43	44	45	46	47	48	49	50
51	52	53	54	55	56	57	58	59	60
61	62	63	64	65	66	67	68	69	70
71	72	73	74	75	76	77	78	79	80
81	82	83	84	85	86	87	88	89	90
91	92	93	94	95	96	97	98	99	100

"In each row, the 10s number stays the same and the 1s number goes up by 1."

"In each column, the 10s number goes up by 1 and the 1s number stays the same."

What patterns do you notice?

▲ Math Words and Ideas, p. 28

Math Words and Ideas | Read Together

100 Chart (page 3 of 3)

Some of the numbers on this 100 chart are missing.

1	2	3	4	5	6		8		10
	12	13	14	15	16	17	18	19	20
21	22		24	25	26	27	28	29	30
31	32	33	34				38	39	40
41	42	43	44	45	46	47	48	49	50
51		53	54	55	56	57	58	59	60
61	62	63	64	65	66	67			
71	72	73	74	75	76	77	78	79	80
81	82		84	85	86	87	88	89	90
91	92	93	94	95	96		98	99	100

What numbers are missing?
How do you know?

Math Words and Ideas, p. 29

Math Words and Ideas | Read Together

Counting Forward

You can use the number line and the 100 chart to count forward from any number. You do not have to start with 1. Max starts with 8 and counts to 14.

"8, 9, 10, 11, 12, 13, 14."

0 1 2 3 4 5 6 7 8 9 10 11 12 13 14 15

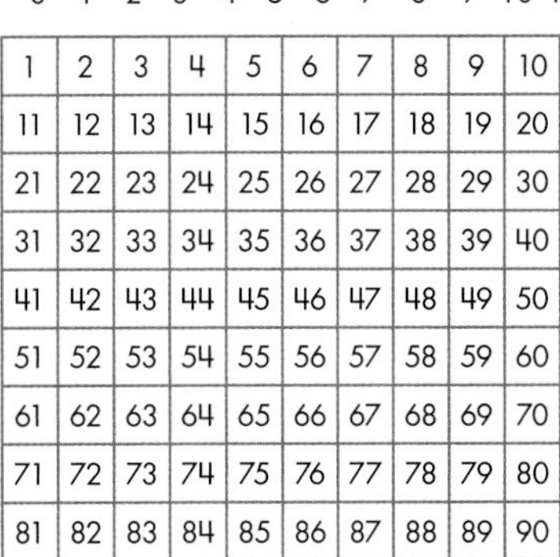

1	2	3	4	5	6	7	8	9	10
11	12	13	14	15	16	17	18	19	20
21	22	23	24	25	26	27	28	29	30
31	32	33	34	35	36	37	38	39	40
41	42	43	44	45	46	47	48	49	50
51	52	53	54	55	56	57	58	59	60
61	62	63	64	65	66	67	68	69	70
71	72	73	74	75	76	77	78	79	80
81	82	83	84	85	86	87	88	89	90
91	92	93	94	95	96	97	98	99	100

Use the 100 chart to count from 38 to 52.

Math Words and Ideas, p. 31

Math Words and Ideas | Read Together

Counting Back

You can use the number line and the 100 chart to count back from any number. Rosa counts back from 33 to 24.

"33, 32, 31, 30, 29, 28, 27, 26, 25, 24."

1	2	3	4	5	6	7	8	9	10
11	12	13	14	15	16	17	18	19	20
21	22	23	24	25	26	27	28	29	30
31	32	33	34	35	36	37	38	39	40
41	42	43	44	45	46	47	48	49	50
51	52	53	54	55	56	57	58	59	60
61	62	63	64	65	66	67	68	69	70
71	72	73	74	75	76	77	78	79	80
81	82	83	84	85	86	87	88	89	90
91	92	93	94	95	96	97	98	99	100

Use the number line to count back from 15 to 9.

0 1 2 3 4 5 6 7 8 9 10 11 12 13 14 15

Math Words and Ideas, p. 32

Math Words and Ideas | Read Together

Solving Addition Problems (page 1 of 5)

Here is a story problem:

Kim has 3 crayons. Sam gives her 4 more.
How many crayons does Kim have now?

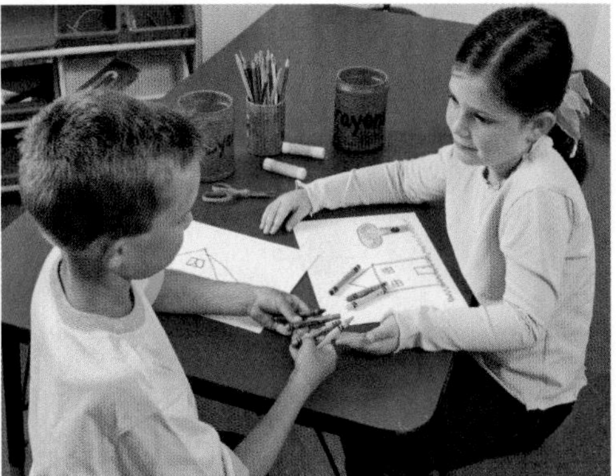

Does Kim have more crayons at the beginning or the end of the story?

Math Words and Ideas, p. 33

Math Words and Ideas | Read Together

Solving Addition Problems (page 2 of 5)

Here is the story:

Kim has 3 crayons. Sam gives her 4 more.
How many crayons does Kim have now?

There are many ways to solve this problem.
Here is what some children did:

Paula took 3 crayons. Then she took 4. Then she counted.	Pei drew 4 lines. Then he drew 3 lines. He counted on from 4.
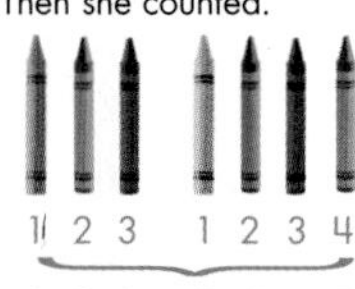 1 2 3 1 2 3 4 / 1 2 3 4 5 6 7	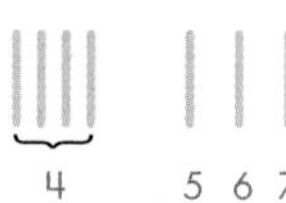 4 5 6 7

How would you solve this problem?

Math Words and Ideas, p. 34

Math Words and Ideas | Read Together

Solving Addition Problems (page 3 of 5)

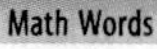

Math Words
- equation
- plus
- equal to
- addend
- sum
- equal sign

Kim has 3 crayons. Sam gives her 4 more.
Now Kim has 7 crayons.

Here are 2 equations for this problem.

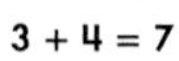

$3 + 4 = 7$

3 plus 4 is equal to 7.

$7 = 3 + 4$

7 is equal to 3 plus 4.

3 and 4 are the addends. 7 is the total, or the sum.

The equal sign shows that 3 + 4 is the same amount as 7.

Math Words and Ideas, p. 35

Math Words and Ideas | Read Together

Solving Addition Problems (page 4 of 5)

Here is a story problem:

Rosa has 8 shells.
Sam gives her 3 more shells.
Max gives her 2 more shells.
How many shells does Rosa have now?

Does Rosa have more shells at the beginning or at the end of the story?

Math Words and Ideas, p. 36

Math Words and Ideas | Read Together

Solving Addition Problems (page 5 of 5)

There are many ways to solve this problem.
This is what some children did:

Paul drew and counted each shell.	Isabel counted on from 8 on a number line.
	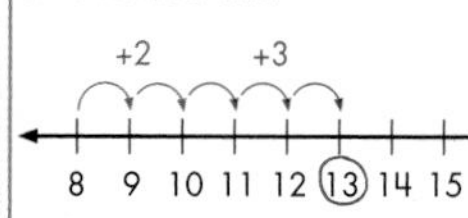

Vic used a combination of 10.

8 + 2 = 10

Then he counted on.

11, 12, 13

How would you solve the problem?

Math Words and Ideas, p. 37

Using Math Symbols

(page 1 of 2)

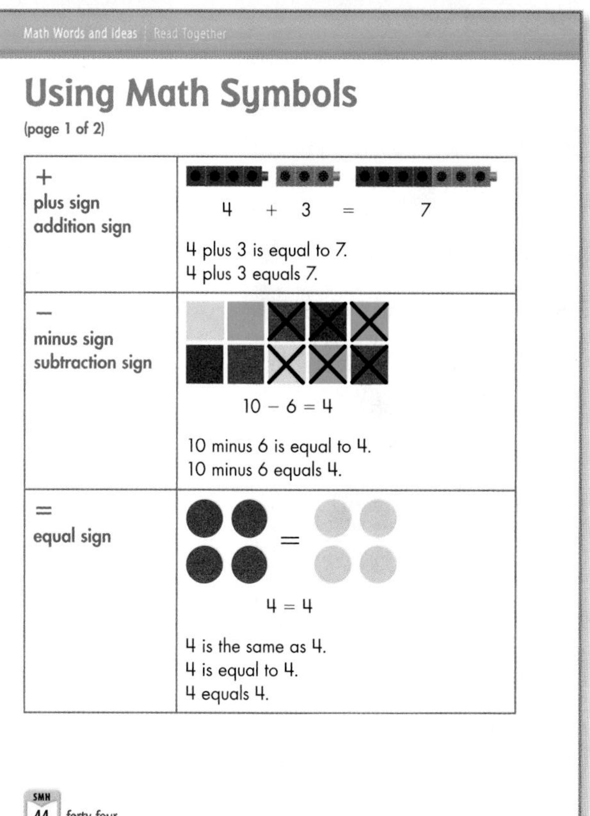

+ plus sign addition sign	4 + 3 = 7 4 plus 3 is equal to 7. 4 plus 3 equals 7.
− minus sign subtraction sign	10 − 6 = 4 10 minus 6 is equal to 4. 10 minus 6 equals 4.
= equal sign	4 = 4 4 is the same as 4. 4 is equal to 4. 4 equals 4.

Math Words and Ideas, p. 44

Using Math Symbols

(page 2 of 2)

Math Words
- **equation**

An equation uses numbers and symbols to show what is happening in a math problem.

8 + 2 = 10 10 − 4 = 6

Here are two ways to write addition or subtraction problems.

$\begin{array}{r} 8 \\ +\ 2 \\ \hline 10 \end{array}$ is the same as 8 + 2 = 10

10 − 4 = 6 is the same as $\begin{array}{r} 10 \\ -\ 4 \\ \hline 6 \end{array}$

Math Words and Ideas, p. 45

How Many of Each? (page 1 of 2)

Here is a story problem.

I have 6 vegetables.
Some are peas.
Some are carrots.
How many of each could I have?
How many peas? How many carrots?

There are many different solutions.

Here is one.

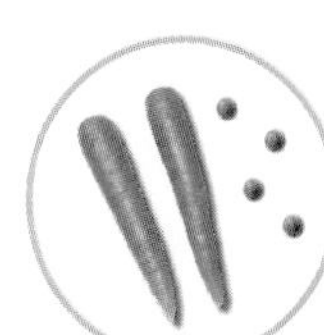

I could have 2 carrots and 4 peas.

6 = 2 + 4

Can you find other combinations of peas and carrots?

Math Words and Ideas, p. 46

How Many of Each? (page 2 of 2)

Here are some children's solutions.

Edgar: 5 peas and 1 carrot

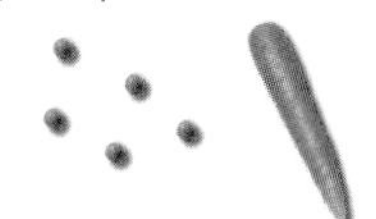

5 + 1 = 6

Allie: 3 peas and 3 carrots

3 + 3 = 6

Nicky: 2 peas and 4 carrots

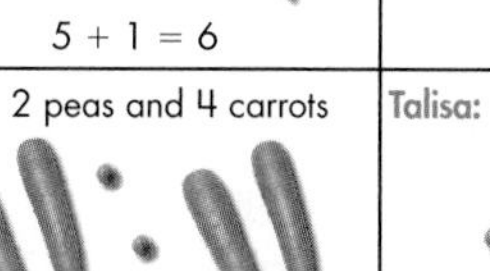

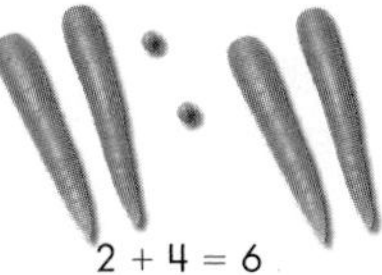

2 + 4 = 6

Talisa: 4 peas and 2 carrots

4 + 2 = 6

Lyle: 1 pea and 5 carrots

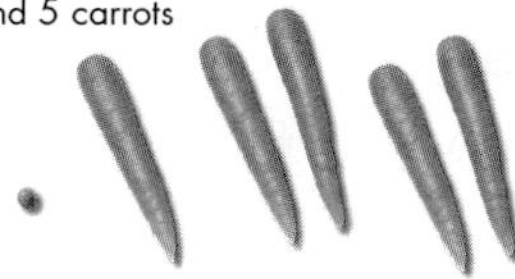

1 + 5 = 6

If there were 7 vegetables, how many peas and carrots could there be? Find as many combinations as you can.

Math Words and Ideas, p. 47

Math Words and Ideas | Read Together

Combinations of 10 (page 1 of 2)

Here are some ways to make 10.

3 + 7 = 10

5 + 5 = 10

9 + 1 = 10

6 + 4 = 10

7 + ? = 10

What card do you need to make 10?
What other ways can you make 10 with 2 cards?
Can you make 10 with 3 cards?

Math Words and Ideas, p. 48

Math Words and Ideas | Read Together

Combinations of 10 (page 2 of 2)

0 + 10 = 10
1 + 9 = 10
2 + 8 = 10
3 + 7 = 10
4 + 6 = 10
5 + 5 = 10
6 + 4 = 10
7 + 3 = 10
8 + 2 = 10
9 + 1 = 10
10 + 0 = 10

What do you notice about these combinations of 10?

Math Words and Ideas, p. 49

Games | Read Together

Collect 20 Together

You need

- dot cube
- counters

Play with a partner. Work together.

1. Player 1 rolls the dot cube and takes that many counters.
2. Player 2 rolls the dot cube and takes that many counters.
3. After each turn, count how many counters you have.
4. Keep playing. Players work together to collect 20 counters.
5. The game is over when you have 20 counters together.

More Ways to Play

- Play with 2 dot cubes.
- Play with 1 dot cube and 1 number cube.
- Play *Collect 25 Together* or *Collect 30 Together.*
- Try to collect *exactly* 20 counters.

Games, G1

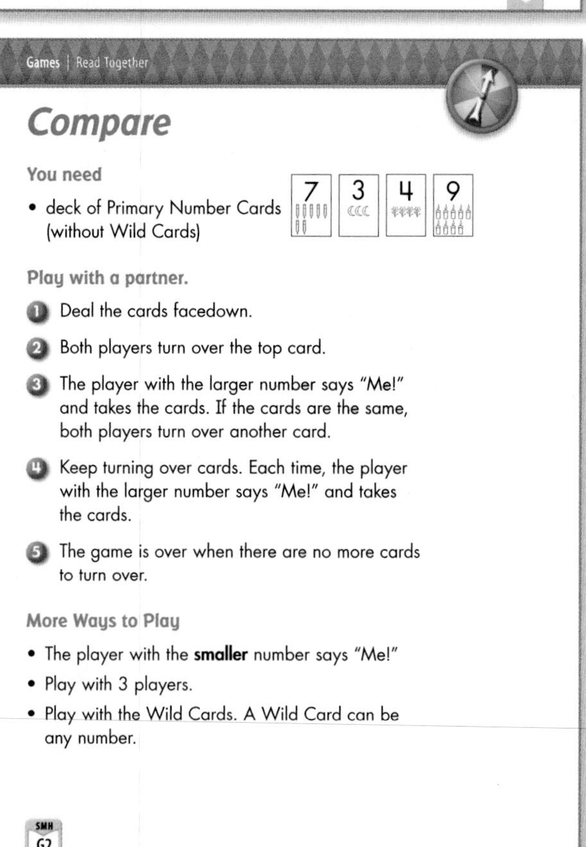

Games | Read Together

Compare

You need

- deck of Primary Number Cards (without Wild Cards)

Play with a partner.

1. Deal the cards facedown.
2. Both players turn over the top card.
3. The player with the larger number says "Me!" and takes the cards. If the cards are the same, both players turn over another card.
4. Keep turning over cards. Each time, the player with the larger number says "Me!" and takes the cards.
5. The game is over when there are no more cards to turn over.

More Ways to Play

- The player with the **smaller** number says "Me!"
- Play with 3 players.
- Play with the Wild Cards. A Wild Card can be any number.

Games, G2

Compare Dots

You need

- Dot Cards

Play with a partner.

1. Deal the cards facedown.
2. Both players turn over the top card.
3. The player with more dots says "Me!" and takes the cards. If the cards are the same, each player turns over another card.
4. Keep turning over cards. Each time, the player with more dots says "Me!" and takes the cards.
5. The game is over when there are no more cards to turn over.

More Ways to Play

- The player with **fewer** dots says "Me!"
- Play with 3 players.

Double Compare

You need

- deck of Primary Number Cards (without Wild Cards)

Play with a partner.

1. Deal the cards facedown.
2. Both players turn over their top two cards.
3. The player with the larger total says "Me!" and takes the cards. If the totals are the same, both players turn over two more cards.
4. Keep turning over two cards. Each time, the player with the larger total says "Me!" and takes the cards.
5. The game is over when there are no more cards to turn over.

More Ways to Play

- The player with the **smaller** total says "Me!"
- Play with 3 players.
- Play with the Wild Cards. A Wild Card can be any number.

Double Compare Dots

You need

- Dot Cards

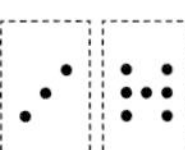 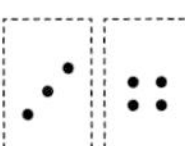

Play with a partner.

1. Deal the cards facedown.
2. Both players turn over their top two cards.
3. The player with cards having more dots says "Me!" and takes the cards. If both pairs of cards have the same number of dots, both players turn over two more cards.
4. Keep turning over two cards. Each time, the player with more dots says "Me!" and takes the cards.
5. The game is over when there are no more cards in the deck.

More Ways to Play

- The player whose cards have **fewer** dots says "Me!"
- Play with 3 players.

Five-in-a-Row

You need

- 2 dot cubes 
- 20 counters 
- gameboard

Play with a partner. Work together.

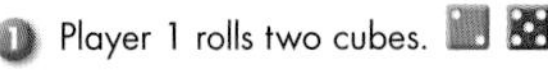

1. Player 1 rolls two cubes.
2. Player 1 adds ⚃ + ⚄.
3. Player 1 covers that sum on the gameboard.
4. Player 2 takes a turn, following steps 1–3.
5. If the sum is already covered, roll again.
6. The game is over when all of the numbers in one row are covered. The numbers can go across, down, or corner to corner.

More Ways to Play

- Play with different gameboards.
- Play with 1 dot cube and 1 number cube.
- Play with 2 number cubes.

Games | Read Together

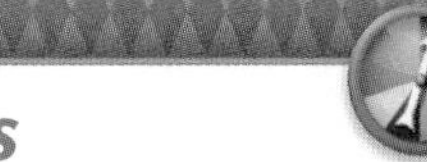

Heads and Tails

You need

- 8–12 pennies

- recording sheet

Play alone.

1. Decide how many pennies to play with. Record this number on the recording sheet.
2. Drop the pennies.
3. Count how many pennies are heads and how many pennies are tails.
4. Record the two numbers on the recording sheet.
5. Keep dropping the pennies and recording how they land.
6. The game is over when the grid is full.

SMH G13

Games, G13

Games | Read Together

How Many Am I Hiding?

You need

- 8–12 connecting cubes
- recording sheet

Play with a partner.

1. Decide how many cubes to play with. Both players write this number on their recording sheets.
2. Make a tower with that many cubes.
3. Player 1 hides some of the cubes.
4. Player 2 tells how many cubes are hidden.
5. Player 1 shows the hidden cubes.
6. Both players count how many were hidden and then record that number on their recording sheets.
7. Keep playing with the same tower. Take turns being Player 1 and Player 2.
8. The game is over when the grid is full.

More Ways to Play

- Play with 5 cubes of one color and 5 cubes of another color.

SMH G14

Games, G14

Games | Read Together

Roll and Record

You need

- 2 dot cubes
- recording sheet

Play alone.

1. Roll 2 cubes.
2. Add the numbers.
3. Write the sum on the recording sheet.
4. The game is over when one column is full.

More Ways to Play

- Play with 1 dot cube and 1 number cube.
- Play with 2 number cubes.

SMH G19

Games, G19

Games | Read Together

Three Towers of 10

You need

- dot cube

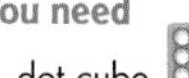

- 30 connecting cubes per player, in 2 colors

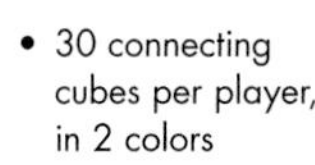

- crayons in 2 colors
- recording sheet

Play with a partner. Work together.

1. Each player picks a color of cubes.
2. Player 1 rolls and makes a tower with that many cubes.
3. Player 2 rolls and takes that many cubes.
4. Player 2 adds the cubes to the tower. A tower can have only 10 cubes. Start a new tower with any extra cubes.
5. The game is over when there are 3 towers of 10 cubes.
6. Both players record. Show how many cubes of each color there are in each tower. Write an equation for each tower.

More Ways to Play

- Make 5 towers of 10.
- Make 3 towers of 15.
- Play with 2 dot cubes.
- Play with 1 dot cube and 1 number cube.
- Play with 2 number cubes.

SMH G25

Games, G25

Index

IN THIS UNIT

W

Z